the
mind
game

GW00655974

PHILLIP DAY

C Credence Publications

Table of Contents

Introduction

Hello. My name is Phillip Day. Thank you for taking the trouble to obtain a copy of this book and read it. May I start by saying how excited I am personally to share the following information with you, as the research I shall be reporting from the desks of some of the world's leading medical and political researchers connects with that most basic and worthwhile of human goals – to live a long and happy life, to prosper in circumstances, both in health and in quality of life and, most importantly of all, to help others.

For the past 17 years I have been researching and reporting on contentious health issues, publishing information that has been deliberately stymied or obfuscated by the political and medical establishments. My organisation is Credence, a research and publishing company with offices around the world dedicated to exposing quackery and hidden agendas within the health industry, which exist because of entrenched error, financial and strategic interests, quite a few of which we will examine later in this book.

As a reporter, I am interested in medical wars - situations where eminent scientists and doctors have done the unthinkable and directly challenged their own establishments over core issues of medical science. On the face of it, this seems to be a foolish move on their part, since to shut up and follow the party line would have guaranteed them the path of least resistance and a perpetuation of their enviable livelihoods and future prospects. But come out of the closet many honest men and women in the medical fraternity have done, to the great dismay of their peers, and there were those like myself ready to report the issues and agendas with which they felt compelled to unburden themselves.

Our researchers and affiliates also compile the latest data on the developing social globalisation of Earth and its strategic implications. We are not Luddites, disdaining every new advance in favour of maintaining a dogged, impractical adherence to the sentiments and traditions of the past. As has been said, 'the only constant *is* change', and to resist this

3

truism is to demonstrate a naiveté completely at odds with observable reality.

OUR BRAVE NEW WORLD

Every new year brings incredible new inventions, new advances in technologies, new medicines, further discoveries in physics, chemistry and the other sciences. There are also new political challenges and military threats. News channels such as ABC, CNN, the BBC and Sky report 24 hours a day on the problems besetting this complicated, restless and fretting planet. Credence Research monitors this prodigious output; our publications division prepares reports and publishes books on these subjects. Our lecturers travel and host public meetings around the world to share this vital information.

But *The Mind Game*, it must be said, has been my most extraordinary and challenging project to date. I believe, after you have finished reading this book, that you also will agree that there are no greater or more important issues facing us as a civilisation than those under discussion in these pages. I speak to thousands of citizens a year during the course of my own touring. Almost to a man, woman or child, my audiences are worried about the world around them. They are at present known as the Silent Majority.

Author and researcher Bruce Wiseman writes: *"Outside our windows, the peaceful streets of years past now harbour violence. In some neighbourhoods, gunfire pierces the night. Police helicopters fly overhead, scanning yards and alleys for runaway criminals.*

We worry about our children. Once-quiet schools are now hothouses of drug-trafficking, promiscuity, and vice unimaginable in days gone by. We hear of an ever declining literacy rate, dwindling test scores, and of graduates who can't even find their home city on a map. We wonder how they will ever make it in the adult world.

In our homes, at our jobs, on our television screens, we see that the once-clear line between right and wrong has become grey and hazy. Virtue is held up to ridicule. The honest man is viewed as a fool. Criminal behaviour is now excused under the banner of 'irresistible impulse' and 'diminished capacity'.

Hardly anyone would argue with the statement that <u>something</u> has been eating at the moral fabric for decades now.... No one questions that

4

there is a palpable, destructive force. In the United States, for example, people are at each other's throats over it. Liberals blame it on conservative policies, right wingers rebuke the left. Many in the religious community have held the entertainment industry accountable." [1]

THE SILENT MAJORITY

The Silent Majority of the public sees these things, yet has remained silent up to now. These are ordinary, decent citizens who have grown exasperated with the ineffectiveness and corruption of their political systems. Many have registered their protests by refusing to vote. Others are frustrated at the media for eschewing its collective responsibility to evaluate the social problems we really face. Most people, as we will learn later, have not the slightest idea which ends the press really serves. Dumbfounded, we look on as our newspapers, TV and cinemas feed us a steady, putrid fare of sex, violence, money and the shenanigans of the famous, instead of promoting the common-sense approaches that could heal our nations, restore our health services and stabilise our societies.

The Silent Majority simmers as it looks around at a culture whose framework has crumbled, whose law and order precepts have been corrupted and repeatedly violated, whose mass communications media and entertainment industries have swamped it and its youth with images of senseless, gratuitous violence and pop-pornography. Many of these families lost loved ones in tragic circumstances in two World Wars which were ostensibly fought to preserve the values our society cherished. Today those values have evaporated, in spite of the sacrifice. The obscenity of where we have arrived as a society today has not gone unnoticed. The Silent Majority has begun to stir itself from its apathy and nurture an understandable and justifiable outrage.

If you, the reader, are one of these ranks, then this book is for you. In the pages that follow, we will trace together the cause of these disasters and identify the perpetrators who are summarily guilty, by the evidence which follows, of introducing, through gross deception, their font of destructive ideologies, and of carrying out a calculated attack on the very fabric of our nations and their cultures.

As we will learn, the 18th and 19th centuries brought with them more than just the technical allure of an industrial revolution. Man himself

---

[1] Wiseman, Bruce, *Psychiatry – The Ultimate Betrayal*, Freedom Publishing, Los Angeles: 1995, pp.5,6

became restless for a spiritual, as well as a physical change in the way he had traditionally regarded himself and his place in the cosmos. New sciences emerged, such as evolution, psychology, psychiatry and the mental health and hygiene movements. Their impacts on our future society were to have fundamental, far-reaching and ultimately tragic consequences in the decades that followed their introduction and broad acceptance by the public at large.

PSYCHIATRY

Psychiatry is one science in particular that comes under scrutiny in this book. At first glance, most would not even acknowledge the incredible changes psychiatric and psychological theories have had on our world. Yet we shall see that they have permeated our courts, our police, our hospitals, our movies and TV, our schoolyards, our governments and even our homes. Who would consider for one moment that psychiatry could have played such a fundamental role in the development of politics, education, entertainment, war and medicine?

OFF THE RAILS?

Many have concluded that mankind itself must be going insane. Indeed, we are told, at no other time in human history has a greater segment of society been diagnosed 'mentally ill' than today. Our nations' governments, schools and courts appreciate this, which is why they are veritably aswarm with armies of politically correct legislators, administrators and the inevitable battalions of psychologists, psychiatrists and other 'mental health' experts. One could expect that with such an impressive arsenal of professional expertise on call, victory itself would be assured. Who would possibly consider for a moment, in their right mind, that these might conceivably be the very same armies responsible for all the chaos?

THOMAS SZASZ

Dr Thomas Szasz is an interesting individual. He is Professor of Psychiatry Emeritus at the State University of New York at Syracuse and Lifetime Fellow of the American Psychiatric Association. Although reaching the pinnacle of his profession, Dr Szasz has repeatedly denounced psychiatry as *"...probably the single most destructive force that has affected American society within the last fifty years."* An author of 23 books, including *The Myth of Mental Illness*, described by *Science* magazine as *"bold and often brilliant"*, the Hungarian-born specialist has covered, in his writings, every type of abuse carried out by his profession. Szasz pronounces psychiatry guilty, not only of gross abuses of power and

6

human rights over its patients, <u>but also for the far-reaching, deleterious effects its philosophies have had on society throughout the world</u>:

"Psychiatry is a part of the general liberal ethos.... Everybody is a victim, everybody has special rights, no responsibilities. This psychiatric view has so completely infiltrated [global thinking], *people don't even think of it as psychiatry."* [2]

THE *MIND GAME* MISSION

This book traces the origins of psychiatry - this 'science of the mind' - and lays bare the startling and unsettling history of the Trojan Horse that has taken up residence in our midst. Without doubt, there are good men and women working with all the best intentions within the various fields of mental health. We will examine and hear from many of these as we proceed. Indeed, it is, in large part, their incredible testimonies and information that have made this extraordinary book possible. Part 1 deals with psychiatry itself, while Part 2 examines the major 'mental disorders' from their true and vital standpoints. And it is here that the good news about our predicament is truly seen. Is there really such a thing as 'mental disease', or is the reality for us and our societies altogether more straightforward and, most importantly, manageable?

For the millions who wrestle with Alzheimer's, Parkinson's, ADD/ADHD, schizophrenia, anorexia, depression, dyslexia and violence in the home, there is great news! My task in the pages that follow is to report to you the leading research on these issues from the mouths of the specialists themselves, so the reader may make up their own mind on how to proceed from here.

For those unsettled and perplexed by the predicaments of the modern world and why seemingly nothing is being done about them, the journey we will shortly take will explain the nature of Wiseman's *"palpable, destructive force"*, and how it has gained so much power over us. More to the point, this book discusses measures whereby the public may retake control over much of what has been given up or taken away. If you are sympathetic to the mission of this book, then take heart, for there are millions of people who think the same way you do. If we are to pass on to our children a future world that contains any legacy at all of decency,

---

[2] Citizen's Commission of Human Rights (CCHR) interview with Dr Thomas Szasz, 17th September 1993

honesty and a moral compass, then we must discuss and resolve the answers to the ultimate question that faces our world today:

"What on Earth is going on?"

- Part 1 -
Psychiatry and Social Control
- A History -

Going Through the Great Change
(Do Not Allow Your Worst Animals to Breed)

The 1800's were a pivotal time for man. Fuelled by the momentum generated by the technological discoveries of Newton, Descartes and the industrial pioneers, the industrial revolution was in full swing. The Victorian era became synonymous with the heady and emotionally buoyant enthusiasm of man gaining the ascendancy over his harsh, unforgiving global environment, especially in Europe and America and their respective principalities. New technologies were being developed yearly. Rail travel, steamships, global trade and travel, the new mail services, banking, electricity, exploration and indeed newspapers to report all such wondrous things opened up a new world for even the most humble member of the public to consider and become amazed. One technological discovery rapidly begot another. Few however were prepared to consider the long-term implications of such rapid advances in science, finance, engineering, textiles, travel, medicine, social order and the justice system. Indeed, the expanding differences these discoveries would make, not only to the material world in which man lived, but perhaps more significantly, the difference this revolution was to have in how man spiritually was coming to view himself, his purpose and his origins, was to change forever his perceptions of the world around him.

THOMAS ROBERT MALTHUS (1766-1834)

Leading British economist Thomas Malthus gave voice to a major problem he believed was dogging society. That, while food production was indeed increasing in a linear fashion, the population was growing exponentially. Malthus saw a future world in which indiscriminate growth of population would soon outstrip mankind's ability to feed itself. Malthus blamed the problem on the expanding working classes. An end had to be put to their 'sexual mania'. His published work, *An Essay on the Principle of Population as it Affects the Future Improvement of Society*, became extremely popular with the British aristocracy, who were noting with alarm the growth of the working classes and already anticipating future social control problems. Malthus' sentiments, to those who adopted them, seemed scientific, well articulated and, more significantly, encapsulated an outline of self-preservation for the upper classes.

Malthus advocated that the wages of the working classes be frozen, so as not to allow the latter the financial resources to afford more children. Welfare should also be abandoned in case it produced laziness in the population and encouraged an increase in the size of families to claim more benefits. Malthus saw social catastrophes, such as famine, starvation, pestilence and war, as natural, even desirable guardians of the population status quo - a belief that still permeates and influences much of Third World population politics today.[3] Malthus was determined to enforce what he deemed necessary measures to curb *"the reckless fertility of the poor"*. He also believed that, if necessary, a nation should *"subject itself to the periodically recurring shrinking of the population surplus through famine, pestilence or war."*[4]

In their book, *Psychiatrists – The Men Behind Hitler*, authors Röder, Kubillus and Burwell articulate the real legacy of Malthus' persuasions:

"Malthus was received in certain circles 'like a divine revelation', writes historian Will Durant. But Malthus was less visionary than he was father of a new kind of witch-hunt – the pursuit of the expendable inferiors. It was Malthus' influence that caused William Pitt, then the British Prime Minister, not only to withdraw the legislation which he had introduced to improve the welfare of the poor, but also to call for cuts in the wages of working people.

In 1834, Malthus achieved one of his biggest successes. The British Parliament passed legislation that provided for the establishment of poor houses in which men and women would be strictly separated – to check "the unstoppable population surplus". Malthus' idea of introducing moral barriers to limit population growth had been legislatively implemented in tangible form."[5]

CHARLES DARWIN (1809-1882)
In his autobiography, naturalist Darwin observed:

"In October 1838... I happened to read for amusement Malthus on Population.... it at once struck me that under these circumstances favourable variations would tend to be preserved and unfavourable ones to be destroyed.... Here then I had at last got a theory by which to work."[6]

---

[3] Ransom, Steven & Phillip Day, *World Without AIDS*, Credence Publications, England: 2001

[4] Durrant, Will, *Die Napoleonische Ära*, Frankfurt, Berlin, 1982, p.91

[5] Röder, Thomas, Kubillus, Volker & Anthony Burwell, *Psychiatry – The Men Behind Hitler*, Freedom Publishing, Los Angeles: 1995, p.12

[6] Durrant, Will, *Die Napoleonische Ära*, op. cit. p.93

To understand the impact Darwin was to have on 19th century science and philosophy, one must appreciate the notion, prevailing at that time, that man's fortunes were indeed in the ascendancy. It must have been intoxicating for Darwin, a privileged citizen of the most powerful empire on Earth, to view the spectacular successes of the new industrial sciences and admire their impact on mankind. Through the development of impressive new military technology, such as battleships, the new breach-loaded artillery and rifle, followed later by the machine gun, science was implicitly teaching that man now held dominion, not only over 'lesser animals', but also over his own glorious destiny. New empires had germinated in America, Germany, Russia, Austria and Japan, buoyant on this passionate, intoxicating new superhuman ethic, now being celebrated in opera, symphony, theatre and the arts.

The new science of archaeology was also uncovering unthinkably large bones, spurring new theories on man's beginnings – beliefs which would bring their supporters into the inevitable, direct challenge to the traditionally held biblical account of the Earth's and man's origins. Against the backdrop of 19th century human achievement and its concomitant belief that man was now capable of anything, religion came to be viewed with a covert, almost apologetic scepticism by the proponents of the new scientific method. As time progressed, the irresistible tide of materialistic advancement emboldened those who defied traditional beliefs and ethics, as the boundless possibilities of science and the new theories offered an unchaining of traditional paradigms, and were reported daily in the newspapers.

Challenges to the teachings of the Christian churches were soon being openly heard and seen. The public sensed a beguiling and forbidden moral liberation in the air. The biblical accounts of man's origins and his place under the yolk of a morally accountable God were soon being written up in the popular press by scientists of the New Way as mythical, fanciful and plain unscientific.

In the 1830's, Englishman Charles Lyell had invented the Geologic Column, which chronologically tabulated the different eras he believed existed since the formation of the world. New and unfamiliar terms such as the Cretaceous, Jurassic, Cainozoic and Palaeozoic Eras became the road-signs describing the ancient ascendancy of man over his environment and other creatures. Vitalised by the novelty of the prehistoric dinosaur, the conundrum of astronomy and the heady possibilities of the new physics and chemistry, science closed ranks around the new knowledge. Theory often became fact as the leading thinkers of the age set their imaginations loose to examine the fundamental, enormous questions surrounding man's distant past, uncertain present and ultimate destiny.

The impact of Lyell on the public mind was epoch-shaping. But it was Darwin, the keen supporter of Malthus' population ideas and Lyell's Geologic Column, who would subsequently solidify the schools of evolutionary thought already in existence by the early 19ᵗʰ century. The 1859 publication of his book *On the Origin of Species and the Preservation of Favoured Races in the Struggle for Life* became a new Bible to the world - an alternative explanation of man's past which, as part of its legacy, brought to those who believed in it the Trojan Horse of a new and unfamiliar moral liberty. The title of Darwin's work alone gives an insight into the race prejudices that were fully formed in his day, prejudices that would have a tragic and far-reaching denouement in the century to follow.

EVOLUTION - THE LEGACY OF LYELL AND DARWIN

The idea of evolution, as expounded by Lyell, Darwin and their supporters, was to explain the origins of life on Earth without the involvement of a Creator God. At the base of Darwin's contention was the theory that somehow *living matter had formed itself from inorganic matter*. A natant, primordial germ had developed, which, over the billions of years following, mutated and bred, through the survival of the fittest transitions, into the different branches of living organisms we recognise today. Insects, fish, amphibians, reptiles, birds, mammals and humans – Darwin held that all living things had originated from the same ultimate, microscopic, simple-celled ancestor, and indeed then began their evolutionary ascent.

Contrary to notions in the church of a biblically derived young Earth, the world of Lyell and Darwin had to be immensely ancient, for otherwise there would not be enough time for evolution's haphazardry to work its plan. Countless scientifically-named epochs had to range off into the dim, misty corridors of the past in order for monkeys to turn into men, reptiles to grow feathers and turn into birds, whales to become cows, rats to morph into bats, and fishes to grow legs, crawl up onto dry land, shed their scales and begin breathing air. Each form had to evolve into a more complex version of its predecessor through beneficial mistakes, in direct opposition to the Second Law of Thermodynamics, the universal scientific maxim which teaches that matter is always breaking down from the complex to the simple, and energy in the universe is becoming more unavailable as time passes.

In the world of the evolutionist, nothing on Earth was constructed by the hand of God. Indeed, to many who followed Darwin, there was no God, no universal right or morality - just blind, random chance. Survival of the fittest. Man had finally become man. Nothing more than an evolved animal. An animal which had survived against huge odds to triumph over its harsh and unforgiving environment.

Anthropologists in the nineteenth century were so obsessed with finding 'the missing link' between apes and humans to provide the necessary scientific underpinning for evolution that one expedition after another set off to scour the Earth for evidence of an upright 'in-between'. Some had noticed from naturalists' sketches that the Australian Aborigines had the requisite protruding brows and other supposed features of a human transitional form. So off the scientists sailed with their shovels and their picks to dig up a few corpses and bring them back for analysis.

The problem was, Darwin's soldiers soon ran out of Aborigine graves to rob, so they began shooting the indigenous natives for specimens. Not one full-blooded, Tasmanian Aborigine escaped the awful genocide that followed and so none exist today. At the present time, there are over 33,000 sets of human remains in the crypts of the American Smithsonian and the British Natural History Museum, stockpiled in an attempt to prove the reality of Darwin's evolution.

Perhaps most sinister was Darwin's strange mix of his own evolutionary sentiments with Malthus' emotional solutions to preserve the British aristocracy, which had so impressed Darwin decades before. In what can now be regarded as a darkly prophetic letter to William Graham, Professor of Jurisprudence in Belfast, Darwin wrote:

"Looking at the world at no very distant date, what an endless number of the lower races will have been eliminated by the higher civilised races throughout the world." [7]

---

[7] Darwin, Charles, Die Abstammung des Menschen und die geschlechtliche Zuchtwahl, Part 1, Stuttgart, 1871, p.146 (translated)

FRIEDRICH WILHELM NIETZSCHE (1844-1900)

Contemporary to Darwin came another of the new thinkers – the German philosopher Friedrich Nietzsche. Nietzsche's iconoclastic declarations, couched in the most momentous rhetoric, would later be condemned by many as some of the most outrageous and inhuman concepts ever to blight humanity. But in the heady 'anything-goes' atmosphere of the mighty surge in scientific development that characterised the 1800's, citizens were becoming increasingly used to having their minds boggled with the latest news in social and technical development. And Nietzsche was only happy to contribute.

Karl Schlechta, perhaps one of the most comprehensive researchers of Nietzsche's works, sums up the philosopher's core beliefs and teachings as follows:

Values and virtues, charity and kindness are an irrelevance and mean nothing: *"Here is an insight, which has been formulated by me for the first time; that there are no moral truths at all.... Morality is only an interpretation of certain phenomena, or, more precisely, a misinterpretation."* [8]

The existence of man and his physical realm are without design or purpose and cannot be comprehended: *"The world – including mankind – as it truly is, is without any purpose, and is nonsense!"* [9]

A woman is an inferior being.

The only life worthy to be lived is that of the 'superhuman', who is characterised by a desire for war, power, and possesses the innate physical strength to use force as a means of achieving control. [10]

War is beautiful - a natural force that should be embraced: *"They [the superhumans] are always looking for an enemy. In some of them is a hatred at first sight. They love peace as a means towards new wars, and they love a short peace more than a long one."*

Certain races are superior to other races.

---

[8] Nietzsche, Friedrich, Book III, p.425
[9] Nietzsche, Friedrich, Book V, p.91
[10] Nietzsche, Friedrich, Book II, p.589

RELIGION DESPISED

Nietzsche's hatred of Christianity marks him as one of the proponents of the new 'free morality'. More profoundly though, Nietzsche conveys the idea to his readers that the concepts of mercy, kindness, charity and love, as expounded by Jesus Christ, are in fact the complete antithesis of the true way, since Jesus, in Nietzsche's view, seeks to help the weak at the expense of the strong:

"Christianity, rooted in Jewish tradition and nothing more than a plant from its soil, is a counter-movement against any morals of the breeding, the race, the privileges – it is the anti-Aryan religion par excellence: Christianity, the transformation of all Aryan values... the evangelism of the poor, the inferior, the complete rise of all the down-trampled, the wretched and poor against the Race...." [11]

Nietzsche loathes the idea that the meek stand even the slightest chance of inheriting the Earth. His ideas about the Master Race, The Cleansing of the Race, the Industrious Race, all revolve around the mythical Aryan ideal. That the Aryans will hold power over the Earth in a glorious struggle is a foregone conclusion to the famous philosopher. The Aryan will triumph over the Deteriorated Races.[12] Here we see, prior to 1900, the idea, fully articulated, of a genetically superior human race – the Aryans – wielding war and power as a glorious, mighty thing to behold. At the same time, the reader is desensitised to the suffering and eventual demise of the unclean and deteriorated races.

FRANCIS GALTON AND THE BIRTH OF EUGENICS

English psychologist Francis Galton, a half-cousin to Charles Darwin, coined the concept of 'social-Darwinism', merging Darwin's evolutionary sentiments on animals with the desire to manipulate human evolution. He named his 'science' *eugenics*. Here Man is essentially an animal, and therefore, to obtain the optimum quality of this animal in society, selective breeding of superior stock, with the simultaneous 'reducing' of inferior or diseased stock, will guarantee the eradication of the negative aspects of natural selection. Evolution needs a hand, after all.

Negroes are closer to ape than humans, and are still in their evolutionary ascent, according to Galton: *"The average intellectual*

---

[11] Nietzsche, Friedrich, Book III, p.428
[12] Nietzsche, Friedrich, Book IV, p.430

standard of the Negro is some two grades below our own." [13] Galton also vocalises on another sector of humanity: *"The Jews are specialised for a parasitical existence upon other nations."* [14]

Galton's ideas are to influence even the influencers. Darwin himself is convinced of the need for eugenics when he writes:

"With the savage, the weak in body or mind are soon eliminated; and those that survive commonly exhibit a vigorous state of health. We civilised men, on the other hand, do our utmost to check the process of elimination; we build asylums for the imbecile, the maimed, and the sick; we institute Poor Laws; and our medical men exert their utmost skill to save the life of every one to the last moment.... Thus the weak members of society propagate their own kind. No one who has attended the breeding of domestic animals will doubt that this must be highly injurious to the race of man. It is surprising how soon a want of care, or care wrongly directed, leads to the degeneration of a domestic race; but excepting in the case of man himself, <u>hardly anyone is so ignorant as to allow his worst animals to breed</u>." [15]

Who wants to wait millions of years before evolution and natural selection have wrought their magic on society? Although the idea of eugenics - in effect, giving evolution a much-needed helping hand - soon gains a significant foothold in the minds of the forward-thinkers of Darwin's day, it is to be a more powerful clique of players who will usurp eugenic social engineering and evolution for their own designs, which in turn are to spawn the racist and nihilistic sub-philosophies which plunge Europe for the next seventy years into the abyss of world war.

---

[13] Quoted in Lapon, Lenny, *Mass Murderers in White Coats*, Springfield, Massachusetts, Psychiatric Genocide Research Institute, 1986, pp.75-76

[14] Quoted in Lapon, Lenny, *Mass Murderers in White Coats*, op. cit. pp.75-76

[15] Darwin, Charles, quoted in Bernhard Schreiber, (San Francisco: Section 5 Books, 1983), pp.11-12

Doyens of the Mind - The New Brain Scientists

Evolution, eugenics and the new sciences of the 1800's also birth a new science of the mind – psychiatry. Although the word means 'doctor [*iatros*] of the soul', psychiatry will ironically deny the concept of a human soul almost from the profession's inception.

Psychiatry as a recognised profession begins humbly enough in the early 1800's, concerning itself with the custodial care of the madman. Since the start of man, the insane and the mentally impaired had always been a enigma for society, requiring care and control. However, this service to society, which began with the localising of the mentally impaired in almshouses and sanitaria, albeit as brutal as the infamous British Bedlam 'hospital' of the thirteenth century with its whips and chains, begins to expand rapidly in the 19th century under the influence of a self-styled American expert on 'the diseases of the mind', Dr Benjamin Rush.

BENJAMIN RUSH
Rush is even today regarded as the founder of the modern mental health movement, so much so that his likeness adorns the seal of today's American Psychiatric Association. Yet Rush's methods and theories were, to say the least, extraordinary. Rush believed crime to be a curable disease. Understanding murder and rape to be symptoms of this disorder, Rush advocated having criminals transferred from police custody to that of psychiatrists.[16]

The doctor's therapies for the insane included revolving them in a specially designed chair for extended periods, torturing them with frigid water baths, bleeding the patient profusely to relieve the 'excessive action' in their brain, and terrifying them with threats of further 'treatments'. *"The deception,"* Rush stated, *"would be a justifiable one if it served to cure him of his disease."* Rush believed that only through the physician exercising total control over his patient in every respect - physically, psychologically and spiritually – could the madness be cured.[17]

---

[16] Rush, Benjamin, "Medical Inquiries and Observations upon the Diseases of the Mind", Published 1812.

[17] Szasz, Thomas, *The Manufacture of Madness*, Harper and Row, New York: 1970, pp.146-147

Influenced by the racist and supremacist sentiments of Weishaupt, Voltaire, Rousseau and Lyell – that the lower animals were in dire need of guidance by a knowledgeable élite – Dr Benjamin Rush's view of the black race was summed up in his theory of 'negritude' – namely that black skin was a disease affliction and that the healthy Negro should be white. Psychiatrist Thomas Szasz quotes Rush, in the latter's *Medical Inquiries*, stating, *"However well they appear to be satisfied with their colour, there are many proofs of their preferring that of the white people."*[18]

American William Cobbett was so vehemently opposed to Rush's views and techniques that he published *The Rush-Light*, a periodical produced specifically to expose Rush and his works. Even after Rush sued and virtually bankrupted Cobbett for defamation, the dogged investigator moved to another state and continued his attacks.[19]

Dr Carl Binger, a modern-day Rush biographer, writes: *"The doubts that Cobbett cast on Rush's claims for his methods were, as a matter of fact, justifiable. Indeed, in the long run, they probably helped discredit a system of medicine that time has not sustained. Cobbett claimed to have established mathematically that Rush had killed more patients than he had cured."*[20]

Rush's subsequent experiments were regarded by many as barbarous and lethal, many of his patients in the Philadelphia area perishing with the trauma of their 'cures'.[21] Yet even today, Rush is still venerated as the consummate mental health authority of his day.

Was Rush simply buying into the élitist sentiments of his 'free-thinking' contemporaries? Bavarian revolutionary Adam Weishaupt's concept of iron obedience wielded by a ruling cryptocracy, if necessary applied through brute force, was designed to produce in the target population a feeling of resignation, apathy and lack of resistance. The idea promoted was that the 'cattle' would be so cowed by the superior power as to believe that all resistance was useless, and thus render themselves far more easily controlled. This concept undeniably became successfully installed as one of the main tenets of psychiatry and the treatment of

---

[18] Szasz, Thomas, *The Manufacture of Madness*, op. cit. p.45
[19] Binger, Carl, *Revolutionary Doctor: Benjamin Rush 1746-1813*, W W Norton & Co., New York: 1966, pp.246-247
[20] Ibid.
[21] Szasz, Thomas, *The Manufacture of Madness*, op. cit. p.157

'mental' patients by Rush. As early as 1810, Johann Christian Reil, Professor of Medicine at the University of Berlin, who first coined the term 'psychiatry', was already articulating this sinister concept, when he wrote:

"Through strong painful impressions we capture the patient's attention, accustom him to unconditional obedience, and indelibly imprint on his heart the feeling of necessity. The will of his superior must be such a firm, immutable law for him that he will no more resist it than he would rebel against the elements." [22]

WILHELM WUNDT

Towards the end of the nineteenth century, psychiatry became restless, impatient to break out of the insane asylum and flex its new ideas. At this time, a psychiatric world-view was in full development and the profession began moving from supervising the custodial insane towards the concept of the prevention and eradication of insanity in general society. Not content just to deal with life's incarcerated human wretches, the pioneers in mental health moved with determination into the public eye with several far-reaching agendas.

Professor Wilhelm Wundt, of Leipzig University in Germany, made his historic declaration in 1879 that man had no soul. Wundt, an ardent evolutionist, reported that man, this higher form of animal, was nothing more than a stimulus-response creature whose behaviour could be controlled using science. Wundt's implicit challenge to the Church's continued right to administer mental and spiritual healing to the populations was the catalyst which brought a new alternative to religious counselling into the public's mind –a new 'science of the mind' that could benefit all society – the science of 'psychiatry'. Psychologist G Stanley Hall, actually an ordained minister, was an avid student of Wundt's and a keen

---

[22] Quoted in Kraepelin, Emil, *One Hundred Years of Psychiatry*, Philosophical Library, Inc., New York: 1961, pp.92-94, translated from the German essay written in 1917.

supporter of the concept of eugenics. Studying at the University of Berlin in 1868, his courses included anatomy, theology, anthropology and psychiatry. Hall's biographer, David Hothersall, writes:

"Given Hall's theoretical position, we should not be surprised that he was interested in eugenics. He was in fact an enthusiastic proponent of eugenic controls and left money in his estate to establish a chair of genetic psychology at Clark University [USA]. Hall was a firm believer in 'higher' and 'lower' human races. He believed the Negro race to be at an early stage of human development, and dependent upon the 'higher', more advanced white race for its development and supervision." [23]

Author Bruce Wiseman agrees that the confluence of materialism, evolutionary theory, revolutionary sentiment against the existing social structures and the exploding influence of science into ordinary citizens' lives in the late 1800's was the ideal womb that subsequently birthed the modern mental health movement:

"Materialism is merely an idea that says that nothing exists but matter - the physical. There is no God, no soul, no validity to religion and its accompanying moral stance. One can readily see the consequences of such a belief riding in on the coat-tails of a rapidly advancing Science and even being passed off as scientific fact – as indeed it has been.

Through intellectual sleight-of-hand, scientific materialism boldly claims that since spiritual matters or the mind or the will can't be measured with physical instruments, they therefore don't exist and have no place in scientific theory." [24]

Wundt's influence on the public to view psychiatry as a 'medical science' dovetailed completely with Darwin's evolutionary and eugenics influences. The spectacle of 'great men of science', such as Wundt and Hall - imposing looking, dignified, well-versed in speech - declaring that man was no more than the result of his random and haphazard evolution, and as such was not responsible for his behaviour, completely rotated 19th century European society's long-accepted view of man being accountable for his actions. Science, materialism and evolutionary view-points became the hot topics of the day. And the public, spurred on by the vivid pictures

---

[23] Hothersall, David, *History of Psychology*, Temple University Press, Philadelphia, 1984, p.268
[24] Wiseman, Bruce, *Psychiatry - the Ultimate Betrayal*, op. cit.

painted for them by the newspapers of a society about to take a quantum leap into a new era of scientific understanding and technological marvels, found themselves enthralled, captivated - impatient for more.

Wundt's philosophies also attacked the concept of 'free will'. If man was now able to assign his behaviour to causes beyond his control, then the Christian religion, which teaches that a person has 'free will' to exercise moral choices and is responsible for his actions, was surely, according to the new science, nothing more than cringing tradition – an embarrassing superstition; at best, a narcotising influence on the masses; at worst, an iron, inflexible barrier to the freeing of man's restless, imprisoned genius.

WILLIAM JAMES

William James, a student of Wundt's, is sometimes regarded as 'the Father of American Psychology'. James' solicitous belittling of religion as 'a therapeutic' which could make people 'feel better', is more properly understood in the context of his age. James biographer Clarence J Karier clarifies:

By the time James published 'The Varieties of Religious Experience' in 1902, Friedrich Nietzsche, in 'Gay Science' (1882), had already declared: 'God is dead. God remains dead. And we have killed him'. With both Nietzsche and James, we pass from a culture with God at its centre to a culture with man at its centre. This fundamental shift in Western thought initiated a corresponding shift in the ideological structure of the social system.... Western society underwent a transformation of the basis for personal and collective values.... Salvation was now a matter of survival, sin became a physical sickness, and such religious rituals as confession, designed to alleviate guilt and atone for sin, were replaced by individual and group psychotherapeutic interventions, designed to alleviate the guilt of anxiety neurosis.

These then were the signs of an emerging therapeutic society, a society born in the closing decade of the nineteenth century and nourished in the secular world of the twentieth century.... William James, as one of the first secular theologians of this new therapeutic society, conceptualised the fundamental ideas that came to underpin that society." [25]

IVAN PAVLOV

Before long, new stars were rising in the 'science of the mind' pantheon. Early in the twentieth century, Russian physiologist and psychologist Ivan Pavlov, together with his colleague, Vladimir Bekhterev, a student of Wundt's, were inducing conditioned responses in dogs, causing them to salivate with the ringing of a bell, having trained the animals to link the bell's tone to food and pleasure. Pavlov's testimony is cited almost invariably in every beginner's psychology textbook – Pavlov, moving the psychology/psychiatric student in the desired direction, namely, to conclude from his work that man, like the dogs, is nothing more than a stimulus-response animal. In later decades, Pavlov's theories on mind conditioning would lead to the barbaric brainwashing and mind control programs carried out in the Soviet Union, China, Great Britain, the United States and Canada.

EMIL KRAEPELIN

German psychiatrist Emil Kraepelin gave the world the word and concept of 'paranoia'. Another dubbed 'the Father of Psychiatry', Kraepelin's evolutionary beliefs also led him down the path of humans-as-animals and the right to 'play God' over those diagnosed 'mentally ill'. At the time of psychiatry's genesis as the new method of diagnosing the mentally disturbed, caring for the latter was a thankless task few wanted, with patients being incarcerated under the most appalling conditions. In

---

[25] Karier, Clarence J, *Scientists of the Mind*, Chicago: University of Illinois Press, 1986, p.28

his *One Hundred Years of Psychiatry*, Kraepelin quotes an anonymous reporter, who, in 1795, was constrained to write:

> *"A humanitarian is bound to shudder when he discovers the plight of the unfortunate victims of this dreadful affliction; many of them grovel in their own filth on unclean straw that is seldom changed, often stark naked and in chains, in dark, damp dungeons where no breath of fresh air can enter. Under such terrifying conditions, it would be easier for the most rational person to become insane than for a madman to regain his sanity."* [26]

The question confronting Kraepelin, Wundt and others who would follow them was simple: could insanity be explained and cured? Psychiatry was labelling 'insanity' a physical disease of the mind, with no proof, and invariably the treatments resorted to a brutalising force to overwhelm the patient mentally and physically. Thomas Szasz writes:

> *"These have included whipping, flogging, the application of ants, scabies and stinging nettles, surgical removal or cauterising (burning) of the clitoris and removing a woman's ovaries. Masturbation, originally considered a mental illness, was treated by circumcision and cauterising the spine and genitals."* [27]

Later, psychosurgery, or lobotomy – the surgical removal of tissues from the brain – would follow, along with electro-convulsive therapy to the brain (ECT) and psychotropic drugs to alter behaviour. Behind the scenes, the terror continued. Dr Elliot S Valenstein reports that within a five-year period in the 1930's, insulin coma, metrazol shock, electroshock and lobotomies were widely prescribed by psychiatrists worldwide. All caused physical damage to the patients. None ever cured. [28]

German authors Drs. Hans Georg Guse and N Schmake recount that Emil Kraepelin had *"...adopted the central thesis of Social Darwinism, whereby a person's social rank is the expression of a natural allotment of qualities and abilities.... Kraepelin then began to consider the mentally handicapped as 'a heavy burden for our nation'. Along with many other academics, he saw the solution to social disorder in a strong leader: 'An*

---

[26] Quoted in Kraepelin, Emil, *One Hundred Years of Psychiatry*, op. cit. p.11
[27] Szasz, Thomas, *The Manufacture of Madness*, op. cit. pp.278, 310-311; also Howells, John G, *World History of Psychiatry*, Brunner/Mazel, Inc. New York: 1975, p.264
[28] Valenstein, Elliot S, *Blaming the Brain*, The Free Press, New York: 1998, p.205

unrestricted ruler with the power to intervene in our way of life would bring about the reduction in insanity within a few decades!' Kraepelin supported the idea of sterilisation for certain psychopaths, maintaining that the passing on of inferior hereditary traits would thus be avoided." [29]

Kraepelin's self-evident support for Malthusian social intervention with an omnipotent authority to purify man of his hereditary insanities was by no means an isolated sentiment. In 1897, Dr M W Barr, president of the American Association for the Study of Feeblemindedness, strongly advocated sterilisation as a eugenics measure. [30]

Bruce Wiseman also reports: *"In the early twentieth century, psychiatrist Edwin Katzen-Ellenbogen, who was ultimately convicted of war crimes as a doctor at Buchenwald concentration camp, 'drafted for the governor the law of sterilisation of epileptics, criminals and the incurably insane for the State of New Jersey.' Other states – 22 in all – followed suit with similar laws."* [31]

It is testament to the mistaken direction psychiatry took from the outset to cure 'mental illness' that the answer to the question of whether so-called mental disorders could be treated and cured at all proved troubling for one of psychiatry's chief architects. A pondering Emil Kraepelin wrote in 1917:

"The impenetrable darkness that hides the innermost workings of the brain and their relation to psychic manifestations, and finally the inadequacy of our instruments for dealing with extremely complicated issues, must cause even the most confident investigator to doubt whether it is possible to make any appreciable progress towards psychiatric knowledge and understanding." [32]

THE 'SCIENTIFIC UNDERPINNING' OF EUGENICS

Kraepelin's observations were to be one of many indictments against psychiatry and its brutal methodologies which followed. By 1914 and the onset of World War 1, the head of the American Medico-Psychological Association, today known as the American Psychiatric Association (APA),

---

[29] Guse, Hans Georg & N Schmake, "Psychiatry and the Origins of Nazism", *International Journal of Health Services*, Vol. 10, No.2, 1980
[30] Lapon, Lenny, *Mass Murderers in White Coats*, op. cit. p.76
[31] Wiseman, Bruce, op. cit. p.62
[32] Kraepelin, Emil, *One Hundred Years of Psychiatry*, op. cit. p.9

was confirming that mental illness was hereditary, and as such should be controlled through the eugenics system:

"That a radical cure of the evils incident to the dependent mentally defective classes would be effected if every feeble-minded person, every imbecile, every habitual criminal, every manifestly weak-minded person, and every confirmed inebriate were sterilised, is a self-evident proposition. By this means we could practically, if not absolutely, arrest, in a decade or two, the reproduction of mentally defective persons, as surely as we could stamp out smallpox absolutely if every person in the world could be vaccinated." [33]

We see here a number of pivotal developments that are already entrenched in the minds of psychiatrists and psychologists by 1914, and the significance of these should not go unnoticed. The above words are spoken at a presidential address to the forerunner organisation of the American Psychiatric Association, the body governing all areas of mental illness at the time. Firstly we learn that the 'benefits' of sterilisation to prevent reproduction by 'mental defectives' are already 'self-evident'. Secondly, we can deduce that presumably only the American Medico-Psychological Association has the expertise to define who is a 'mental defective' and who isn't, thus giving eugenics concepts 'a scientific respectability'. Thirdly, alcoholism is now a mental illness and habitual crime a mental derangement rather than the result of greed, social factors or just the plain, 'sane' desire of a person to commit a crime.

SIGMUND FREUD

Another shaper of the age, Sigmund Freud, proposed that man was a product of his past experiences. With Freud we once again see man as the sum total of the effect of his environment and thus, not in control of his actions. Under Freud, past psychological abuse becomes the explanation for current criminal behaviour or stress, however extreme. Therefore, although culpable of the crime, the criminal is not responsible, if evidence can be found in his past to 'justify' why he committed the crime.

Freud, himself owning a serious and well-known libido-stimulating cocaine addiction (which no doubt influenced his views on sex), preached

---

[33] Castel Robert, Castel Francoise & Anne Lovell, *The Psychiatric Society*, (Translated by Arthur Goldhammer), Columbia University Press, New York: 1982, pp.46-47. Source for quote is Carlos F MacDonald, "Presidential Address", *American Journal of Insanity*, July 1914, 71:9

sexual promiscuity, even with children, to free man of his 'inhibitions' and all that stress: *"Free sexual intercourse between young males and respectable girls"* was urgently required, or society was *"doomed to fall victim to incurable neuroses which reduce the enjoyment of life to a minimum, destroy the marriage relation, and bring hereditary ruin on the whole coming generation."*[34]

In a personal interview, Al Parides, Professor of Psychiatry at UCLA in Los Angeles, declared that psychiatric values had been *"very influenced, especially by the Freudian influence in regard to sex and morality generally.... If you look at the personal lives of all Freud's followers – his initial disciples – these people certainly have an unbelievable amount of particular problems in the sexual area.... The amount of deviancy as far as their sexual behaviour and so forth is enormous. If you are saying that psychiatry promotes a certain form of morality that is a deviant morality in regard to many areas including sexual behaviour - yes, I would agree."*[35]

Freud had a particular passion for denouncing religion. Religion was the Enemy. The implacable Spoiler of Carnal Pleasures. The Jailer of the Emotions and Stern Guardian over the Primeval, Stone-Age Urges of Humankind. Freud predicted with some relish the eventual death of religion – especially Christianity:

"The scientific spirit generates a certain posture towards matters of this world; before matters of religion it stops for a while, hesitates, at last there too crosses the threshold. In this process there is no stopping; the more the treasures of our knowledge become accessible to people, the more the defection from religious belief will spread, at first only from its obsolete, offensive vestments, but then from its fundamental presuppositions as well."[36]

Thomas Szasz's research highlights an interesting fact. *"Although an entire volume of the Standard Edition of Freud's collected works is devoted to an index, there is no entry for 'responsibility' in it. True to the*

[34] Mindless, Harvey, *Makers of Psychology: The Personal Factor*, Insight Books, New York, 1988, p.32

[35] Interview between Bruce Wiseman and Al Parides, 17th December 1993

[36] Freud, Sigmund, *The Future of an Illusion*, SE XXI, p.38

faith of the master, his acolytes must have felt that responsibility was so unscientific a concept that it was not worth indexing." [37]

Freud today has been widely discredited in professional circles, but still remains, in the public's mind, a giant in the field of mental health. Psychology professor Frank Sulloway, author of *Freud: Biologist of the Mind*, believes *"Freud was wrong in almost every respect."* [38]

ALEISTER CROWLEY

The encroaching influence of psychiatry's architects at the turn of the 20th century were to have a dramatically hostile and disastrous impact upon religion. The banishment of God by this time has also spawned a strong interest in the occult, encouraging a proliferation of tarot readings, séances and Luciferian doctrines, along with their eccentric proponents. No investigation into the huge change in social and religious attitudes of this period can be properly understood without appreciating the extent to which occultism had already penetrated European life by 1900. In 1904, one of Britain's most devious free-thinkers, Aleister Crowley, sits down to write a book. Crowley is originally a member of the Christian Plymouth Brethren sect, but evidently from his youth is a difficult child exhibiting alarming behaviour traits. His own mother brands him 'spawn of Satan'.

Crowley becomes influenced by the writings of Madame Helena Petrovna Blavatsky, a Satanist and founder of the Theosophical Society.[39] Crowley admits he does not know precisely what caused his defection from Christianity: *"I accepted the theology of the Plymouth Brethren. In fact, I could not conceive of the existence of a people who would doubt it. I simply went over to Satan's side and to this hour cannot tell why.... I was not content to believe in a personal devil and serve him in the ordinary sense of the word. I wanted to get hold of him and become his chief of staff."* [40]

---

[37] Szasz, Thomas, *Insanity: The Idea and its Consequences*, John Wiley & Sons, New York: 1987, p.245

[38] Horgan, John, *The Undiscovered Mind*, The Free Press, New York: 1999, p.74; McFarling, Usha Lee, "Analyze This: Why Freud, Discredited, Still on Minds", *The Commercial Appeal*, 21st May 2000

[39] Blavatsky, Helen P, *The Secret Doctrine*, Theosophical University Press, 1989

[40] Symonds, John & Kenneth Grant, *The Confessions of Aleister Crowley*, Viking Penguin, 1989

Crowley claims *The Book of the Law,* first published in 1908, was dictated to him by a spirit he later identifies as Satan.[41] Crowley, it seems, has been instructed to prepare the world for the coming One World Order of the Antichrist, a future world ruler who would be Satan's incarnation on Earth.

Crowley's constant usage of the term 'New Aeon' leads to the popularity of the phrase, 'New Age'. In his widely read and revered *The Book of the Law,* Crowley's aims are expounded upon with deadly seriousness. According to his writings, the coming New Age will be ushered in on a wave of hallucinogenic drugs, strange music and free sex - an odd and improbable prophecy to be given back in the first century of the post-Victorian era. Later, the 1960's arrive and people rapidly begin changing their minds.

Aleister Crowley

Crowley's watchword is *"Do what thou wilt shall be the whole of the law"* (do whatever you want) – a complete unhinging of society from the moral concepts of personal accountability and right/wrong, couched in the quasi-biblical language of the occult. The world seems ill-prepared for the psychedelic explosion of moral rebellion that follows in the 1960's. Psychiatric mind-bending drugs, such as heroin, cocaine, Thorazine, methadone and LSD flood into society, relentlessly promoted by those such as psychologist and pop-drug mystic Timothy Leary, who invites the world to study Crowley and 'turn on, tune in and drop out.' Parents begin losing their children to a more alluring force, one against which, they realise, they have no power.

Crowley is run out of France for his evil ways. At one point he is considered the most wicked man on Earth, having owned up to child sacrifice. Nevertheless, in contrast to his nefarious character is the fact

---

[41] Crowley, Aleister, *The Book of the Law,* Samuel Weiser Inc., 1989

that Crowley is privately admired by many for his ability to go to the max. Posthumously, Crowley becomes the 'patron saint' of rock stars. Thus canonised, his philosophies would be taken up and sung from a thousand stages in a hundred nations to over a billion attentive and impressionable minds around the world in the years which follow.

Getting God off the Backs of the People

That the moral and religious revolutions of the 19th and 20th centuries can be laid at the door of Darwin, Galton, Wundt, Freud, Pavlov and James, is clear in the minds of Dr Parides and Bruce Wiseman. The latter author, former chairman of the Department of History at the John F Kennedy University and US national president of the Citizen's Commission on Human Rights (CCHR), a mental health watchdog organisation, states in his *Psychiatry – The Ultimate Betrayal*:

"Yet while its progress has indeed remained minimal, psychiatry's materialist and anti-religious slant has survived and even prospered. In a 1976 survey of members of the American Psychological Association, 95% reportedly admitted to being atheists and agnostics.[42] So did a majority of psychiatrists in an American Psychiatric Association Task Force report.[43] Dr Al Parides, a former California state chairman for the American Psychiatric Association, confirmed this, saying psychiatrists are 'more likely to be atheists'."[44]

But as the power and influence of the medical and media establishments grew, so too did their commensurate and unrepresentative influences on society. Wiseman puts this into perspective:

"Webster's defines an atheist as one who 'rejects all religious belief and denies the existence of God'. Statistical Abstracts of the United States shows that less than a half percent of the population of North America is atheist. Even if one includes persons 'professing no religion, non-believers, agnostics, free thinkers, and dereligionised secularists indifferent to all religion', they still amount to only 7 percent of the population.

It is an odd situation. Obviously the beliefs of psychiatrists are utterly out of synchronisation with what the rest of the continent is thinking. Yet in their attempts to enlighten society, mental practitioners

---

[42] Larson, David B, et al. "Systematic Analysis of Research on Religious Variables in Four Major Psychiatric Journals", *The American Journal of Psychiatry*, Vol.143, No.3 (March 1986), pp.329-334

[43] *American Journal of Psychiatry*, "Report of the Task Force on Religion and Psychiatry – Phase III", 135:6, June 1978, p.776

[44] Interview between Bruce Wiseman and Al Parides, 17th December 1993

have gone to great lengths to convince the rest of us that we should come around to their way of viewing things." [45]

Wiseman's last point is an important one. A powerful clique, whose revolutionary sentiments represented those of only the smallest minority of the rest of society, were able to influence the majority, especially through the reporting of their agendas in sympathetic newspapers and, later, by eventually soliciting the official stamp of approval from government and medicine.

RELIGION REVILED

As we have seen, the Europe of the 1800's is undergoing massive social change. The French imperial decadence preceding the Napoleonic era has seen the rapid transference of man's beliefs from the religious to the carnal. Historian J R Kantor writes: *"No factor in the evolution of scientific psychology stands out more prominently than the doctrines of French Materialism in the eighteenth century and German Materialism in the nineteenth century.... Materialism is essentially a non-scientific movement, a phenomenon of social transformation and change. In the religious domain, a materialist is simply an atheist."* [46]

The theory of evolution has the ultimate effect for many of getting God off the backs of the people, paving the way for a socially graded, 'acceptable atheism'. For centuries the Christian church had held sway over the morals of man, presiding over pastoral duties, counselling the sick and mentally disturbed, ideally determining, through the application of biblical morality, what was right and wrong. The Church's many lapses into brutality, hypocrisy, simony, extortion and murder however, along with the desire for control over the masses, had not gone unnoticed through the ages. The Catholic Church and its Popes, who had intermittently for centuries carried out tortures, burnings, impalings and a wholesale slaughter of those opposed to the control of Rome, were not the only religious institution to have taken the words of their prophets on occasion and usurped the power of the religious ethic to impose their sovereignty through naked force. The Mohammedans, reformists, Protestants, Jews and a hundred diverse religions, sects and sub-sects all had vied for violent and murderous control over their congregations throughout the centuries. Europe and the Middle East had seen the Christians killing in the name of a disbelieving Jesus; the Mohammedans

---

[45] Wiseman, Bruce, Psychiatry – The Ultimate Betrayal, op. cit. p.13
[46] Kantor, J R, *The Scientific Evolution of Psychology*, Principia Press, 1969, p.186

carrying the sword to the infidel in the name of an unwilling Mohammed; Protestants killing Catholics ironically in the name of Jesus; the Jews defending their very existence, holding before them the flickering torch of the eternal promise of Abraham.

By the time the era of science had dawned with the Reformation, progressive thinkers were already chafing under religious hypocrisy, murder in the name of a Jesus who expressly forbade murder, and the medieval omnipresence of an infallible Church. In 1533 England's King Henry VIII directly challenged the might of the Vatican over the latter's refusal to grant Henry a divorce from his first wife, Katherine of Aragon. In the face of determined Vatican resistance, Henry declared his marriage to Katherine invalid, married Anne Boleyn, broke ties with the Church of Rome, dissolved and plundered its monasteries in his kingdom, and appointed himself head of a new 'Church of England'.

A highly intelligent and brilliant ruler, an accomplished sportsman and a charismatic, complex and flawed individual, Henry was replete with hypocrisies. His disconcerting ability to manipulate his newly-formed Anglican Church to achieve his own earthy ends, together with his raising of the new term 'Majesty' for man, became the true paradox of his age. But the religious power of the Roman Church, which had held civilisation in its moral and political grip for centuries, had been challenged. And Rome had lost.

The age of the New Materialism and Science gathered momentum in the following two centuries and ignited the spark which exploded into the industrial revolution. Suddenly and dramatically, mankind becomes empowered, intellectually, scientifically, spiritually and physically. His thoughts soon turn to grading himself against the lesser fortunates of his own society. But it is in the realm of mental development that man begins to dream a fantastic possibility – a new quantum leap in evolution, aided by a new 'science of the mind'. Off the back of the new evolutionary thought, the 19th century spawned a tremendous surge in interest in examining radical new social ideals through the lens of evolution and eugenics.

THE ILLUMINATI
One of the most influential of these new thinkers in Europe was Adam Weishaupt, an avid follower of Francois Voltaire's atheistic materialism. A brilliant professor of canon law at Ingolstadt University, Bavaria, Weishaupt had been educated by Catholic Jesuits whom he hated.

34

Weishaupt's extreme and revolutionary sentiments entered their operational phase when, on 1st May 1776, he founded the Order of the Illuminati of Bavaria ('the Enlightened Ones'), a secret sect espousing world domination, the suppression of 'inferior' human stock, and violent anti-Christian sentiments. It is thought that Weishaupt stole the name for his new cult from the Order of the Alombrados, a Spanish sect founded in 1520 and covertly supported by the founder of the Jesuits, Ignatius Loyola.

Weishaupt would have been dismissed as a 'crackpot', were it not for the fact that he was influenced by the leading masons of Europe - men like Massenhausen, Von Zwack, the Marquis of Constanza and Baron de Montgelas, who were to assist him in launching his new crusade. Weishaupt's political allegiances were republican and spiritually steeped in the Luciferianism of the Order of the Golden Cross and the system of the Rosicrucians. Weishaupt realised that the quickest way to spread support of his doctrine of world domination to the powerbrokers who would take it seriously was to infiltrate and subvert established Freemasonry to his aims by any and all means possible. Weishaupt saw that Masonry was where the true power and kudos lay. It is a fact that his order would soon have perished but for the assistance of one Baron Adolph Von Knigge, a Templar who had successfully championed Weishaupt's cause and was instrumental in persuading the Masonic orders to adopt the new-born organisation.

Only the cream of the crop in Weishaupt's day were initiated into the Illuminati, the latter having nine conspiratorial rings: Preparation, Novice, Minerval, Illuminus Minor, Freemason, Presbyter, Regent, Magus and Rex - the Rex, or king, being Weishaupt himself, who had adopted the code-name 'Spartacus'. Those in the lower degrees were told then, as they are today, that the grand purpose of the order was: *"...to make of the human race without any distinction of nation, condition or profession, one good and happy family."*

G Edward Griffin tells us: *"By the time the initiate had advanced to the level of 'Presbyter', or priest, his oath of absolute secrecy and obedience had become deadly serious. Only then was he allowed finally to see the ultimate goal of the order. It was the destruction of all religion, replaced by the worship of reason, or humanism, and the destruction of all independent governments, replaced by a New World Order, a world government ruled from behind the scenes by the Illuminated Ones. Needless to say, most members were never allowed to see these goals."*[47]

'Spartacus' Weishaupt himself even poured contempt on the lower echelons of his own organisation, remarking: *"These good folks swell our numbers and fill our money-box. Set yourselves to work. These gentlemen must be made to nibble at the bait. But this sort of people must always be made to believe that the grade they have reached is the last."*[48]

Weishaupt was also cleverly able to coerce key Christians into his sect by sugar-coating his manifestos with quasi-biblical doctrines, ably put together by the tireless Von Knigge. After one leading Protestant figure joined his ecumenical efforts, Weishaupt was ecstatic: *"You can't imagine what respect and curiosity my priest-degree has raised; and, what is wonderful, a famous Protestant divine* [priest], *who is now of the Order, is persuaded that the religion contained in it is the true sense of Christianity. O Man, Man! To what mayest thou not be persuaded? Who would imagine that I was to be the founder of a new religion?"*[49]

Weishaupt's control grew exponentially within Freemasonry. The man was a reckless braggart who incurred enemies as quickly as converts. His organisation gained control of lodges across Europe before being penetrated by agents of his enemies, the Jesuits and sectarian Rosicrucian orders. The Illuminati was briefly exposed in 1785, after one of its members, a priest named Jacob Lang, was struck dead by lightning while out walking with Weishaupt in Ratisbon. The priest's body was placed in the chapel of Saint-Emmeran where a Benedictine monk later found a list of Illuminati members sewn into the clothes of the corpse. Raids by the Elector of Bavaria on the home of prominent Illuminati attorney Von Zwack soon uncovered the conspiracy of Weishaupt's order. The latter was banished to Saxe-Gotha where he lived under the patronage of the Duke Ernest-Louis until his death in 1812.

Exposés of the Illuminati by its members have been few and the public record of Weishaupt's organisation is quite brief. A few early Christian initiates who became horrified after discovering Weishaupt's hidden

---

[47] Griffin, G Edward, *The Capitalist Conspiracy*, a video documentary, American Media, Westlake, CA, 1992
[48] Ibid.
[49] Robison, John, *Proofs of a Conspiracy*, Boston: Western Islands, 1967 (orig. 1798), p.86

agenda - and indeed the ultimate object venerated within his organisation, Lucifer - spoke out and were subsequently murdered. At a secret Masonic conference held at Wilhelmsbad on 16th July 1782, terror was cast into some, such as the Comte de Virieu, who began to see the true evil intent of the new super-organisation emerging. It is said that the assassination of King Gustav of Sweden was ordered at this Congress in full hearing of disbelieving members. De Virieu, in a letter to a friend, wrote about 'tragic secrets' he had brought back with him from the conference: *"I will not confide them to you. I can only tell you that all this is very much more serious than you think. The conspiracy which is being woven is so well thought out that it will be, so to speak, impossible for the Monarchy or the Church to escape from it."* From this time onwards, says his biographer, M. Costa de Beauregard, *"the Comte de Virieu could only speak of Freemasonry with horror."*[50]

Weishaupt's plan for global domination was a bold and ingenious stroke that appealed to those already prepared by the anti-Christian rhetoric of Voltaire and Rousseau. Plainly the Church and monarchies were to be subverted and controlled, and all opposition to the plan swiftly silenced. So successful was the penetration of the Illuminati into established Freemasonry and the Church, that Thomas Frost, in his *Secret Societies of the European Revolution* (vol.1, p.53), has leading Mason Barruel reporting, *"...that the whole of the Masonic lodges comprised in the Grand Orient, 266 in number, were 'illuminated' by the end of March 1789..."*

Weishaupt foresees a world whose populations are controlled by an élite unrestrained by conventional values. The plan is to conquer nations economically and psychologically, leading their governments and 'cattle', as the population is termed, through different psychologically damaging steps which will eventually exhaust them and allow them willingly to be controlled by the élite. Weishaupt's manifesto includes the destruction of Christianity and Judaism, the abolition of private property, the abolition of inheritance, the dismantling of the family unit, the destruction of patriotism, the abolition of all national government - all in order *"that the Luciferian ideal of totalitarianism may be imposed upon all Mankind."*[51]

---

[50] Webster, Nesta H, *World Revolution*, Constable & Co., London: 1921

[51] Griffin, G Edward, op. cit.

COMMUNISM

In 1848, wealthy Illuminati capitalist Friedrich Engels writes a comprehensive distillation of Weishaupt's original plan, which later becomes known as the Communist Manifesto. Karl Marx, often believed to have been the original architect, is a minor advisor whose name is added to the document 18 years after its first publication. Marx himself rises in the constellation of the progressive thinking élite with the publication of his book, *Das Kapital*. On the flyleaf of his manuscript, Karl Marx has attempted to write a dedication in the top right-hand corner which reads: *"To Charles Darwin, from a sincere admirer - Karl Marx."*

Marx sees the theory of evolution as the perfect psychological template for Communism. The man-centred, humanist philosophy Marx espouses preaches power to the people and a clear downing of the Old Way of monarchy and religion. France has successfully shrugged off the yolk of imperial monarchy during its civil war, and the doctrines of Weishaupt, Marx and Engels find immediate favour with those of a strong revolutionary bent. The idea of a coming New Age or New World Order of 'freedom' is sold to the public; an order which will apparently liberate man from the shackles of royalty, poverty, moral control by the Church and its vengeful God. Yet underneath the shiny exterior of this promise of a New Age, the true intentions of its architects lurk, revealing a darker infamy. All aspects of the lives of citizens are to be controlled for their own good down to the last detail. The wealth of nations is to be aggregated into the hands of a few powerful banking dynasties, and the people's reliance on established religion and family ethics will be attacked and eliminated. The New World Order will be headed by a new world government, perpetually controlled behind the scenes by the 'Illuminated Ones'.

Vultures over Europe

In 1901, Britain's Queen Victoria dies. For many, the passing of Britain's longest-living monarch symbolises the ending of an age. Many have known no different, millions having lived and died during the period of her monumental reign. A definite and significant passing is sensed by all – even an end it seems to the visible, moral austerity of the Victorian Era. The sobriety that characterises her magnificent funeral and the period of her mourning eventually passes, and the peoples around the world, raised under her sceptre, begin gathering themselves to contemplate their future.

Inventions, railways, the first airplanes, communications, electric street lamps and the advent of a new century promise the birth of a more alluring future - a bright, sophisticated new modern age of materialism, presided over by Victoria's son, the womaniser and profligate, King Edward VII. People relax and begin to have fun. Britain's power is at its zenith. The sun never sets on the British Empire. Merchants bring their goods to the West from the marvellous and exotic lands of Kipling. Excitement fires a million imaginations. Many sense the dawn of a New Age. The possibilities seem endless. And the soft but determined breeze of change caresses the cheeks of those whose faces are turned expectantly, searching towards the horizon of their future.

PROMOTING HATE

But the new science of the mind and its racist sub-philosophies are to have tragic repercussions for Europe in the first half of the 20th century. Psychiatry produces the necessary flame of racism towards the end of the 1800's by pathologising into 'a disease' the hatred for others. Authors Röder, Kubillus and Burwell report:

"In 1850, psychiatrist C T Groddeck was awarded a doctorate for his dissertation entitled "The Democratic Disease – A New Form of Insanity". In Groddeck's view, every democratically inclined person was insane. In 1854 his colleague, C J Wretholm, 'discovered' the 'Sermon Disease'. Psychiatrist P J Möbius lectured shortly thereafter on the 'psychological feeble-mindedness of the woman'.

Not long thereafter, the leading proponents of psychiatry in Germany were advocating the theory that anyone who refused military service for religious reasons was abnormal and 'sick'. A psychiatrist named Adolf Hoppe characterised conscientious objection to military service as an 'unmistakable expression of ethnic inferiority'. One of psychiatry's leading figures, Richard von Krafft-Ebing, added to his list of varieties of mental disorders 'political and reformatory insanity' – meaning any inclination to form a different opinion from that of the masses. An excellent tool was thus created for politicians to denounce opponents. With the help of psychiatric classifications, it was now possible to perform the character assassination of a political enemy in the wink of an eye – anyone who disagreed was obviously insane." [52]

By 1871, the trend is in full-swing. Psychiatrist Carl Stark publishes a treatise entitled "The Psychical Degeneration of the French People", in which he presents the concept that the French have degenerated into mass-delusion, warmongering and delirium. Now, with being French a mental illness, others come forward. Löwenfeld discusses 'the national character of the French and its sickly excesses':

"The kind of mental abnormalities emerging nowadays belong to a borderline area which I label as psychopathy, psychopathic inferiorities, psychopathic conditions, and so on. I believe therefore that it is justified now to talk about a 'psychopathia gallica', which should by now be obvious." [53]

Psychiatry is soon seen adopting the paradox of glorifying war and xenophobia while at the same time denouncing pacifism and tolerance of minorities. The warmongering pronouncements of Nietzsche, Houston Stewart Chamberlain, Joseph-Arthur, Comte de Gobineau and others of their persuasion have, by the first decade of the 1900's, taken firm root and primed Europe for war. The Illuminati cryptocracy and its banks, championed by the Rothschild dynasty, are forever courting powerful leaders. They have not been idle in their efforts to subvert nationalism, denigrate and dismantle national sovereignty, corrupt the money supply with their inflatable paper notes of debt (paper currency), and plant in the minds of many the desirability to move towards a world order. Europe has become a patchwork of national treaties which compel countries to go to the aid of their treaty partners in the event that war is declared upon the partner. All that is needed is a spark.

---

[52] Röder, Thomas, Kubillus, Volker & Anthony Burwell, *Psychiatry – The Men Behind Hitler*, op. cit. p.23
[53] Löwenfeld, L, ber den Nationalcharakter der Franzosen und dessen krankhafte Auswüchse, Wiesbaden, Germany: 1914

INTO THE BREACH

On the 28th June 1914, Archduke Franz Ferdinand visits the troubled Austro-Hungarian rebel province of Serbia and enters Sarajevo in a motorcade. As the car carrying the Archduke and his wife Sophie halts to correct a wrong turning, Serbian nationalist Gavrilo Princip steps out of the crowd outside Moritz Schiller's delicatessen and blasts two shots into the vehicle, hitting the Archduke in the throat and Sophie in the abdomen.

The subsequent deaths of the Archduke and his wife set into motion the now famous catastrophic treaty landslide. On 27th July, Austria severs diplomatic ties with Serbia. The following day, spurred on by Austro-Hungarian public outrage over the shooting of Ferdinand by 'a degenerate', Austria declares war on Serbia. The Russians react by mobilising to the aid of their treaty partner, Serbia. Austria reacts by calling in its treaty partner, Germany. On 2nd August, Berlin demands passage for its troops through Belgium. On 3rd August, Germany declares war on 'degenerate' France. On 4th August, Britain comes to the aid of its treaty partner, France, and declares war on Germany. On 5th August, Austria declares war on Russia. World War 1 has begun.

The outbreak of hostilities on a scale hitherto unseen introduces Nietzsche's long-awaited Aryan war. That this is a glorious thing is regularly expounded upon in the almost unbelievable psychiatric literature of the day. Yet not even after the Dantéan phenomenon of millions dead and 20 million wounded will psychiatry be repentant of the role it played. By way of illustrating psychiatry's surviving, racist ethos following World War 1 and the implications of this for psychiatry's involvement in another future war, witness Dr Johannes Bresler, editor-in-chief of the *Psychiatrisch-Neurologische Wochenzeitschrift* (Psychiatric Neurological Weekly), who later in 1926 ominously remarks:

"The world war [WW1] was sacred to us and will remain sacred to us for all eternity. It was <u>and is our just cause</u>." [54]

'WAR NEUROSES'

One of the major battles fought in World War 1 is at Verdun. This battle is fought between France and Germany and begins with an artillery bombardment unprecedented in ferocity. The French draw up over four miles of hub-to-hub artillery and on the opposing front, the Germans have

---

[54] Bresler, Johannes, "Betrachtungen ber geistige Prophylaxe (Schlua)", *Münchner Medizinische Wochenschrift*, 1926, pp.285-288

a similar strike force waiting. It takes France eight days of total national production and all their transportation facilities to haul the newly produced ammunition to the front in preparation for the opening artillery barrage. The Germans begin the attack on 21st February 1916.[55]

Both sides fire millions of artillery rounds before the actual infantry advances begin. Over half a million men are lost during the ten months of battle which follow. First the Germans advance and then the French, driving back the Germans with the help of the British, who open up a major action on the River Somme. During the four-month Battle of the Somme alone, the repeated, atrocious engagements with artillery and machine guns claim the lives of 600,000 Allied troops, two-thirds of them British. German losses are estimated at 450,000. All day long, soldiers are ordered out of their trenches into the vulnerable line of sight of enemy machine guns and slaughtered. Many of the soldiers have their hearing blown out by the unbelievable detonations of the apocalyptic artillery barrages preceding the attacks, and are incapable of hearing orders above the din.

Significantly, psychiatry introduces the new concept of 'war neurotics' to the world as unprecedented numbers of soldiers experience fits of quivering, crying, hysteria and vomiting. Widespread desertions from frontline units alarm the German authorities of the day, ever promoting the 'glorious war' ethic and the struggle for 'Teutonic supremacy'. The unsettling, un-German problem of the 'war neurotic' is quickly passed to the psychiatrists. The aim is to render these soldiers fit for active duty again as quickly as possible. Drastic remedies are showcased, such as electroshock therapy, which sometimes has the desired effect of galvanising 'slackers' back to the front even before treatment, due to its appalling effects and rapidly spreading sinister reputation. Hamburg-based psychiatrist Dr Max Nonne recalls:

"The war brought us in Eppendorf a tremendous workload. We soon got to see sad pictures of men who were amputated, half-paralysed through head wounds, paralysed down to the legs, the bladder and the rectum because of bullets in the spine, of epileptics who had seizures because of head wounds. But after a few months, we saw a sight we had rarely seen before – the sight of hysteria virilis, the 'manly hysteria', which had once been described to us by Charcot in Paris. We had said

---

[55] Hermann, William Paul Bacon, *The Holocaust: From a Survivor of Verdun*, Harper & Row, New York: 1972

then: 'This only happens to the French. In Germany, hysteria of the men does not exist.' But now we saw it often and in all forms: as paralysis of the vocal cords, as dumbness, as paralysis of the upper and lower extremities, as trembling in all parts of the body, as spasms of single muscles and muscle groups, as deafness, as inabilities to see and walk, and as dislocations in the most confounded forms." [56]

LESS THAN MANLY

Röder et al agree that some of the trench problems of the First World War soldier are extremely embarrassing for the German military authorities, who are eager at the time to promote the manly virtues of the Great War:

"Sometimes in place of war neurosis, German psychiatrists used terms like 'traumatic neurosis', 'fright neurosis', 'grenade shock' or 'war hysteria'. In other countries, such as Britain, this hysteria was described as 'shell shock', 'concussion neurosis', 'gas neurosis' or 'battle fatigue'. However in 1915, the German army medical services forbade the use of the word 'hysteria' in military psychiatric diagnosis because it was contrary to the noble concept of honour befitting a warrior. In the eyes of the army, the diagnosis of a hysterical reaction was dishonourable and, therefore, banned. No doubt the German army was offended in part by the suggestion that its soldiers might be less than 'manly'. After all, 'hysteria' comes from the Greek 'hyster', meaning 'uterus', and connotes a woman's suffering, not the illness of a soldier." [57]

Denying that soldiers are in any way 'sick' and therefore exempt from combat, German war authorities are able to use psychiatry as a justification for denying the symptoms that are cropping up in medical offices such as Dr Nonne's. Front-line commanders are expressly forbidden from sending the 'tremblers' and 'hystericals' away from the fighting. 'Kaufmann Therapy' awaits those who shirk battle and 'feign symptoms'. This controversial approach follows the line that war neurosis is a 'constitutional, psychopathic inferiority', and those suffering from it are plainly too weak to endure the beauty of the war.[58]

---

[56] Nonne, Max, *Anfang und Ziel meines Lebens*, Hamburg: 1971, pp.177-178

[57] Röder, Thomas, Kubillus, Volker & Anthony Burwell, *Psychiatry – The Men Behind Hitler*, op. cit. p.25

[58] Wohlmuth, Georg: Feinstrom, Gavanisatoren, catalogue 1929, p.8 (StaHH 352-3, 10 1-60)

Those undergoing the therapy are prepared with pre-shock suggestions. Then a strong alternating current is passed through the patient's head while the therapist repeats strong military commands in the form of 'psychic driving'. The patient is under the strict enforcement that he must be healed in one session.[59] At the annual conference of the Gesellschaft Deutscher Nervenärzte in Bonn on 29th September 1917, Dr M Raether, head doctor of the Provinzial Heil und Pflegeinstitut, includes a demonstration of 'Kaufmann Cure' in his lecture.[60]

Even in the eyes of the most forward-thinking psychiatrists of the day, the concept of treating shell shock with electric shock is radical and uncomfortably close to plain, old-fashioned torture. With no scientific evidence at all to back up the supposed efficacy of his treatments, Kaufmann and his followers are nevertheless allowed to continue, disciplining 'malingerers' with high voltage, hauling them back to the front, thereby cementing up embarrassing breaches in the honour and nobility of German military service.

An electric shock box was also available near the front for use by psychiatrists to kill their own soldiers. Dr Emil Gelny, later a Nazi Party member from 1933, founded electro-execution:

"Once a patient went unconscious from the effects of the electricity, the caretakers then had to attach four other electrodes to the hands and feet of the patient. Dr Gelny ran high voltage through them and after ten minutes at the most, the death of the patient would set in." [61]

In spite of psychiatric measures like Kaufmann's being couched in pseudo-scientific terminology, and attempting to pass themselves off as 'cutting-edge medicine', there are those in the scientific community of the day who see their psychiatric colleagues *"...sinking back into the barbarism of the Middle Ages."* Röder et al report that psychiatry predictably had an ingenious answer to its attackers at this time:

"It took considerable courage to denounce the psychiatric movement of the era because critics were liable to be labelled with an unfavourable diagnosis by the very subjects of their criticism. This was no idle fear. In

---

[59] Kaufman, Fritz, Münchener Medizinische Wochenschrift, 1916
[60] Riedesser, Peter & Axel Verderber, Aufrüstung der Seelen. Militärpsychologie und Militäpsychiatrie in Deutschland und Amerika, Freiburg: 1985, pp.15-17
[61] Röder et al, op. cit. pp.207-208: footnote 12

1927, a professor of psychiatry from Hamburg named Ernst Ritterhaus actually came up with the diagnosis of 'mass psychosis of hostility toward psychiatry' for all critics of the psychiatric movement. In other words, 'if you disagree with us or challenge our methods, you are insane.'

The same diagnosis was applied to a large number of journalists, doctors, officers, legislators, manufacturers and law professors as well as the victims of psychiatry who had dared to challenge the utility and ethics of inhuman therapies. By then, it was almost impossible to argue logically against psychiatry – psychiatry was too irrational to allow for it." [62]

In his extraordinarily arrogant declaration in 1899, leading psychiatrist P J Möbius had elevated psychiatry to the post of 'Judge of all Human Things', a position still occupied at that time in the minds of most by God Himself:

"The psychiatrist should be the judge about mental health, because only he knows what 'ill' means. If one views psychiatry in this way, then it turns from a servant into a ruler, and becomes what by nature it should be. The psychiatrist then becomes the judge of all human things, a teacher of the lawyer and theologian, a leader of the historian and the writer."

Plainly, even by the turn of the 20th century, German psychiatry already saw itself poised to influence the legislature, the media, religion and even history itself in its grandiose designs for control. The tools to enforce this control were by this time already nearing completion:

"The formula was as simple as it was chilling in its implications. Beneath a shroud of a few impressive-sounding, Greek- and Latin-based words, and cloaked with the presumed authority of a medical science, to shut up your critic, simply pronounce him or her insane and do so from the point of view of the omniscient expert." [63]

THE CAULDRON RISING – BETWEEN THE WARS

By the turn of the 20th century, Weishaupt's master plan for world social, economic and political domination had kicked into high gear for those attempting to implement it. As the seeds of Weishaupt's and Engels'

---

[62] Röder et al, op. cit. p.28
[63] Ibid. p.29

Communism were watered into growth by Marx, Trotsky and Lenin, its branches spread out across Tsarist Russia. Other peoples, dissatisfied with the old imperialism of the 19th century, began to examine ways in which this novel and revolutionary new way of structuring society could be applied in their own nations. That 'Spartacus' Weishaupt's original thesis still forms the underpinning of Communism well into the 20th century is clearly seen with the formation of groups of German Communist revolutionaries in the chaotic aftermath of post-World War 1 Europe.

Known as 'Spartacists', their leaders included Rosa Luxemburg and Karl Liebknecht, who were later hunted down by the German Chancellor, Friedrich Ebert, captured and shot. In Hungary, Communist revolution broke out under Béla Kun in March of 1919, resulting in the establishment of a Communist satellite state. Kun himself would later resign and move to Moscow, where he ironically became one of hundreds of thousands of loyal Communists shot during Stalin's purges.

'LIFE UNWORTHY OF LIVING'
European psychiatry predictably survives World War 1 in great shape. In the eyes of many, the horrors of the Great War cannot be adequately explained by the Church as the intervention of any loving God. However the mental sciences, with their evolutionary/eugenic underpinnings and cloak of indefatigable science, offer their own explanations for why man does the things he does. Studies in genetics, ongoing since the turn of the century, are redefining in the minds of the public the haphazard nature of man. Eugenics states that any perceived physical or mental abnormality in the population is evidence of a genetic trait that must be eradicated to prevent its proliferation. Into this context comes the first mention of the concept of 'life unworthy of living'.

Many try to process the horrors of the Second World War without an understanding of the framework behind *why* the atrocities happened. Many times we read of the grotesque incongruity of the Nazi officer - a cultured and educated man, lover of Wagner and the arts, whilst at the same time capable of committing acts of genocide with an everyday banality of spirit. But it is precisely the explanation behind this paradox, so studiously avoided by Spielberg in *Schindler's List*, which gives us the chief reason why so many in Europe go along with the policies of the SS and their enforcer, SS-General Reinhard Heydrich. Heydrich is Himmler's deputy, head of the Reich security apparatus, and perhaps one of the most feared men in Germany.

The German people have been sold on evolution; on the superiority of the white, Aryan race; on the need to sterilise or kill those whose lives are deemed 'of no value'; sold on the utter conviction that Germany is to be the seat of the New Order which will haul it from the ignominious ashes of the First World War. Indeed Hitler's book, *My New Order*, espouses these very concepts. But the underlying groundwork providing the cultural acceptability of these fatal philosophies has already been laid down by the eugenicists, psychiatrists and Darwinists of the previous fifty years. Bruce Wiseman reports:

"Alfred Hoche, a professor of psychiatry, and Karl Binding, a German jurist and retired professor of Wundt's alma mater, the University of Leipzig, published 'The Release of the Destruction of Life Devoid of Value' in Leipzig in 1920. It went a step further than the recommendation of mere sterilisation. It advocated the outright killing of mental defectives, 'euthanasia' as it was called: 'For the idiots... the continuation of life for society as well as for the person himself has no value.'

By 1922, at a psychiatric congress in Dresden, Germany, a proposal was put forward requesting legalization of euthanasia. The psychiatric social experiment called Eugenics had embarked on a road from which there was no turning back."[64]

Throughout the 1920's and '30's, the language grows increasingly sinister and apocalyptic as the German proponents of racial hygiene and eugenics face scant opposition. Germany is in turmoil following the humiliation of the Treaty of Versailles after World War 1. After signing the Treaty on 28th June 1919 in the famous railway carriage, English premier David Lloyd George is asked what has been accomplished. The English statesman replies, *"Gentlemen, I have just signed the document which guarantees war in 20 years."* These words are repeated in Lloyd George's memoirs, published after his administration in 1923.

Lloyd George's extraordinary admission is understood when one appreciates that the Treaty of Versailles is designed to leave Germany with nothing, not even the wherewithal to rebuild its economy and physical infrastructure from within. Fifteen years later Japan will encounter the same problem. A nation faced with such a future must go to war eventually to free itself and this is precisely the platform Hitler uses to gain power

---

[64] Wiseman, Bruce, op. cit. p.63

and control in the late 1920's after the financial collapse of the Weimar Republic.

The tremendous nationalistic vacuum generated by the hardships in Germany following World War 1 becomes the fertile soil which germinates the latent supremacist philosophies of Darwin, Malthus, Weishaupt, Wundt, Galton and Kraepelin. Germany wants to feel clean. Efficient. Redeemed.

In charge again.

ERNST RÜDIN

By 1930, a rising psychiatric luminary named Ernst Rüdin is articulating his beliefs on the urgent need for Germany to *"...do something about the positive and negative eugenics before it is too late. For the negative, the sterilisation of the genetically sick has to be closely looked at.... It would be a blessing to know that genetically incompetent, unhappy people would not be produced anymore. Much more national expansion would be created through positive eugenics than we can imagine.*

The fertility rate of the genetic undesirables is so great today that we have every reason in the interest of humanity to address ourselves to the prevention of the genetically weak. The increase of the hereditarily healthy that is so necessary to us as a nation today will cause less of a headache in the future." [65]

The significance of the above statements, made by a man who will be the key player in implementing the racial hygiene policies of the Nazis in the years to come, is stark and shocking when one considers that *these ideas are fully formed by psychiatry a full three years before the Nazis even came to power.* <u>Thus it is not the Nazis who are the creators of the eugenics program which will later underpin the Holocaust, it is German psychiatry</u>. And it is psychiatry also which will, in the dark and hopeless years to follow, design, draw up and implement the murderous policies which will attempt to rid the Nazis of their 'mental defectives', political opponents, habitual criminals, 'genetically weak' and those whose lives will be deemed 'unworthy of living'.

---

[65] von Gruber, Max, *Docent Ernst Rüdin*, Fortpflanzung, Verebung Rassenhygiene, Munich: 1931, p.279f.

The marriage of psychiatry to Nazism is to prove propitious. In 1933, when the Nazis ascend to power, a legal brief describing a new law gives the reader a chilling insight into the appalling turn Germany is about to take:

"With the passing of the Law for the Prevention of Genetically Diseased Children, the German Nazi government took an important step for the future of our nation. Because of their nature, our previous government could not come to a decision, since German parliamentarianism has generally shown itself to be incapable of innovative steps for the salvation of our nation... Only the Nazi world view has reoriented us to the future, we have again remembered the learning of our lives, the purpose of the state, the fight for survival and life of our families, the species and the race! Hitler writes in his book 'Mein Kampf': 'Who is not healthy bodily or mentally is not allowed to perpetuate his malady in the body of his child....' Therefore, this Act is a complete break from the small-mindedness of an outdated philosophy of life and the overblown and suicidal charity of past ages." [66]

---

[66] Gött, Arthur, Ernst Rüdin, Falk Ruttke, explaining *Gesetz zur Verhülung erbkranken Nachwuchses vom 14. Juli 1933*, Munich: 1934, p.5

Deliver Those You Cannot Heal!
(Germany Descends into the Abyss)

"I am sure it would be sensible to restrict as much as possible the work of these gentlemen [psychiatrists]*, who are capable of doing an immense amount of harm with what may very easily degenerate into charlatanry."* – Winston Churchill, December 1942

"Since sterilisation is the only sure thing to prevent further transmission of mental illness and serious hereditary afflictions, it must therefore be viewed as an act of charity and precaution for the upcoming generation." – Prof. Ernst Rüdin, Director of the Kaiser Wilhelm Institute for Psychiatry, Munich, Germany, 1936

"We should make a law which helps nature have its way. Nature would let a creature which is not equipped starve to death. It would be more humane for us to give it a painless, mercy killing. This is the only option which is proper in such cases and it is a hundred times more noble, decent and humane than the cowardice that hides behind the idiocy of humanitarianism and which burdens both the creature with its own existence, and the family and the society with the burden of supporting it." – Das Schwarze Korps (The Black Corps), 18th March 1937

No more stark and frightening insight into the marriage of eugenics with Nazism can be provided than the above Black Corps declaration, which illustrates the deadly intent of Hitler's National Socialists to implement their policies to 'cleanse' Germany of its undesirables. And psychiatry is deemed the 'science' that has the expertise and will to determine who is undesirable in this Germany of the future. Thus it is psychiatry which must play the defining role in spearheading the selection of these undesirables for processing under the laws which will soon be drafted. Clearly, the measures that will follow - measures forever seared into the Post-War collective conscience of a horrified world citizenry - cannot, by any grotesque manipulation of the imagination, be categorised as 'a hundred times more noble, decent and humane'.

As we have already learned, the path to the gas chambers can be clearly traced back to the attitudes and bogus science propagated decades before. And it is through the process of gradualism that the 'sophisticated' public's perceptions of man and his place in the cosmos endure a quantum shift, to the point where the unthinkable eventually becomes thinkable.

50

NOT JUST NAZI GERMANY

Insanity initially was frowned upon and locked away from the general public where it was monitored by those in charge. Later, 'mental disorders', and those exhibiting the growing list of them, became Kraepelin's 'heavy burden for our nation'. The evolutionary beliefs of Darwin, Lyell and Galton formed the bedrock for the eugenics movement with its desire to 'perfect evolution' by breeding out 'undesirable traits', and 'feeble-mindedness' in different races. By 1914, mental illness was professionally regarded as 'hereditary', when the American Medico-Psychological Association (later the modern-day American Psychiatric Association) stated that *"... a radical cure of the evils incident to the dependent mentally defective classes would be effected if every feeble-minded person, every imbecile, every habitual criminal, every manifestly weak-minded person, and every confirmed inebriate were sterilised."* [67]

It is important and fair to appreciate that these beliefs were not wholly restricted to those of the burgeoning German psychiatric community. They were also held by many 'forward-thinkers' elsewhere. Lewis M Terman, professor of psychology at Stanford University, USA, believed in 1916 that *"...if we would preserve our state for a class of people worthy to possess it, we must prevent, as far as possible, the propagation* [breeding] *of mental degenerates."* [68]

Houston Stewart Chamberlain, born in Britain in 1855, married the daughter of composer Robert Wagner and became a German citizen in 1916. Chamberlain's works lionised Aryan world philosophy, denigrated Jewish influence as negative and inferior, and promoted German supremacy. Chamberlain's élitist views are clear when he remarks that *"...moderate talent... is frequently the character of bastards; one can easily observe this daily in cities where, as in Vienna, the various peoples meet each other; at the same time one can also notice a particular laxity, a lack of character, in short, the moral degeneration of such people."* [69]

---

[67] Castel, Robert, Castel, Francoise & Anne Lovell, *The Psychiatric Society*, (Translated by Arthur Goldhammer), Columbia University Press, New York: 1982, pp.46-47. Source for quote is Carlos F MacDonald, "Presidential Address", *American Journal of Insanity*, July 1914, 71:9

[68] Lapon, Lenny, *Mass Murderers in White Coats*, op. cit. p.78

[69] Röder et al., op. cit. p.19

A young Adolf Hitler would echo these same sentiments in 1925: *"...those who are physically and mentally unhealthy must not perpetuate their suffering in the body of their children."* [70] By 1933, after the Nazis come to power, Hitler is busying himself with the implementation of legislation entitled The Nazi Act for Averting Descendants Afflicted with Hereditary Diseases. Within six years, 375,000 forced sterilisations are carried out. Even the physically 'unfit' are not exempt.

Psychiatrist Ernst Rüdin is the catalyst and organiser of the operational phase of the Nazis' eugenics policy. With the scientific credibility of his professorship at Munich University to drape his acts with the requisite legitimacy, Rüdin is fêted for his fidelity and unswerving loyalty to the Reich. Upon his sixty-fifth birthday, the Munich psychiatrist is honoured for having *"...just recently received the Goethe Medal for the Art and Science from the Führer 'in recognition of his achievements in the development of German Racial Hygiene'."* Fellow racial hygiene advocate Dr Alfred Ploetz continues at the festivities to announce that *"...the Reichminister of the Interior, Dr Frick, sent him* [Rüdin] *the following telegram: 'To the indefatigable champion of racial hygiene and meritorious pioneer of the racial hygiene measures of the Third Reich, I send my sincerest congratulations on his 65th birthday'."* [71]

EUTHANASIA

The concept of sterilisation is soon to have another sinister bedfellow: euthanasia. The murder of those whose lives are deemed Devoid of Human Value commences with a landmark episode in 1938. Dr Werner Catel, Professor of Neurology and Psychiatry at the University of Leipzig, advises the father of a deformed child that the latter write to the Führer seeking permission to end his own child's life. In response, Hitler sends his personal physician, Professor Karl Brandt, to discuss the matter with Catel. The significance of a father requesting a mercy death for his own son fascinates the public. The child is subsequently killed.

Such an event is to have major repercussions in the realm of public psychodrama now the state has sanctioned euthanasia:

"A group of physicians was called to the Reich Chancellory to form a Euthanasia Committee. Dr Herbert Linden, psychiatrist and ministerial

---

[70] Hitler, Adolf, *Mein Kampf*, translated by Ralph Manheim, Houghton Mifflin & Co., Boston, USA: 1971, p.255
[71] Quoted in Schreiber, Bernard, op. cit. p.18

advisor for health in the Reich Ministry, was appointed its director. Of the four other doctors on the committee, two were psychiatrists, including the influential Dr Werner Catel. Shortly, another seven psychiatrists were added.

In 1939, the following document was signed and released by Hitler: 'Reichleader [Philipp] Bouhler and Karl Brandt MD are charged with the responsibility of enlarging the authority of certain physicians to be designated by name in such a manner that persons who, according to human judgment, can upon most careful diagnosis of their condition of sickness, be accorded a mercy death.'" [72]

Journalist Joseph Harsch makes an important point in his analysis of the above ruling by Hitler:

"Those who proposed [the plan for euthanasia] are understood to have asked Hitler for a written edict or law which would officially authorise them to proceed with the 'mercy killings'. Hitler is represented as having hesitated for several weeks. Finally, doubting that Hitler would ever sign the official order, the proponents of the project drafted a letter for him to sign which merely expressed his, Hitler's general approval of the theory of euthanasia as a means of relieving incompetents of the burden of life. While this letter did not have the character of the law, it was adequate in Nazi Germany. The Führer had expressed approval of the practice. It went ahead." [73]

EUROPE EXPLODES

Meanwhile, throughout the first seven months of 1939, the Nazi industrial dynamo was churning out weaponry, aircraft, submarines and warships. In spite of Hitler's assurances to Britain's Neville Chamberlain that England and Germany were not in danger of war, events inexorably built during the spring and summer. In the second week of August, Hitler ordered German troops to mass along the border with Poland. Late on the night of 31st August 1939, Hitler's government informed the world that Polish troops had stormed a German radio station in Upper Silesia and, after murdering the technicians there, had broadcast an appeal to the Polish people inciting them to war with Germany.

---

[72] Wiseman, Bruce, op. cit. p.64; also Schreiber, Bernhard, op. cit. p.41
[73] Harsch, Joseph, *Pattern for Conquest*, quoted from Schreiber, Bernhard, op. cit. p.45

Historian Martin Gilbert reminds us of the tragic farce that followed: *"No such Polish provocation had taken place. The Polish troops were Germans dressed up as Poles. The dead German – for there was indeed one – was a common criminal taken from a concentration camp and killed by his fellow Germans to give credence to the tale of a Polish attack. The incident was a crude fabrication, but in the early hours of 1st September, citing this bogus incident us the reason, Hitler ordered German troops to cross into Poland.... On 3rd September 1939, Britain and France declared war on Germany."*[74]

CLEANING UP THE HUMAN DETRITUS

By 1939, a telling documentary film is circulating Germany and its provinces, entitled 'Existence Without Life' ('Dasein ohne Leben'). Featured in the 1991 documentary 'Selling Murder', the German piece is designed to educate and influence public opinion in the controversial area of euthanasia. Wiseman states that all the latest film techniques are used to give the project every chance of success:

"The main character was a professor... used 'to add spurious scientific respectability' to the film. The documentary explains, 'The [film's] script demands that demonically mad faces arise like a spectre out of the scene.... Unedited film shows the techniques used such as sharp, underneath lighting to make the patients appear grotesque.... His [the professor's] lecture, scripted by psychiatrists.... first claims that care for the sick has become indiscriminate and too costly.'

The professor closes the movie with a dramatic appeal to all: 'We call upon a merciful destiny to liberate these regrettable creatures from their existence without life.... Allow me to close with a few purely human and personal remarks and so extend the framework of this lecture. If I knew that I – and this could happen to anyone – would be struck down by the disaster of some incurable mental illness and that such an existence without life would lie before me, I would do anything for this not to happen. I would rather die. I am convinced all healthy people think like this. But I am also convinced that every incurable mental patient or idiot, if he could recognise his position, would prefer an end to such existence. No sensible human being could deny him the right to die. Is it not the duty of those [psychiatrists] who care for the incapable - and that means total idiots and the incurable mental patients – to help them exercise

---

[74] Gilbert, Martin, op. cit. p.263

their rights? Is that not a sacred demand of charity? Deliver those you cannot heal!' [75]

T4 AND THE 'MERCY KILLINGS'

The deliverings, or 'mercy killings', of mental patients are carried out under the organisation of the infamous T4 centre[76], so named for its Berlin address at Tiergartenstrasse 4. According to the Nuremburg Trial transcripts, some 275,000 mental patients are murdered between 1939 and the cessation of hostilities in 1945 under Operation Gnadentod ('Operation Mercy Killing'). Even before the killing centres have been properly set up and tested, psychiatrists are rounding up mentally sick patients from institutions in Meseritz, Pomerania (Poland) and shipping them into the forests. Here they are executed by SS firing squads and buried. Later in the war, these bodies, some 3,500 of them, are hastily exhumed and burned by the SS to prevent their discovery by the approaching Russian Army.

Two of the first killing facilities are set up at Castle Grafeneck and Brandenburg by T4, under control of 'politically reliable' psychiatrists, doctors, nurses and orderlies who oversee the murders. Psychiatrist Werner Heyde moves from Würzburg to Berlin to head up T4. Heyde's job is to oversee the Reich's euthanasia program and supervise its consulting staff of approximately 30 physicians, most of whom are psychiatrists. The T4 psychiatric team will 'evaluate' patients and decide on their fate. The *Los Angeles Daily News* agrees that the first medical killings of mental patients in Germany were to pave the way for mass murder in the years to follow:

"The systematic 'treatment' of Jews under T4 began in April 1940, with a proclamation from the Reich Interior Ministry that within three weeks all Jewish [mental] patients were to be registered. In June the first gassing of Jews took place: 200 men, women and children were killed in the Brandenburg facility; they had been transported to the killing centre in six buses from the Berlin-Buch mental institution." [77]

---

[75] Wiseman, Bruce, op. cit. p.65; Burleigh, Michael, *Selling Murder*, directed by Joanna Mack, Domino Film Production, 1991

[76] T4 was originally known as The Working Association of Sanitaria and Caretaking Facilities of the Republic.

[77] *Los Angeles Daily News*, "Medical killings led Nazis to mass murder", 28th September 1986

The original method of murder is carbon monoxide gas. It is chosen for its obvious lethality and lack of smell. Specially constructed 'shower rooms' lure the unwary victims inside. The gas is then pumped in until all visible movement ceases. After the excess gas is extracted, the bodies are removed and taken to the nearby crematoria for incineration. Later, the appalling plumes of smoke cause many a local inhabitant to complain to the authorities. In time, the nefarious purpose of these facilities, first as rumours and then as truth, soon becomes known. By this time however, public complaints about the centres themselves become a cause for the arrest and deportation of 'troublemakers'.

Author and psychiatrist Dr Frederic Wertham describes a student tour of one of the mental facilities actively involved in the Nazis' Operation Mercy Killing: *"In the fall of 1939, a group of psychology students were given a tour of the state psychiatric institution Eglfing Haar in Nazi Germany. Dr Hermann Pfannmüller, a psychiatrist and director of the institution, explained the 'euthanasia' or 'mercy killing' program that was being used on the inmates. In the children's ward, twenty-five children were being starved to death. They ranged in age from one to five years. Pfannmüller lifted up one emaciated child who was near death and told the students that food is withdrawn gradually, not all at once. 'With this child,' he said, 'it will take another two or three days.'"* [78]

Ludwig Lehner, one of the students attending that visit to Dr Pfannmüller's institution, commented in a sworn statement at Nuremburg: *"I shall never forget the look of that fat, grinning fellow with the whimpering little skeleton in his fleshy hand, surrounded by the other starving children."* [79]

At first, it is the 'mental defectives' who are killed. As these 'mercy killings' proceed however, criteria for selection are steadily widened. That psychiatrists themselves are only following orders and are not actually instigators of the brutal killings is roundly refuted by surviving documentation. Psychiatrist Dr Wertham:

"It has been stated that psychiatrists were merely following a law or were being forced to obey an order. Again and again we read – as if it were historical fact – of Hitler's secret order to exterminate those

---

[78] Wertham, Frederic, *A Sign For Cain: An Exploration of Human Violence*, Robert Hale Ltd, London: 1966, p.180
[79] Mielke, F, *The Death Doctors*, Elek Books, London: 1962, p.248

suffering from severe mental defect or disease.... There was no law and no such order. The tragedy is that the psychiatrists did not have to have an order. They acted on their own. They were not carrying out a death sentence pronounced by someone else, they were the legislators who laid down the rules for deciding who was to die; they were the administrators who worked out the procedures, provided the patients and the places, and decided the methods of killing; they pronounced a sentence of life or death in every individual case; they were the executioners who carried the sentences out, or – without being coerced to do so – surrendered their patients to be killed in other institutions; they supervised and often watched the slow deaths." [80]

By the middle of 1941, the killing of the mentally ill was well underway throughout the Reich and its conquered lands. T4 expanded the definition of those deemed 'unworthy of life' and a full training program was instigated to coach those in the skills of mass extermination. An accomplished authority on the mental health system of Nazi Germany, Dr Wertham further states:

"The 'material' for all this training was mental hospital patients. On them the methods were tried out and tested before they were later applied to Jewish and other civilian populations of the occupied countries. Technical experience first gained with killing psychiatric patients was utilised later for the destruction of millions.

Towards the end of 1941, the gas chambers in the death institutions were dismantled, transported to the east, and then freshly erected for their new tasks in concentration camps.... Some were the same psychiatrists who selected patients in hospitals, went to concentration camps and selected death candidates there. Heinrich Himmler had the idea of having the inmates of these camps examined to 'comb out' those to be eliminated. He needed suitable physicians, so the central bureau of the 'euthanasia' program [T4] supplied him with 'experienced psychiatrists'.... In 1941, a commission of five went to the concentration camp at Dachau to select prisoners to be transferred to Mauthausen to be killed. All five men were psychiatrists, and their chief was a professor of psychiatry at the University of Berlin." [81]

---

[80] Wertham, Frederic, op. cit. pp.164-165
[81] Wertham, Frederic, ibid. pp.181-182

BRANCHING OUT THE PROGRAM

The success of the euthanasia program, inasmuch as the public remains largely unaware of what is occurring, spurs more imaginative ways to dispose of the mentally ill. New facilities are opened in occupied Poland, equipped with 'shower rooms' and machine guns. Specialised gassing trucks are constructed and painted to look like 'Kaiser's Coffee' delivery vehicles. Carbon monoxide gas is fed from steel canisters into the interior of the vehicles while the latter drive to the disposal sites to off-load the bodies for cremation.

There is money in the killing. Questionnaires are sent in to T4 from the mental institutions for each patient to be evaluated. Psychiatric consultants, under the guidance of T4 chief Heyde, go over the questionnaires and, on the basis of the information learned, place a red mark on the form for those to be killed and blue for those to be spared. By October 1940, a psychiatrist working as a euthanasia consultant is receiving 100 marks per patient evaluation up to a total of 500 questionnaires. Bonuses are also being earned: 200 marks per evaluation up to 2,000 questionnaires, 300 marks up to 3,000 and 400 marks for all questionnaires above that.

Records show that the above-mentioned Dr Hermann Pfannmüller, for instance, completed 2,000 registration forms in only three weeks, while another, Dr Schreck, 'very conscientiously' completed 15,000 in nine months, according to his own testimony. One witness, states researcher Ernst Klee, *"even worked while drinking wine in a public restaurant."* [82]

And then a strange thing happens. On 24th August 1941, Hitler calls a halt to the T4 euthanasia killings. Some say that Hitler has become politically uncomfortable as the public learns of the truth. A psychiatrist named Menneckes, involved in the euthanasia killings in the Rhenish Eichberg Institute, later, in an open session of the Eichberg proceedings on 3rd December 1946, declared:

"One day when Hitler was travelling on his special train from Munich to Berlin, it had to make a stop at a station at Hog. To find out why, he went to the window and was spotted by a crowd standing outside that had been witnessing the shipment of mentally ill patients. When the crowd saw Hitler at the window, they became irate, as they

---

[82] Klee, Ernst, *'Euthanasie' im NS-Staat*, Frankurt am Main, 1989, testimony of an eye-witness (Mauthe) on 18th October 1948, pp.120-121

knew what would happen with the patients. This demonstration of dissatisfaction against Hitler prompted him to call off what had been going on until then." [83]

Other surviving documents demonstrate that Hitler's policy of distancing himself from the carnage is being recognised at the bureaucratic level. One physician, giving testimony after the war, states:

"The discontinuation of the extermination program was skilfully exploited, according to a physician of the Weissengau Institute, by spreading a whisper campaign that it had happened because of Adolf Hitler, who prior to that had not been aware of the killing." [84]

But researchers Röder, Kubillus and Burwell surmise another, perhaps more prosaic explanation for Hitler's order to cease the euthanasia killings. In their *Secret Activities of the Third Reich*, the authors demonstrate with research that by August 1941, T4 has actually reached its quota of 70,000 persons euthanised. In fact, it has actually exceeded its target by exactly 273 persons. The original program has accomplished its preset targets and is now being shut down. Are the Nazis merely calling in a breathing space while those in charge decide what to do next?

REINHARD HEYDRICH

By the beginning of 1942, the concept of expanding the slaughter of the mentally ill into the conquered territories to an even wider criteria of 'inferior citizens', such as Jews, gypsies, homosexuals, habitual criminals and political undesirables, is being contemplated and sanctioned by the Nazi High Command. On 20th January, Himmler's deputy, Reinhard Heydrich, convenes a meeting of 15 senior Nazi officials at a villa at the beautiful lakeside retreat of Wannsee, ostensibly to examine the options of ridding Europe of 'parasitic Jewry'.

Heydrich is Hitler's *Wunderkind* - an operations genius who has just been appointed 'Reich Protector' of Bohemia and Moravia in September 1941. Heydrich's career with the Nazis has been spectacular and meteoric. Having organised the entire Nazi secret police and intelligence services (SS and SD) even before his party gained power, Heydrich was trusted by the Nazis for his incredible capacity for organisation on a large scale. It

---

[83] Ibid, p.341

[84] Dr Bischoff, 10th December 1945, quoted by Klee, E, op. cit. p.341

was Heydrich who had removed Nazi opponents quietly and effectively to Dachau, near Munich. It was Heydrich who, by 1934, had all the political police of the Reich under his iron control. It was Heydrich who had organised four special task forces to follow Operation Barbarossa, Hitler's invasion of Russia, liquidating all Communist officials, saboteurs, agitators and Jews as the Nazis advanced. By the time the Wannsee meeting is convened, wholesale murder of the Jews in Russia has become routine. Historian Martin Gilbert tells us:

"From the first days of the German invasion of the Soviet Union, the SS Special Task Forces took Jews out of their homes to the nearest wood or ravine, and shot them down. Tens of thousands of Jews were murdered in the first few weeks; hundreds of thousands in the months ahead; as many as a million by the end of the year. As the executions spread from town to town and village to village, babies and small children were thrown into the deep pits in which their parents had been shot." [85]

Reinhard Heydrich

In spite of the brutality of his command, there is compelling evidence that Heydrich, born in Prussian Saxony the son of a music director and minor composer, is secretly disgusted with the scale of the worst tasks he is called upon to perform. That Heydrich is not just the simple Nazi monster he is often painted to be is evident when one studies the amazing social reforms the SS-General is able to introduce into Czech society through his own initiatives. Heydrich understands that the carrot and the stick are both of use in maximising the productivity of conquered people brought under the heel of the Reich. Heydrich discovers that Czech farmers have been holding out on the true number of cattle they have registered. He orders all surplus animals to be slaughtered and the meat added to the rations of the factory workers. On Labour Day 1942, Heydrich distributes thousands of free cinema, theatre and football tickets to the working population to reward them for their hard endeavours. New national insurance cover, pension rights, new wage levels and holiday entitlements are agreed with the Czech trade unions.

---

[85] Gilbert, Martin, *History of the Twentieth Century*, HarperCollins, 2001, p.276

Ignoring the safety risks, Heydrich often tours the factories of his protectorate, telling the dumbfounded workers to their faces what an inspiration they all are - even to the Nazis.

WANNSEE – MURDER OVER CIGARS AND COGNAC

It is this complex Heydrich, part monster, part operations genius, that sits down at the conference table at the villa at Wannsee in January 1942 to discuss what is to be done permanently with the inferiors, mental degenerates, habitual criminals and the Jews across the German empire. Heydrich's mind has no moral conflict with what it has to do. The minutes of this meeting have survived and from them we can piece together a chilling montage of what was agreed and understood between the various parties attending.

Clear is the fact that Hitler himself will issue no such order sanctioning the murder of eleven million Jews, although clearly the mass exterminations which follow can never go ahead without the Führer's approval. Hitler's quandary and subsequent refusal to issue a written order for the exterminations, according to researcher Ernst Klee, appears to be centred on the fact that it is actually still illegal at this time in Nazi Germany to murder people:

"Everyone involved knows that Hitler rejects a legal ruling for political reasons." [86]

Heydrich himself makes this expressly clear at Wannsee when some of the incredulous attendees, after hearing of Heydrich's proposal for the extermination of the Jews, timidly request the whereabouts of an official written order from the Führer. Heydrich once again pointedly reminds his audience of the need to purge Germany of undesirables. He is counting on their unanimous support to overcome the logistic problems of ceasing the propagation of 'inferior stock'.

In his book, *The Villa, The Lake, The Meeting: Wannsee and the Final Solution*, British scholar Mark Roseman uses the minutes from the infamous meeting to paint an almost unbelievable portrait of cultured men gathering in a stately, picturesque location, eating superb food, smoking cigars and sipping cognac, discussing the fate of such 'mental degenerates' as remain, along with the removal of up to 11 million Jews from European society. The meeting, conducted in cultured tones, begins

---

[86] Ibid. p.86

with the question of deportation of undesirables. References are made to the success of the previous T4 euthanasia program.

Although the question of sterilisation is openly discussed in connection with the desire to prevent 'inferior races' from propagating, it is quite evident from the minutes that Heydrich is dissatisfied with the costs and manpower associated with extending this kind of operation. At Wannsee, we see the indomitable Heydrich presenting the top brass at Wannsee with a *fait accompli* with his Endlösung, his Final Solution for the Jews - a package of measures already thoroughly planned, costed down to the last detail, and bearing the Heydrich stamp of approval.

SETTING UP THE FINAL SOLUTION

There are historians who attempt to minimise Hitler's involvement in, and cogniscence of Heydrich, Eichmann and Himmler's Final Solution. But clearly, from documentation and later testimony at Nuremburg, Hitler is in the loop and always in overall command. Roseman agrees and reports that, within weeks of the meeting at Wannsee, the random massacres of 'degenerates' throughout the empire, including thousands of Russian prisoners of war falling into German hands as a result of Operation Barbarossa, give way to highly organised and documented industrial extermination.

Psychological propaganda is all-important in breaking the will of the Soviets, contemptuously regarded by leading Nazis as sub-human animals. But some Wehrmacht commanders are shocked at the savagery that has by now overtaken the soldiers under their command. On 26th June 1941, four days after the launch of the German invasion of the Soviet Union, General Lemelsen, commander of the 47th Panzer Corps, is protesting to his subordinates about the 'senseless shootings of both prisoners-of-war and civilians'. Yet the savagery on both sides continues unchecked both within the beleaguered Soviet Union as well as across occupied Europe. The world now witnesses something it has not seen before. A war between millions, not of conquest, but of annihilation.

At dinner with Himmler and Heydrich on 25th October 1941, Hitler had reminded his guests of his 'prophecy' in 1939 that a world war would result in the complete destruction of European Jewry. He added: *"Let no one say to me, we cannot send them into the swamp.... It is good if our advance is preceded with fear that we will exterminate Jewry."* [87]

This is one of many examples illustrating that Hitler is sanctioning the continued murder program and aware that the SS are drowning Jewish women and children in the Pripet marshes. Just ten days after the Wannsee meeting, while Hitler is celebrating the ninth anniversary of his coming to power, he reminds a huge crowd in Berlin: *"The war will not end as the Jews imagine it will, namely with the uprooting of the Aryans, but the result of this war will be the complete annihilation of the Jews."* [88]

THE WAR WIDENS

Worsening relations with America and a deteriorating war with Russia had long since caused the Nazis to abandon their original idea of sending European Jews on 'luxury ships' to any nation who would have them. And then the Japanese attack the US Pacific Fleet in Pearl Harbor on 7th December 1941 and pound US airfields in the Philippines. On 11th December, believing with elation that the Japanese will score a quick and easy victory over the United States, Hitler declares war on America. The Führer is relieved to receive this Japanese boost to his endeavours. Operation Barbarossa has bogged down in Russia with the record shocking winter, temperatures falling as low as -35°C. Stalingrad is the turning point in the war. Yet it is one of the overriding and tragic ironies of World War 2 that, at precisely the time when it is dawning on the more prescient of Hitler's staff that the war may already be lost, Hitler embarks upon his full-scale war on the Jews.

At Wannsee, Heydrich is speaking with the voice of Hitler. Adolf Eichmann, Heydrich's operations chief, records in his memoirs and later 1961 trial in Israel that Heydrich's proposal for genocide of the Jewish people is enthusiastically and unanimously endorsed by all attendees at Wannsee. The Wannsee protocol is specific in its evolutionary stance: any Jews surviving the attempt to work them to death for the benefit of the Reich *"...will have to be dealt with appropriately, because otherwise, by natural selection, they would form the germ cell of a new Jewish revival."* [89]

---

[87] Roseman, Mark, *The Villa, the Lake, the Meeting: Wannsee and the Final Solution,* Allen Lane, 2002
[88] Gilbert, Martin, *History of the Twentieth Century,* HarperCollins, 2001, p.281
[89] Ibid.

THE DEATH CAMPS

Meanwhile the psychiatrists at T4 are experimenting with new, more efficient forms of annihilation. Decrying the increased costs of firing-squad ammunition and the shipping of carbon monoxide to the extermination facilities in Poland, arrangements are made for the off-the-shelf pesticide gas, Zyklon B, to be manufactured on-site by chemical giant I G Farben's subsidiary DEGESCH, an acronym for the German Corporation for Pest Control. In the purpose-built extermination facilities in Poland, the gassing of Russian prisoners of war, together with the continuous stream of victims provided by T4 psychiatrists from the KZs (concentration camps) across the empire, proceeds apace. The Polish death centres of Belzec, Sobibor and Treblinka, according to reliable estimates, carry out the murders of over 1.7 million souls alone. Approximately 100 T4 psychiatrists are transferred from the Berlin headquarters to the Polish extermination sites to supervise and implement Heydrich's Final Solution. The original gas chambers are built to contain 500 people at a time. At the height of the extermination program, up to 1,500 people are herded into the rooms to prepare for what some camp guards refer to sarcastically as 'the peaceful sleep'.

Nazi psychiatrist Ernst Rüdin's racial hygiene program reaches its appalling denouement between 1942 and 1945 as further extermination facilities spring up like evil blooms across occupied Europe. Numerous eyewitness accounts testify to the brutality of Heydrich's hated SS, who preside over the genocide with ruthless efficiency:

"After the arrivals were taken to the location next to the crematorium, they had to undress entirely because they were told they would have a shower. They were then chased – often with beatings – by the SS into the so-called bath, which in reality was a gas chamber...." [90]

" [in the dressing room of the crematorium], people's blood-stained and battered heads and faces proved that there was scarcely anyone who had been able to dodge the truncheon blows of the yard. Their faces were ashen with fear and grief.... Hope and illusions had vanished. What was left was disappointment, despair and anger.

They began to bid each other farewell. Husbands embraced their wives and children. Everybody was in tears. Mothers turned to their

---

[90] Among eye-witness accounts documented by Lifton, Robert Jay, *The Nazi Doctors*, Basic Books, 1986, p.170

children and caressed them tenderly. The little ones... wept with their mothers and held on to them....

After a while, I heard the sound of piercing screams, banging against the door, and also moaning and wailing. People began to cough. Their coughing grew worse from minute to minute, a sign that the gas had started to act. Then the clamour began to subside and to change to a many-voiced dull rattle, drowned out now and then by coughing...."[91]

The killing continues up until the end of the war - and even beyond. On 8th May 1945, the war ends in Germany. In the camps however, the killing continues, masked by the uncontrolled chaos of a German empire in ruins. The mental institutions also appear to be functioning as before. Röder el al report:

"In the extermination institutes, they either kept on killing, or let the patients starve to death. As late as 29th May 1945, a four-year-old feeble-minded boy was murdered in Kaufbeuren, and on 7th July, a Munich newspaper made a horrifying discovery which proved that the loss of World War 2 had had no effect on the overall intentions of those who still operated the human slaughterhouses.

On 2nd July 1945, Robert E Abrahams walked into the district hospital of Kaufbeuren to find the warm, swinging body of a physician who was junior only to the director. He had hanged himself. Twelve hours earlier, the last adult had died. In Irsee, soldiers found the bodies of men and women who had died just hours earlier, most of them through starvation."[92]

THE FINAL HOURS

As often in the tragedy of war, a retrospective look at the eventual outcome of World War 2, this most destructive conflict in human history, yields a million tragic tales of callousness, brutality, personal courage and fatal heroism. The relentless march of the Allies across Europe and the eventual fall of Berlin to the Soviets eventually end the mass killings, the aerial bombings, the artillery and tanks battles, the firing squads in the woods and forests, as well as the emotional torment of the populations previously yolked under Nazi rule. The smoke of a thousands fires, from

---

[91] Ibid.
[92] Röder et al, op. cit. p.70

Dresden to Hamburg, from Warsaw to Normandy, show the world the funeral pyre of German National Socialism.

Hitler kills himself with a pistol in his Berlin bunker on 30th April 1945. His mistress, Eva Braun, whom he has just married, takes poison. Hitler's propaganda and psychology chief Josef Goebbels arranges for his six children to be given a lethal injection by an SS doctor. He then has himself and his wife Madga shot by an SS orderly. The Allies frantically try to account for all the major human rights violators in the complete chaos that is Europe at the end of the Second World War.

A SPRING DAY IN PRAGUE

But SS-General Reinhard Heydrich survives only a few months after Wannsee. On 27th May 1942, the SS chief is assassinated in Prague by two British-trained Czech agents, Kubis and Gabcik, as he takes the beautiful drive from his villa at Panenske Brezany to his headquarters in the capital. As his Mercedes slows to negotiate a hairpin bend in the Prague suburbs, Kubis and Gabcik attack the vehicle with a Sten gun that jams, and a specially prepared fragmentation grenade that doesn't. Heydrich is mortally wounded, his spleen and diaphragm pierced by shrapnel as well as cloth and leather fragments from the vehicle's upholstery. Nine days later, on 4th June, Heydrich dies in agony from his wounds.

WAGNER AND PAGEANTRY

Heydrich is buried with all Nazi honours in the Veteran's Cemetery in Germany's capital. The Berlin Philharmonic Orchestra plays Wagner's funeral march. Heydrich's state funeral, designed to be broadcast to the world as a great show of Nazi solidarity and power, features all the Nazi leadership and literally thousands of black-uniformed SS guarding the awesome pageantry of the procession. Hitler gives an emotional eulogy of the dead man. Himmler praises Heydrich as a *"...gentleman of breeding and bearing"* who had been *"feared by lower racial types and sub-humans, hated and defamed by Jews and criminals."* [93]

As Heydrich's coffin, draped in the swastika, is drawn by four jet-black horses in procession towards the Veteran's Cemetery, the retaliation hundreds of miles to the south in Czechoslovakia has already begun. The Führer is beside himself with rage. Hundreds of Czechs of doubtful political allegiance are rounded up and shot. The entire village of Lidice, thought to have sheltered Heydrich's assassins at some point during their

---

[93] Garbutt, Paul, *Assassin!*, Ian Allan Ltd., England, 1942, p.87

five-month preparation, has its entire male population machine-gunned and its women and children driven away to concentration camps.

The assassins are eventually tracked down to an Orthodox Church in Ressel Street, Prague. Hundreds of SS surround the building while their officers puzzle out how to finish the stand-off. Finally the pride of Heydrich's officer corps orders the Prague fire department to pump water from the River Vltava into the crypt to drown 'the vermin'. Later the bodies of the priests, assassins and collaborators are recovered. All are found to have died either fighting or having committed suicide with the last of their bullets before the water could reach them.

JUSTICE FOR ALL?
Adolf Eichmann is later tracked down by the Israeli Mossad and in 1961 is kidnapped from his hideout in South America and returned to Israel for trial. Eichmann gives his account professionally and unemotionally before the world's cameras. He is found guilty and hanged. Nazi psychiatrist Professor Paul Nitsche is sent to the guillotine on 25th March 1948 in Dresden. T4 doctor Carl Schneider, recruited by the Nazis to carry out pathology work on the brains of children gassed in the extermination institutions, is found guilty at Nuremburg and hanged. Dr Leonardo Conti, the Reich's Minister for Health from 1939 to 1945, commits suicide. Fleeing from Allied authorities, psychiatrist Dr Max de Crinis, one of the leaders of the T4 euthanasia program, practises murder even in his final hour. The Austrian physician poisons his wife and children with potassium cyanide before taking his own life in the same manner.

POSTSCRIPT
Were the war-time psychiatric abuses only attributable to the Nazis? Dr W H Kay, reviewing his military service during World War 2, later reported that he had found an American psychiatrist up to his old tricks: *"Electroshock was indicated to help in the management of insane soldiers, who would become quite meek and manageable after a session with the 'thing....'"* [94]

---

[94] Kay, W H, *We Can't All Be Sane!* Collectors Publications, Los Angeles: 1965, pp.117-119

Rounding up the Cattle
Examining the Mechanics of Political Control

"Behind the ostensible government sits enthroned an invisible government owing no allegiance and acknowledging no responsibility to the people. To destroy this invisible government, to befoul the unholy alliance between corrupt business and corrupt politics is the first task of the statesmanship of the day." - President Theodore Roosevelt, 19th April 1906

"There is a power so organised, so complete, so subtle, so pervasive, that they had better not speak above their breath when they speak in condemnation of it." - President Woodrow Wilson

In 1905 an infamous document known as *The Protocols of the Learned Elders of Zion* had surfaced and caused a stir. The Protocols appeared to be a dissertation on the ABCs of world take-over and had apparently been written to look like the work of evil Jews. The media react to the exposing of the Protocols with disdain and mockery that anyone could ever take them seriously. Ever since, the Protocols have courted controversy and criticism. *The Los Angeles Times*, 28th November 1993, writes, "Russia Rules Anti-Semitic Tract a Fraud." Other news headlines include, "Codebook for World Take-Over or Anti-Semitic Nonsense?" and "The Conspiracy Conspiracy". What's interesting is that while everyone seems very vocal in denying the authenticity of the Protocols, no one ever quotes them. Could there be a reason for this? That if they were quoted, the reader might quickly learn that they are a series of self-fulfilling prophecies, uncomfortably close to mankind's current predicament?

That the Protocols are a modernisation and distillation of Weishaupt's original manifesto is beyond doubt when one studies them. The use of Jewish terms and the overall style is clearly designed to finger the descendants of Abraham as the culprits and conspirators. Notes and emphasis have been added to the following by this author where appropriate.

PROTOCOL #1 (EXTRACT) EXPOSED 1905
Behold the alcoholised animals, bemused with drink, the right to an immoderate use of which comes along with freedom. It is not for us and ours to walk that road. The peoples of the goyim [cattle] are bemused with alcoholic liquors; their youth has grown stupid on classicism and

from early immorality, into which it has been inducted by our special agents – by tutors, by lackeys, governesses in the houses of the wealthy, by clerks and others, by our women in the places of dissipation frequented by the goyim.

Our countersign is – Force and Make-Believe.... Far back in ancient times, we were the first to cry among the masses of the people the words, "Liberty, Equality, Fraternity", [French Revolution] words many times repeated since those days by stupid poll-parrots.... The abstraction of freedom has enabled us to persuade the mob in all countries <u>that their government is nothing but the steward of the people who are the owners of the country</u>, and that the steward may be replaced like a worn-out glove [the process of 'democracy']. It is this possibility of replacing the representatives of the people, which has placed them at our disposal, and, as it were, given us the power of appointment.

PROTOCOL #2 (EXTRACT) EXPOSED 1905
It is indispensable for our purpose that wars, so far as possible, should not result in territorial gains. The intellectuals of the goyim will puff themselves up with their knowledge and without any logical verification of them will put into effect all the information available from science, which our agentur specialists have cunningly pieced together for the purposes of educating their minds in the direction we want.

<u>Do not suppose for a moment that these statements are empty words; think carefully of the successes we arranged, for Darwinism</u> [Evolution], Marxism [Communism], Nietzscheism [later- Nazism]. <u>To us Jews, at any rate, it should be plain to see what a disintegrating importance these directives have had on the minds of the goyim.</u>

PROTOCOL #3 (EXTRACT) EXPOSED 1905
Hunger creates the right of capital to rule the worker more surely than if it were given to the aristocracy by the legal authority of kings. By want and the envy and hatred, which it engenders, we shall move the mobs and with their hands we shall wipe out all those who hinder us on our way [a preview of the Bolshevik Revolution to follow].

When the hour strikes for our Sovereign Lord of all the World to be crowned [viewed by Christians as the Antichrist], it is these same hands which will sweep away everything that might be a hindrance thereto. <u>The goyim have lost the habit of thinking</u> unless prompted by the suggestions of our specialists.

69

PROTOCOL #4 (EXTRACT) EXPOSED 1905

Who or what is in a position to overthrow an invisible force? And this is precisely what our force is. Gentile Masonry blindly serves as a screen for us and our objects, but the plan of action of our force, even its very abiding-place, remains for the whole people a mystery.

It is indispensable for us to undermine all faith, to tear out of the minds of the goyim the very principle of Godhead and the Spirit, and to put in its place arithmetical calculations and material needs.

The intensified struggle for superiority and shocks delivered to economic life will create, nay, have already created, disenchanted, cold and heartless communities. Such communities will foster a strong aversion towards the higher political offices and towards religion. Their only guide is gain, that is Gold, which they will erect into a veritable cult, for the sake of those material delights, which it can give.

Has it already been decided how societies are to be ruled in the future? Has a future Earth been planned – one populated by a narcotised, dumbed-down worker-class hooked on material pleasures, whose every need and desire has been anticipated and envisioned by an all-powerful élite – indeed a self-elected élite who will henceforth call the shots for the sake of world stability? Let us examine further.

Several examples of how well Weishaupt's plan appears to be proceeding on a number of different fronts can be seen with the dramatic developments in America and other leading nations in more recent times. On 17th June 1963, the Supreme Court of the United States bans school Bible reading in the Abington versus Schempp case. The court explains its psychiatry-influenced decision as follows: *"If portions of the New Testament were read without explanation, they could be... and had been psychologically damaging to the child."* One can only imagine what American founding father James Madison would have thought about the Bible causing brain damage to the children.

PSYCHIATRY FROM GOD

Psychiatry had begun infiltrating the churches during the 1920's. The theory of evolution was widely accepted, even by many churchgoers. Man was nothing but a stimulus response animal, after all. And he did need expert help. By the 1950's, certain 'progressive' divinity schools, such as the Fuller Theological Seminary in Pasadena, California, were introducing a melding of traditional biblical teaching with psychiatric and psychological counselling. The establishment of the Academy of Religion and Mental Health in 1954 launched programs such as conferences on psychological testing for ministerial selection and 'clinical' (psychological, pastoral) training for the clergy.

Today, we find Christian 'psychology' everywhere – in the pulpit, on Christian radio and a myriad of cable TV stations around the world. There are even Christian psychiatric clinics, where drugs and bonhomie are dispensed presumably as extensions to the Christian religion. One Christian psychiatric chain, Minirth-Meier, began when Frank Minirth announced to both the president and academic dean of the world-famous Dallas Theological Seminary, *"God is calling us to teach psychology in Dallas"*.[95]

Predictably, the rot set in. Today, churches have been fooled into becoming referral institutions for psychiatrists. Where once a parishioner would turn to his spiritual leader when in need, now he was being told he was mentally ill and needed psychiatric, not spiritual, care.

By 1991, a *Christianity Today* survey found that 29% of its readers had received counselling for themselves or a close family member within the last three years, and that they were three times more likely to receive it from a psychiatrist or psychologist than from a pastor. The results of a similar survey in *Today's Christian Woman* were even higher—38%.[96]

THE GREAT APOSTASY
CHURCH ATTENDANCE FALLS AWAY

What has been the result of the multi-forked attack on Christianity? According to church poll findings since the 1950's, more than four out of five Americans consider themselves 'Christians' (82%), yet actual church attendance reached an all-time low in 1996. In West Germany, church membership dropped 14.5% from 1963 to 1994. Between 1992 and 1993, almost 350,000 people resigned from the German Catholic Church.[97] In the United Kingdom, only 11.7% stated that they attended church once a

---

[95] Stafford, Tim, "The Therapeutic Revolution", *Christianity Today*, 17th May 1993, p.31.
[96] CCHR, *Psychiatry – Destroying* Morals, Los Angeles, 2000; also, Stafford, Tim, "Franchising Hope", *Christianity Today*, 18th May 1992, p.24
[97] "Church Resignations", *Awake*, 1994. Citing statistics from the German Catholic newspaper, *Christ in der Gegenwart*.

week or more in 1993,[98] prompting one researcher to declare: *"It is not exaggerated to conclude that between 1960 and 1985, the Church of England as a going concern was effectively reduced to not much more than half its previous size.... For a supposed national church, the Anglican figures were – and still are – a pretty catastrophic situation to come to terms with."* [99]

In the Netherlands, a nation which, under the recommendations of its psychiatrists, legalised euthanasia and pot smoking, 75% of the population were churchgoers in 1950. By 1991, this had dropped to 50%, with a further decline to 25% expected in the near future.[100]

In 1980 it became illegal for copies of the Ten Commandments to be publicly displayed in American school buildings. The US Supreme Court decision for Stone versus Graham is characterised by the following statement: *"If posted copies of the Ten Commandments are to have any effect at all, it will be to induce school children to read, meditate upon... perhaps even to venerate and obey the Commandments....*[i.e. 'Thou shalt not commit murder', 'Thou shalt not steal', etc.] *this is not a permissible objective."* [101]

In the 1960's, psychiatry stepped up the heat in driving the nails into the coffin of organised religion. One such example was psychologist William Coulson, who was responsible for corrupting some two dozen religious orders through the deliberate introduction of 'humanistic' psychology and 'non-directive counselling'. The result of his work was the complete destruction of the religious order of the Sisters of the Immaculate Heart of Mary and their 59 schools in less than a year and a half. In 1993, Coulson came clean to the press after realising the evil he had perpetrated. He later renounced his psychiatric philosophy, stating:

"We corrupted a whole raft of religious orders on the West Coast in the 1960's by getting nuns and priests to talk about their distress.... The IHM's [Sisters of the Immaculate Heart of Mary] *had some 60 schools*

[98] "1993 British Social Attitudes Survey", *Social Trends* 25 (1995), Section 13.15, "Religious Attendance", p.222

[99] Davie, Grace, *Religion in Britain since 1945. Believing Without Belonging,* Blackwell, Boston, Mass: 1994, p.53

[100] *Awake,* op. cit.

[101] Proactive, *A Nation Adrift,* a video documentary, 1627 W Main Street #213, Bozeman, MT 59715 USA

when we started; at the end, they had one. There were some 560 nuns when we began. Within a year after our first interventions, 300 of them were petitioning Rome to get out of their vows. They did not want to be under anybody's authority, except the authority of their empirical inner selves....

We did similar programs for the Jesuits, for the Franciscans, for the Sisters of Providence of Charity and for the Mercy Sisters. We did dozens of Catholic religious organisations. We provoked an epidemic of sexual misconduct among clergy and therapists...."[102]

Peter Hoagland, a Nebraska state senator, contended on radio in 1983 that *"...fundamental, Bible-believing people do not have the right to indoctrinate their children in their religious beliefs because we, the state, are preparing them for the year 2000, when America will be part of a one-world order global society and their children will not fit in."*

SILENT WEAPONS ASSAULTS ON CHRISTIANITY
Protocol #17 (extract) Exposed 1905
We have long past taken care to discredit the priesthood of the goyim, and thereby ruin their mission on Earth, which in these days might still be a great hindrance to us. Day by day its influence on the peoples of the world is falling lower. Freedom of conscience has been declared everywhere, so that now only years divide us from the moment of the complete wrecking of that Christian religion, as to other religions we shall have still less difficulty in dealing with them [monotheistic religions: Judaism and Islam].

When the time comes finally to destroy the papal court [Catholic Church], *the finger of an invisible hand will point the nations towards this court. When however the nations fling themselves upon it, we shall come forward in the guise of its defenders as if to save excessive bloodshed. By this diversion, we shall penetrate to its very bowels and be sure we shall never come out again until we have gnawed through the entire strength of this place.*

ALL UNDER ONE ROOF
On the finance side, Dr John Coleman illustrates the extent of the financial monopoly now owned by the banking élite: *"To show the*

---

[102] An interview with Dr William Coulson, "We overcame their traditions, we overcame their faith," *The Latin Mass*, Special Edition

concentration of power, note that 50 banks control 64% of the world's assets. 50 insurance companies control 80% of all insurance assets worldwide. Only 100 corporations in the US control over 58% of the industrial assets in the US. In total, there are only about 4,300 leadership positions (positions of authority and power controlling over half the assets in the US) in the corporate sector.

There are 300 families in the United States (while only 100 in the UK and even less in Russia) that are involved in the control of this nation. A closer examination shows many tie-ins of control that go back to the Satanic hierarchy for corporate leaders. All of America's 300 families are co-operating with the Committee of 300. Occasionally there are members who stray from the co-operation such as the Kennedy and Hunt brothers...."[103]

PROTOCOL #5 (EXTRACT) EXPOSED 1905

The principal object of our directorate consists of this: to debilitate the public mind by criticism; to lead it away from serious reflections calculated to arouse resistance; <u>to distract the forces of the mind towards this sham fight of empty eloquence</u>.

In order to put public opinion into our hands, we must bring it into a state of bewilderment by giving expression from all sides to so many contradictory opinions and for such length of time as will suffice to make the goyim lose their heads in the labyrinth and come to see that the best thing is to have no opinion of any kind in matters political, which it is not given to the public to understand.

<u>There is nothing more dangerous than personal initiative</u>. We must so direct the education of the goyim communities [dumbing down], *that whenever they come upon a matter requiring initiative, they may drop their hands in despairing impotence. From this collision arise grave moral shocks, disenchantments, failures. By all these means we shall so wear down the goyim that they will be compelled to offer us international power of a nature which, by its position, will enable us, without any violence, gradually to absorb all the State forces of the world and to form a Super-Government.*

---

[103] Coleman, John, *Conspirators' Hierarchy: The Story of the Committee of 300*, American West Publishers, 1992

74

Like Churchill before him, John F Hylan, Mayor of New York between 1918 and 1925, articulates his own fears for his country: *"The real menace to our Republic is the invisible government which, like a giant octopus, sprawls its slimy legs over our cities, states and nation."* [104]

PROTOCOL #9 (EXTRACT) EXPOSED 1905
It is from us that the all-engulfing terror proceeds. We have in our service persons of all opinions, doctrines, restorating monarchists, demagogues, socialists, Communists, and utopian dreamers of every kind. We have harnessed them all to the task: each one of them on his own account is boring away at the last remnants of authority, is striving to overthrow all established form of order. By these acts all States are in torture; they exhort to tranquillity, are ready to sacrifice everything for peace. But we will not give them peace until they openly acknowledge our international Super-Government, and with submissiveness.

Division into fractional parties has given them into our hands, for, in order to carry on a contested struggle, one must have money - and the money is all in our hands.

The goal of a global world order is succinctly enshrined in the United Nations World Constitution: *"The age of nations must end. The government of nations have decided to order their separate sovereignties into one government to which they will surrender their arms."* [105]

George Bush Sr, a Skull and Bones initiate from Yale University, 'born again' after ritualistically climbing into a coffin naked before his university peers,[106] sees no conflict in declaring treason in 1992 whilst president of the United States: *"My vision of a New World Order foresees a UN with a*

---

[104] Kershaw, Peter, *Economic Solutions*, Quality Press, 2888 Bluff Street #315, Boulder, CO USA 80301

[105] Kershaw, Peter, op. cit.

[106] George Bush's membership of the élite, occultic Skull and Bones Society of Yale University has been the subject of many a public report: Aronson, Steven M L, "George Bush's Biggest Secret", *Fame* magazine, August 1989, pp. 82-89; "Skull and Spare Ribs", *The Economist*, 2nd November 1991; "God, Men and Bonding at Yale", *Newsweek* magazine, 29th April 1991, p. 66; "Yale Women Barred from Secret Society", *Los Angeles Times*, 6th September 1991, p. A28; "So George, What About Those Swastikas?" Winnipeg Free Press, reprinted in *Sun*, 17th October 1989; "Old New World Order?" Christopher Hutchens in *The European*, 14th-16th June 1991, p.10.

revitalised peacekeeping function. It is the <u>sacred principles</u> enshrined in the UN charter <u>to which we henceforth pledge our allegiance</u>." [107]

Even the crusty, improbably named Zbigniew Brzezinski, National Security Advisor to Carter and four other presidents, is at it in his book, *Between Two Ages*: *"The technetronic era involves the gradual appearance of <u>a more controlled society. Such a society would be dominated by an élite, unrestrained by traditional values</u>."*[108]

In his famous novel, *1984*, George Orwell writes of his fictitious controlled society: *"In the past, no government had the power to keep its citizens under constant surveillance. The invention of print however made it easier to manipulate public opinion - film and radio carried the process even further. With the development of television... private life came to an end. Every citizen could be kept, for twenty-four hours a day, under the eyes of the police with all other channels of communication closed. The possibility of enforcing not only complete obedience to the will of the state, but complete uniformity of opinion on all subjects, now existed for the first time."* [109]

Thomas Macawley, writing to H S Randall, sees the danger posed by Weishaupt's burgeoning movement even as early as 1857: *"Either some Caesar or Napoleon will seize the reins of government with a strong hand, or your republic* [America] *will be as fearfully plundered and laid waste by barbarians in the Twentieth Century as the Roman Empire was in the Fifth; with the difference that the Huns and Vandals who ravaged the Roman Empire came from without, and your Huns and Vandals will have been engendered from within your own country and by your own institutions."* [110]

Ted L Gunderson, former head of the FBI in Los Angeles, Memphis and Dallas, testifies to this gradual encroachment of the Illuminati in a 1995 interview with Radio Free America talk-show host, Anthony Hilder, in the latter's TV documentary, *Reichstag '95*:

"There is no question that the Satanic movement, which has been with us for two thousand years, was really well organised back in 1776

---

[107] Kershaw, Peter, op. cit.

[108] Brzezinski, Zbigniew, *Between Two Ages*, Greenwood Publishing Group, 1992

[109] Orwell, George, *1984*, NAL/Dutton: 1976, p.206

[110] Kershaw, Peter, op. cit.

when the Illuminati was founded and became active. There's no question that they have been working at this for years.... I have information, documentation, that these people, this element in our society, has infiltrated virtually every level: doctors, lawyers, politicians – oh, by all means, politicians...."

PROTOCOL #10 (EXTRACT) EXPOSED 1905

It is indispensable to trouble in all countries, the people's relations with their governments so as to utterly exhaust humanity with dissension, hatred, struggle, envy and_even by the use of torture, by starvation, by the inoculation of diseases_, by want, so that the goyim see no other issue than to take refuge in our complete sovereignty in money and in all else. But if we give the nations of the world a breathing space, the moment we long for is hardly likely ever to arrive.

PROTOCOL #11 (EXTRACT) EXPOSED 1905

The goyim are a flock of sheep, and we are their wolves. And you know what happens when the wolves get hold of the flock.... There is another reason also why they will close their eyes: for we shall keep promising them to give back all the liberties we have taken away as soon as we have quelled the enemies of peace and tamed all parties.... It is not worthwhile to say anything about how long a time they will be kept waiting for this return of their liberties....

THE ROLE OF THE MEDIA

Total domination of global politics, economics and the military can never be accomplished without total control of the media. Many scoff at the notion that the press can be appropriated and controlled, citing as obvious example the various 'exposés' that rock our nations from time to time in the newspapers. Sceptics who disbelieve that there exists a Media and Information Super Highway Old Boys' Club may wish to obtain the September 1998 edition of *Vanity Fair* which contains Annie Liebovitz's remarkable photograph.[111] Thirty-seven of the world's top mass communications purveyors gather in an Idaho wood for a photo-call. Their combined wealth totals $1.4 trillion. Their average age is 50 and between them they own 14 film studios, 43 music labels, 52 magazines and 124 daily newspapers. Cast your eyes down the following list of names and ask yourself a couple of questions:

---

[111] The photograph is also printed in the *Evening Standard*, 10th September 1998, pp.8-9

- Are these busy people?
- What does it say about collective co-operation that they take valuable time off (some of them to travel halfway around the world) just to attend a photo shoot for *Vanity Fair* in Idaho, of all places?

Herbert A Allen, president, Allen and Company; **Edgar Bronfman Jr**, president, Seagram; **Howard Stringer**, president, Sony (US); **Gerald Levin**, chairman, Time Warner; **Richard Parsons**, president, Time Warner; **Michael Jordan**, chairman, CBS; **Jeffrey Katzenberg**, partner, Dreamworks SKG; **John Malone**, chairman, TCI; **Nathan Myrvold**, chief technology officer, Microsoft; **Michael Ovitz**, chairman, CKE Associates; **Jeff Berg**, chairman, ICM; **Warren Buffet**, chairman, Berkshire Hathaway; **Michael Armstrong**, chairman, AT&T; **Ted Waitt**, chairman, gateway; **Ron Meyer**, president, Universal; **Bob Pittman**, president, America Online; **James Kennedy**, chairman, Cox Enterprises; **Nobuyuki Idei**, president, Sony; **Sumner Redstone**, chairman, Viacom Inc; **Terry Semel**, chairman, Warner Bros; **Michael Bloomberg**, partner, Bloomberg; **Frank Biondi**, chairman, Universal; **Leo Hindrey Jr**, chairman, TCI; **Andrew Grove**, chairman, Intel; **Stephen Case**, chief executive, America Online; **Jonathan Dolgen**, chaiman, Viacom Entertainments Group; **Katherine Graham**, proprietor, Washington Post; **Donald Graham**, chief executive, Washington Post; **Barry Diller**, chairman, USA Networks; **David Geffen**, partner, Dreamworks SKG; **Rupert Murdoch**, chairman, Newscorp; **Bob Wright**, president, NBC; **Herbert Siegel**, president, Chris-Craft; **Gordon Crawford**, senior vice president, Capital Research; **Peter Chernin**, president, Newscorp; **Brian Roberts**, president, Comcast; **Bill Gates**, chairman, Microsoft.

PROTOCOL #12 (EXTRACT) EXPOSED 1905
We shall deal with the press in the following way: What is the part played by the press today? It serves to excite and inflame those passions, which are needed for our purpose, or else it serves selfish ends of parties. It is often vapid, unjust, mendacious, and the majority of the public has not the slightest idea which ends the press really serves.

Literature and journalism are two of the most important educative forces, and therefore our government will become proprietor of the majority of the journals. This will neutralize the injurious influence of the privately-owned press and will put us in possession of the tremendous influence upon the public mind....

Those fools who will think they are repeating the opinion of a newspaper of their own camp will be repeating our opinion or any opinion that seems desirable for us. In the vain belief that they are following the organ of their party, they will in fact follow the flag which we hang out for them.

We shall have a sure triumph over our opponents, since they will not have at their disposition organs of the press in which they can give full and final expression to their views, owning to the aforesaid methods of dealing with the press. We shall not even need to refute them, except very superficially. Not a single announcement will reach the public without our control.

Head Illuminatus David Rockefeller was recorded saying the following words at the clandestine Bilderberger meeting in Baden Baden, Germany, in June 1991.

"We are grateful to the Washington Post, the New York Times, Time magazine and other great publications, whose directors have attended our meetings and respected their promise of discretion for almost forty years.... It would have been impossible for us to develop our plan for the world if we had been subject to the bright lights of publicity during those years. But today the world is more sophisticated and prepared to march towards a world government. The supranational sovereignty of an intellectual élite and world bankers is surely preferable to the national auto-determination practised in past centuries." [112]

---

[112] Liberty Lobby, *Bilderbergers: Spotlight on the Bilderbergers*, Deep River Books, Los Angeles, CA. The Bilderberg meetings were founded by HRH Prince Bernhard of the Netherlands, a former SS officer and employee of Nazi chemical empire, IG Farben. The group was named after the Bilderberg Hotel in Oosterbeck, Holland, where the first meeting took place in 1954. Comprising international financiers, politicians, media and other key global leaders, and by invitation only, the Bilderberg meetings are conducted in the strictest secrecy, at varying world venues, the agendas unpublicised, and the group's existence almost entirely unreported. All attempts by Credence to gain further information on the May 1998 Bilderberg meeting held at the Turnberry Hotel, Scotland, were met with *"No comment."* 1998 Turnberry attendees included Conrad Black, chairman UK *Telegraph Newspapers*, Anatole Kaletsky, associate editor UK *Times,* Christopher Hogg, chairman *Reuters,* Jim Hoagland, associate editor *Washington Post,* David Rockefeller, chairman of *Chase Manhattan Bank*, Henry Kissinger, *Kissinger Associates*, James Wolfensohn, president *World Bank*, Jan Leschly, CEO *SmithKline Beecham Pharmaceuticals*. For an insight into Bilderberg

INTELLECTUAL PROSTITUTES

John Swinton, the former chief of staff of the *New York Times*, was called by his associates 'the dean of his profession'. As a luminary of international journalism and widely regarded as one of the most experienced newshounds of his day, Swinton was asked to toast 'an independent press' at the New York Press Club. In so doing, some monumental statements about the servile and controlled condition of the media were made before an astounded, but not entirely disbelieving audience:

"There is no such thing at this date of the world's history, in America, as an independent press. You know it and I know it. There is not one of you who dares to write your honest opinions, and if you did, you would know beforehand that it would never appear in print. I am paid weekly for keeping my honest opinions out of the paper I am connected with. Others of you are paid similar salaries for similar things, and any of you who would be so foolish as to write honest opinions would be out on the streets looking for another job. If I allowed my honest opinions to appear in one issue of my paper, before twenty-four hours my occupation would be gone. The business of the journalist is to destroy the truth; to lie outright; to pervert; to vilify; to fawn at the feet of mammon, and to sell his country and his race for his daily bread. You know it and I know it, and what folly is this toasting an independent press? We are the tools and vassals for rich men behind the scenes. We are the jumping jacks, they pull the strings and we dance. Our talents, our possibilities and our lives are all the property of other men. We are intellectual prostitutes." [113]

Acclaimed children's author Roald Dahl makes the common mistake of misidentifying the quasi-Jewish façade of the Illuminati[114] in a comment made shortly before his death in 1990: *"We all know about Jews and all the rest of it. There aren't any non-Jewish publishers anywhere. They control the media - jolly clever thing to do...."* [115]

---

influence over the current British, European and US governments, visit www.watch.pair.com/discernment.html and related links.

[113] Kershaw, Peter, op. cit.

[114] See also Holy Bible, KJV, Revelation 2:9; 3:9

[115] *Daily Mail,* 7th January 1999

Richard M Cohen, senior producer of CBS political news: *"We are going to impose our agenda on the coverage by dealing with issues and subjects that we choose to deal with."* [116]

Richard Salant, former president of CBS News: *"Our job is not to give people what they want, but what we decide they ought to have."* [117]

DESENSITISING THE PUBLIC TO VIOLENCE

Glorying in the gore dulls the senses and perverts the mindset. Apathy and a deep kind of sexual thrill are experienced by the viewer who watches scenes of social as well as sexual degradation nightly on the television or at the movies. The lasting effect is a dulling of the blade of morality and a quenching of the desire to help others who have become victims. Author Michael Hoffman:

"I remember Budd Dwyer's televised suicide. The Pennsylvania official prefaced his broadcast TV self-immolation with a quote from one of his associates who told Dwyer that the American people had become too jaded about 'routine' investigations into political corruption on TV's 60 Minutes and 20/20 to care very much about the corruption Dwyer sought to expose.

Mr Dwyer decided that a population so jaded would need a spectacular sacrificial victim to shake it awake from its apathy and therefore he shot himself in front of TV cameras at a news conference.

But his televised suicide did no such thing. Instead it became, like virtually everything else that appears on television, a trivialised part of the entertainment videodrome. It merely raised the stakes for the next human life to exceed, in terms of violence and horror and brutalisation, as public fare." [118]

THE ART OF MANAGING CONSPIRACY

The press plays an important part in the dissemination and controlling of 'conspiracy', whether it is JFK, UFOs, the death of Princess Diana or any other 'latest scoop'. The public is bombarded with TV 'specials', giving so many different angles and theories on the event in

---

[116] Kershaw, Peter, op. cit.

[117] Ibid.

[118] Hoffman, Michael, *Secret Societies and Psychological Warfare*, Wiswell Ruffin House, 1992, p.90

81

question that, just as the Protocols predicted, the viewing public eventually becomes apathetic, loses interest and goes resignedly back to its everyday life. How many JFK and 'X Files' programs does it take to cultivate the cynicism, apathy and a disinclination seriously to look any further? Are we not happy just to canonise the slain subject in question, register our sometimes huge outpourings of grief, and remember how they could have been? It's sentimental mush for all - a big game of 'Let's Pretend', with the mass communications media inflaming those fickle passions we all have within us:

"The whole aim of practical politics is to keep the populace alarmed, and hence clamorous to be led to safety, by menacing it with an endless series of hobgoblins, all of them imaginary." H L Mencken

Without the media, who would today's terrorism play to? Who's going to blow up a building or destroy an airliner if they are not able to gain the leverage of a world stage from which to put their case? Without free, worldwide exposure for his agenda, martyrdom or a 'thirty stretch' in jail suddenly doesn't seem such a bargain to the anarchist. *"But the media exposes all kinds of atrocities!"* people cry. Of course, and that's why we believe we need the media. Have you ever wondered why they don't tell us any good news? Only *News at Ten* used to do a little good news spot almost as an afterthought - Trevor McDonald smiling, *"...and finally...."* and going on to tell his audience about 'The Tamworth Two' - a couple of pigs who escaped from the slaughterhouse and were currently on the run from their executioners.

Indeed.

Michael Hoffman again: *"It is one thing for the media, the police, the judiciary and the killers themselves to commit terrible acts without our knowledge and consent. It is quite another matter, with grave repercussions in the realm of psychodrama, public ritual and advanced mind control, when these crimes are committed with our consent. It is an ancient rule of both the moral and common law that silence connotes consent - silence and a lack of meaningful action constitute consent in the face of these crimes.*

"They brag to us about what they've gotten away with and we're thrilled by it. That's our only significant response, that and the anticipation of the next thrill.

"Thus the old strategy of exposing the cryptocracy, when applied blindly in the belief that this in itself is a potent weapon against the cryptocracy, is bankrupt. Exposure and publicity by themselves, without a broader understanding of the [issues] *involved, is worse than useless, it actually plays into the hands of the conspirators."*[119]

PROTOCOL #13 (EXTRACT) EXPOSED 1905

In order that the masses themselves may not guess what they are about, we further distract them with amusements, games, pastimes [leisure activities], *passions* [soap operas, movies and theatre], *people's palaces* [Disneyland, Lifestyles of the Rich and Famous]... *Soon we shall begin through the press to propose competitions of art, in sport of all kinds* [World Cup, FA Cup, Test Cricket, NBA, Superbowl, the Olympics, with the famous torch of illumination, etc.]. *These interests will finally distract their minds from questions in which we should find ourselves compelled to oppose them. Growing more and more disaccustomed to reflect and form any opinions of their own, people will begin to talk in the same tone as we, because we alone shall be offering them new directions for thought....of course through such persons as will not be suspected of solidarity with us.*

SILENT WEAPONS ASSAULTS ON GOVERNMENTS
Protocol #14 (extract) Exposed 1905

The errors of the goyim governments will be depicted by us in the most vivid hues. We shall implant such an abhorrence of them that the peoples will prefer tranquillity in a state of serfdom to those rights of vaunted freedom which have tortured humanity and exhausted the very sources of human existence; sources which have been exploited by a mob of rascally adventurers who know not what they do [government scandals, Profumo, Kennedy, Hart, Clinton, Nixon, Davis, Mandelson, etc]... *In countries known as progressive and enlightened we have created a senseless, filthy abominable literature* [tabloid newspapers, gossip magazines and pop-pornography].... *Our philosophers will discuss all the shortcomings of the various beliefs of the goyim, but no one will ever bring under discussion our faith from its true point of view* [Luciferianism], *since this will be fully learned by none save ours, who will never dare betray its secrets.*

---

[119] Hoffman, Michael, op. cit.

CREATING WILLING SLAVES

The disintegrating effects of the New Materialism and its turning away from traditional morality is seen every day in the newspapers. Today in the United States, 57 people will be murdered. 251 women will be raped. 54,000 men are serving long-term prison sentences. 3,000 teenage girls will discover they are pregnant. 3,133 unborn infants will be aborted. Ten years after the Abingdon versus Schempp ruling took the Ten Commandments out of the school system, they had to put the metal detectors in. Today 135,000 weapons will go onto school campuses. 3.3 million problem drinkers will go to school. 40 students will be shot on campus. 4.4 million children will take psychiatric medication to cater for their 'special needs'. 623 students will discover they have a sexually transmitted disease.[120]

And the assault on the family? Protocols or not, America again illustrates the trend. 60% of all American married men have admitted to adultery. 69,000 Californian students were assaulted last year on campus. This weekend, 30% of America's students will be drunk. In 1990, 700,000 high school graduates could not even read their own diplomas. Over 200,000 children will be sexually abused this year. Only 7% of America's families today consist of a father who works, a mother who is making a home, and children. One hundred years ago the average vocabulary of an American sixteen-year-old was 70,000 words. Today it is just 15,000.[121]

WIND OR WISDOM?

Many have asked questions such as: "Were the Protocols deliberately exposed?" or "Are they genuine?" The reader must be the judge. Author Wendy Wallace, from her Christian perspective, points out that the exposure of the Protocols themselves may actually serve its own special purpose: *"The majority of the populace is so benumbed and jaded at this point that exposing the 'hidden works of darkness' does little more than titillate and further enslave them, since they no longer have a will to fight their continuing degradation.... If you haven't read the Protocols, get a copy while they're still legal in this country. Reading them is most 'enlightening'. As the Holy Bible shows us the mind and purpose of God, the Protocols show us the mind and purpose of Satan and the plan for*

---

[120] Schatzer, Vaughn, *The Truth Behind the Declaration of Independence*, a video commentary, PROACTIVE, 1627 W Main Street #213, Bozeman, MT 59715 USA
[121] Ibid.

world domination that has been effectually pursued to this day, with ever-increasing speed and efficiency." [122]

SUMMARY OF THE PROTOCOLS
When one studies them in their entirety, it isn't hard to recognise the outworking of each 'unlikely' Protocol in our everyday lives today, suggesting of course one of two explanations: either that the authenticity of the Protocols, their current operation and overwhelming effect on society is entirely provable by what we are witnessing, or alternatively that society has somehow followed the outworkings of these 'fictitious' Protocols through a series of improbably remote coincidences. The fact that they were exposed in 1905 implies, if they are genuine, that their planning and operational phases were actioned much earlier.

More than a few leaders in the 20th century 'appear' to have become alarmed at a Zionist conspiracy to rule the world after the Protocols were exposed. Hitler was encouraged by his own beliefs and opinions, as well as rogue elements within the Catholic Church, into taking the most extreme action against the Jewry of Europe - actions which were ironically funded by Illuminati 'false Jews' and their banks, who had promoted the National Socialists (bankers such as Warburg, Thyssen, Von Schroeder and Rothschild).[123] Today, anti-Semitism still appears to play an important role in protecting the working of the system. No one dares publicly oppose the apparent 'Jewishness' of the Illuminati for fear of being labelled 'another Hitler'.

ILLUMINATI SUB-AGENDAS
On 10th January 1963, the US Congressional Record, pp. A34-A35, listed the long-term goals of the Marxist/Illuminist agenda, as they were being applied in America. This catalogue also appeared in *The Naked Communist* published by ex-FBI agent, Cleon Skousen.[124] The main agendas are itemised below and could equally apply to policies which have been, and still are implemented by the British government and others across the world. The object, as with the Communist Manifesto and the

---

[122] Wallace, Wendy, *Four Horsemen of the Apocalypse and the New World Order,* POB 3109, Prescott, AZ, 86302 USA, pp.28-29
[123] *"There is a mountainous, unquestionable body of evidence demonstrating, directly or indirectly, that the investment and banking firm of which George Bush's father was a major figure gave early financial backing to Adolf Hitler and Nazi officials such as Rudolf Hess."* Marrs, Texe, *Dark Majesty,* Living Truth Publishers, Austin, TX: 1992, p. 168
[124] Kershaw, Peter, *Economic Solutions,* op. cit.

Protocols, seems to be to mould nationalistic populations into a homogenous, subservient, controllable people that can be governed by a centralised world government:

- US acceptance of coexistence as the only alternative to atomic war.
- Develop the illusion that total disarmament by America would be a demonstration of moral strength.
- Permit free trade between all nations regardless of Communist domination.
- Allow all Soviet satellites individual representation at the United Nations.
- Provide American aid to all nations regardless of Communist domination.
- Promote the United Nations as 'the only hope for mankind'. If its charter is rewritten, demand that it be set as a one-world government with its own independent armed forces.
- Resist any attempt to outlaw the Communist Party.
- Do away with all loyalty oaths.
- Continue giving Russia access to the US Patent Office.
- Capture one or both of the political parties of the US.
- Use technical decisions of the courts to weaken basic American institutions by claiming their activities violate civil rights.
- Get control of the schools. Use them as transmission belts for socialism and current Communist propaganda. Get control of the teachers' associations. Soften the curriculum (dumb down). Get the party line into textbooks (evolution, humanism, outlawing of monotheistic religion, especially Christianity).
- Gain control of all student newspapers.
- Use student riots to foment public protests against programs or organisations which are under Communist attack.
- Infiltrate the press. Get control of book review assignments, editorial writing, policy-making positions.
- Gain control of key positions in radio, TV and motion pictures.
- Eliminate all laws governing obscenity by calling them censorship and a violation of free speech and free press.
- Break down cultural standards of morality by promoting pornography, drug-taking and obscenity in books, magazines, motion pictures, radio and TV.
- Present homosexuality, degeneracy and promiscuity as 'normal, natural, healthy'.

- ➢ Infiltrate the churches and replace revealed religion with 'social' religion. Discredit the Bible and emphasise the need for intellectual maturity which does not need a religious 'crutch'.
- ➢ Eliminate prayer or any phrase of religious expression in the schools on the grounds that it violates the principles of 'separation of church and state'.
- ➢ Discredit the American Constitution by calling it inadequate, old-fashioned, out of step with modern needs, a hindrance to co-operation between nations on a worldwide basis.
- ➢ Discredit the American Founding Fathers. Present them as selfish, deviant aristocrats who had no concern for the 'common man'.
- ➢ Belittle all forms of American culture and discourage the teaching of American history on the grounds that it was only a minor part in the 'big picture'.
- ➢ Support any socialist movement to give centralised control over any part of the culture-education, social agencies, welfare programs, mental health clinics.
- ➢ Discredit the family as an institution. Encourage promiscuity and easy divorce.
- ➢ Emphasise the need to raise children away from the negative influence of parents.
- ➢ Give the World Court jurisdiction over nations and individuals alike.

"The American people will never knowingly adopt socialism. But, under the name of liberalism, they will adopt every fragment of the socialist program, until one day America will be a socialist nation, without knowing how it happened." (Norman Thomas, US Socialist Party Presidential candidate).[125]

The deleterious effects on society, as the first of Weishaupt's strategies are implemented by governments upon their populations in the early part of the 1900's, comes first to the notice of the astute. Lady Queenborough (Edith Starr Miller) writes:

"In the course of my researches as an international political investigator into the causes of social unrest, I have probed the depths of infamy which now surrounds, not ours only, but also the next generation, whose right to lead a decent life should be as good as was ours. As a woman of the world I have witnessed things the existence of which I did

---

[25] A full list of these agendas may be found in Kershaw's *Economic Solutions*.

not suspect and I have realised that, due to my 'protected' position in life, they should never have been expected to come to my knowledge. Let me tell every woman, however much 'protected', whether Dairymaid or Duchess, that the safeguards which she imagines to be thrown around herself are but a mirage of the past. Her own and her children's future are at the mercy of those 'forces', the activities of which it has been my business, for the last ten years, to follow as one of a group of investigators.

Today, most of the good people are afraid to be good. They strive to be broadminded and tolerant! It is fashionable to be tolerant – but mostly tolerant of evil – and this new code has reached the proportions of demanding intolerance of good. The wall of resistance to evil has thus been broken down and no longer affords protection to those who, persecuted by evil doers, stand in need of it." [126]

SILENT WEAPONS FOR QUIET WARS

It is important to appreciate that, by the architects' own admission, the 'New World Order' has been designed to succeed with the full consent and approbation of a dumbed-down, servile world citizenry. It cannot triumph any other way. This blind acquiescence is being achieved through the application of what the Illuminati term 'Silent Weapons', which work against the public through the process of gradualism. Quoting from its 'Silent Weapons for Quiet Wars' manuscript:

The objective of such studies is to acquire the know-how to set the public economy into a predictable state of motion or change, even a controlled, self-destructive state of motion, which will convince the public that certain 'expert' people should take control of the money system and re-establish security (rather than liberty and justice) for all. When the subject citizens are rendered unable to control their financial affairs, they, of course, become totally enslaved, a source of cheap labour.

Diversion: The Primary Strategy. *Experience has proven that the simplest method of securing a silent weapon and gaining control of the public is to keep the public undisciplined and ignorant of basic systems principles on the one hand, while keeping them confused,*

---

[126] Miller, Edith Starr, *Occult Theocracy*, privately published, The Christian Book Club of America, 1933. The author, also known as Lady Queenborough, elected that her book be published only after her death to avoid the persecution she felt would have inevitably followed.

disorganised and distracted with matters of no real importance on the other hand.

This is achieved by:

- *Disengaging their minds; sabotaging their mental activities; providing a low-quality program of public education in mathematics, logic, systems design and economics; and discouraging technical creativity.*
- *Engaging their emotions, increasing their self-indulgence and their indulgence in emotional and physical activities by:*
- *Unrelenting emotional affrontations and attacks (mental and emotional rape) by way of a constant barrage of sex, violence and wars in the media – especially the television and newspapers.*
- *Giving them what they desire – in excess – 'junk food for thought' – and depriving them of what they really need.*
- *Rewriting history and law and subjecting the public to the deviant creation, thus being able to shift their thinking from personal needs to highly fabricated outside priorities.*

These preclude their interest in, and discovery of the silent weapons of social automation technology. The general rule is there is profit in confusion; the more confusion, the more profit. <u>Therefore the best approach is to create problems and then offer solutions.</u>[127]

Speaking from the vantage-point of February 1920, as Europe drags itself out of the mud and carnage of World War 1, British statesman Winston Churchill remarks in the popular press on Weishaupt's sinister political undertow. By the early years of the 20th century, Communism has gained sufficient momentum to engulf Russia in the Bolshevik Revolution, depose the old imperialism, and establish a new and mighty Soviet regime which would change the face of history for the next seventy years:

---

[127] The *'Silent Weapons For Quiet Wars'* document was first exposed after a manuscript was 'discovered' on 7th July 1986 inside an IBM photocopier purchased at a surplus sale. It is a clandestine work giving chilling details of the methods required to control and manipulate societies. The document's authenticity is validated by the measures contained within it subsequently coming to pass. A full transcript of this document is contained in William Cooper's, *Behold a Pale Horse*, Lite Technology Publishing, 1991.

"From the days of 'Spartacus' Weishaupt, to those of Karl Marx, Trotsky, Rosa Luxemburg and Béla Kun, this worldwide conspiracy for the overthrow of civilisation has been the mainspring of every subversive movement during the nineteenth century, and now at last has gripped the Russian people by the hair of their heads and become the undisputed master of that enormous empire." [128]

---

[128] *Sunday Illustrated Herald*, London, 8th February 1920

The Wolf and the Sheep

"The criminal court... is not of the opinion that the extermination of the mentally dead and the 'empty human husks', as Hoche has called them, is absolutely immoral per se. There can be extremely differing opinions about this. Long ago, the removal of 'life unworthy of living' went without saying.... All these details... lead us to the conclusion that the question of the shortening of life unworthy of living is, of course, a highly contested problem, <u>but that its execution can in no way be called a measure which conflicts with the general moral code</u>."

Criminal Court 1 of the District Court of Hamburg on the issue of child euthanasia on <u>19th April 1949</u>

The new 'sciences' of the mind had won their spurs during World War 2, proving invaluable in fooling the enemy with propaganda, exhorting home populations to provide extra effort, conditioning them to accept hardships they normally would not, and, perhaps more sinisterly, in being able, through gradualism, to denigrate or finger as 'undesirables' those persons or groups who were deemed 'the enemy'. But it is the incredible survival and indeed future prosperity of the hundreds of other key figures involved in the Nazi extermination program of World War 2 which provide the real scandal of the post-war clear-up. Psychiatry and psychology, of course, not only survive the war, but are destined to take their eugenics and racist philosophies into the decades of the 20th century which follow.

The above court ruling occurs after the war and is used as justification for freeing twenty Nazi psychiatrists from charges of war crimes. Hoche's 1920's tract espousing eugenics and the weeding out of 'empty human husks' during the Nazi era had been expanded to absurd and devastating proportions, as we have seen. Röder et al comment on the above ruling:

"The court's opinion represents the post-war marriage of the psychiatric and official authorities who had initiated and advocated mass extermination being quoted as justification of why the mass extermination could not automatically be condemned even in retrospect. It was in fact the only official reason why the court of Hamburg exempted the twenty accused Nazis from prosecution for war crimes, four years after Hitler was defeated." [129]

---

[129] Röder et al, op. cit. 84-85

SCOT FREE

Psychiatrist Werner Heyde, Erstwhile head of T4, escapes after his 1947 arrest and resumes work as a 'Dr Sawade'. Acting as a consultant for the courts of the Schleswig-Holstein district of Germany, it seems incredible that Heyde is not only able to continue work as a well-renowned psychiatrist, but carry out his assignments within Germany itself! The well-known serpentine secrecy among former Nazis assures that records go missing, aliases are maintained, and eyes studiously turned the other way when the unwelcome, searching questions are asked. Researcher Ernst Klee remarks that *"...numerous professors, the Director of the Social Court, a district court councillor, a Social Court counsellor, two presidents of the Senate and even a federal judge all knew that Professor Heyde was also Dr Sawade."* [130]

That silence is the unspoken code of secrecy among psychiatrists will be amply demonstrated as we proceed. That this silence was exercised among proponents of psychiatry in post-Nazi Germany is attested to when ex-Nazi eugenicist Dr Hans Bürger-Prinz told a parliamentary investigation into Dr Heyde/Sawade in 1961:

"With the exception of the clergymen, I do not believe that there exists a profession in which silence plays as big a role as with us [psychiatry], *and by this, I mean with respect to everything.... Silence is very important to us and is not limited to the legal requirement concerning confidential medical communication...."* [131]

Bürger-Prinz's own involvement with Nazi atrocities has never fully come to light, such is the misty web of disinformation that shrouded such characters after the war. He is the same Bürger-Prinz though, quoted in a *Der Spiegel* article in 1988, who reminded his colleagues in 1935 to 'register' young children 'afflicted with a hereditary disease' before 'fertility' in order to 'pick them out and exclude them from procreation.'

The *Der Spiegel* article continues: "[Bürger-Prinz] *became an ordinary professor in Hamburg! Konrad Lorenz, who would later win a Nobel Prize, stood up in 1940, demanding the 'more stringent eradication of ethical inferiors', only to concern himself after the war with writing*

---

[130] Klee, Ernst, *'Euthanasie' im NS-Staat*, op. cit. p.414

[131] Klee, Ernst, Was sie taten – was sie wurden. Ärzte, Juristen und andere Beteiligte am Kranken – oder Judenmord, Frankfurt, 1988, p.146

bestsellers, only generally about the 'so-called evil', not about his own past.

Johannes Heinrich Schulz, the father of 'autogenic training' and a no-nonsense expert on hereditary disease and homosexual behaviour, sent homosexuals to the concentration camps if they could not have intercourse with a woman while he watched. After 1945, Schulz became one of the most popular medical educators in the country. The professor died in 1970, as old as Methuselah and highly honoured.

Hans-Joachim Rauch, who, as court psychiatrist was very active in Stammheim, was for decades afterwards a full professor in Heidelberg. During the Nazi era, he was a pathologist who dissected the brains of gassed children. The small patients were brought to the killing institute of Eichberg, near Heidelberg. This institute thus satisfied Rauch's desire for their freshly slaughtered organs." [132]

Denazification programs carried out after 1945 were thwarted at every turn. The occupying powers often tacitly allowed entire infrastructures of the German judiciary to return to office, due to an absence of qualified, German-speaking personnel to administer the chaos of the post-war, devastated nation. Röder et al describe the astonishing result:

"Given the amount of complicity in high positions in Germany, the post-war halls of justice were every bit as polluted with Nazis as were the halls of academia. The courts held a plethora of judges and prosecutors whose tenures were interrupted, but not concluded, by military defeat. It is therefore not surprising that Germany's justice system did little to overcome Germany's bloody past in the days following the Third Reich's decline. The truth is that many Nazis returned to positions as judges and prosecutors with little or no scrutiny from those supposedly responsible for supervising the administration of justice." [133]

The *Der Spiegel* series on this subject concurs that most professional Nazis experienced but a momentary hiccough in their careers:

"Most of the murderers were only overcome through the advance of time, through their own old age. After the founding of the Federal

---

[132] Spiegel-series 1988; *Die Mörder sind noch unter uns* ['The murderers are still among us'], issue 25, p.116
[133] Röder et al, op. cit. p.84

Republic of Germany, they advanced again to the ranks of head physicians, medical officers and professorships, respected as academics and college teachers, and finally woven back into the political fabric of justice, bureaucracy and archives, protected by their old comrades.... The Nazi idea... was forgotten, suppressed and glossed over, right from the start." [134]

THWARTED AT EVERY TURN

Dr Rudolf Degkwitz was a persistent advocate of denazification, holding that former Nazis should immediately be sacked from office and stand trial in the event of reasonable evidence of war crimes. Degkwitz typified the problems Germans faced at the time in bringing culpable Nazis into the courts. Degkwitz was the Dean of the Medical Faculty and President of the Health Department in Hamburg. He was constantly thwarted by the very ex-Nazi authorities he was trying to unmask. Professor Hendrik van den Bussch, a leading authority on Nazi medicine and its advocates, describes the problems facing the stoic Degkwitz:

"According to his opinion, every physician who had been a member of the Nazi party should be dismissed from state service. With this opinion, Degkwitz stood very much apart. Neither the British military authorities nor the Hamburg Senate, not to mention the senate of the university of the faculty, shared this viewpoint in the least. When Degkwitz tried nevertheless, all by himself and not always in orthodox ways, to push this intention through, he very quickly became in medical circles the most hated man in Hamburg." [135]

ROLL-CALL OF SHAME

The list of Nazi psychiatrists, especially those who were actively involved with T4 either as staff or consultants, reads as a *Who's Who* of post-war psychiatry, especially those who eventually ended up as presidents of the German Society for Psychiatry and Neurology (GSPN):

Ernst Rüdin (1874-1952)

President of GSPN 1935-1945 – former head of the Nazis' sterilisation, euthanasia and racial hygiene program, Rüdin was still being lionised by the prestigious Max Planck Institute in 1992 for *"...following*

---

[134] Spiegel-series 1988, op. cit. p.116
[135] Bussche, Hendrick van den, Medizinische Wissenschaften im Dritten Reich. Kontinuität, Anpassung und Opposition an der Hamburger Medizinischen Fakultät, Berlin and Hamburg, 1989, p.427

his own convictions in 'racial hygiene' measures, co-operating with the Nazis as a psychiatrist and helping them legitimise their aims through pertinent legislation." [136]

Ernst Kretschmer (1888-1964)
President of GSPN 1948-1951
Nazi psychiatrist and eugenicist who advocated sterilisation of the mentally ill to avoid their reproduction. Kretschmer also included *"drunkenness, criminality and epilepsy"* within the *"more or less unspecified lot of degenerations"* which are the *"actual great sphere of action for eventual eradication".* [137]

Werner Villinger (1887-1961)
President of GSPN 1952-1954
Nazi psychiatrist and one of mental hygiene's most outspoken advocates. Listed as a T4 consultant. Villinger was involved with the drafting of the post-war Sterilisation Act that was enacted with the approval of American occupation forces by the Health Committee of the Stuttgart Council of the Länder.

Friedrich Mauz (1900-1979)
President of GSPN 1957-1958
Nazi psychiatrist, T4 consultant and mental hygienist. Mentored by Ernst Kretschmer. Klee comments: *"In the list of consultants for T4, some famous people are recorded. Besides professors Heyde and Nitsche, we can also find the names of professors Polisch and Panse (Bonn), Carl Schneider (Heidelberg), Erich Straub (Kiel), Friedrich Mauz (Konigsberg), Berthold Kihn (Jena)... while Villinger (Breslau), as we have seen, was involved for much longer."* [138]

Honoured for his 'special accomplishments' on 17th May 1980, a year after his death, Mauz incredibly surfaces in London in 1948 as a participant in the International Congress of Mental Hygiene. During this conference, the World Federation of Mental Health is founded. One of Mauz's 'special accomplishments' was the development of a law in 1940 'ending the suffering' of the 'incurably ill'.

---

[136] Acknowledgement of Ernst Rüdin in the Institute's publication: "75 Years of the Max Planck Institute for Psychiatry, Munich 1917-1992".
[137] Kretschmer, Konstitutionslehre und Rassenhygiene in Rüdin: *Erblehre und Rassenhygiene im völkischen Staat*, Munich, 1934, p.186
[138] Klee, E, op. cit. p.227

Hans Bürger-Prinz (1897-1976)
President of GSPN 1959-1960
Nazi psychiatrist Bürger-Prinz, as the military district psychiatrist in charge of the Neuropathy Clinic in Hamburg from 1937 to 1970, never distanced himself from what happened to the mentally ill during the Nazi period. Bürger-Prinz's career is characterised by a desire to continue his work, unsobered by war, unbroken by the post-war occupation of his country. Strong evidence exists, demonstrating that Bürger-Prinz may have been trained in the killing activities of the mentally ill and attempted to profit from them.[139]

Heinrich Kranz (1901-1979)
President of GSPN 1961-1962
Twins researcher who, although less radical than his colleagues Rüdin and Luxenburger, bowed to pressure during World War 2 and joined in enforcing the compulsory sterilisation laws and commitments to asylums. Later these inmates were transferred to the killing institutions.

Friedrich Panse (1899-1973)
President of GSPN 1965-1966
Nazi military district psychiatrist and T4 consultant. Panse becomes infamous for applying 'Pansing' techniques on battle-shocked soldiers who are suspected of malingering and 'pension-neuroses'. This involves electroshock treatment, reminiscent of the methods used by Kaufmann in World War 1. Acquitted of atrocities through lack of evidence after the war, Panse rises in honour and prestige in post World War 2 psychiatry.

* * * * *

ROBERT FELIX – THE US NIMH
With its infamous role during World War 2 being played down, and its psychological warfare benefits promoted to government and the public as an essential national asset, psychiatry now enters a new and significant era. In the post-WW2 world, the mental hygiene movement is able to 'institutionalise' itself into open society when, in 1946, the United States National Institute of Mental Health (NIMH) is formed with psychiatrist Dr Robert Felix as its first director. The ambitious Felix outlines the new strategy and goals of his institution, which are to establish community

---

[139] Ibid.

mental health programs aimed at fostering 'the prevention of mental illness' before it occurs.[140]

Felix exhorts colleagues to become involved with *"education, social work, industry, the churches, recreation and the courts"* so that *"mental health services"* can be *"fully integrated into, and a regular and continuing part of, the total social environment."* [141]

Henceforth the promises made by psychiatry become profuse. Authors Foley and Sharfstein write: *"The extravagant claims of enthusiasts – that new treatments were highly effective, that all future potential victims of mental illness and their families would be spared the suffering, that great economies of money would soon be realised – were allowed to pass unchallenged by the professional side of the professional-political leadership."* [142]

G BROCK CHISHOLM

G Brock Chisholm, one of the 20th century's most influential mental health advocates and former president of the World Federation for Mental Health, chillingly verifies the collective aim of his profession to continue in its original aim of freeing man from the chafing constraints of righteousness:

"The reinterpretation and eventually eradication of the concept of right and wrong which has been the basis of child training, the substitution of intelligent and rational thinking for faith in the certainties of the old people, these are the belated objectives of practically all effective psychotherapy.... The fact is, that most psychiatrists and psychologists and other respectable people have escaped from these moral chains and are able to observe and think freely." [143]

Chisholm's position of influence would confirm to society and his peers the notion that mental doctors and *"other respectable people have*

[140] Shrag, Peter, *Mind Control*, Pantheon Books, 1978, p.42

[141] Sharkey, Joe, *Bedlam: Greed, Profiteering, and Fraud in a Mental Health System Gone Crazy*, St Martin's Press, New York: 1994, p.174; Felix, Robert, *Mental Health and Social Welfare*, Columbia University Press, New York: 1961, p.21

[142] Foley, Henry & Steven S Sharfstein, *Madness and Government*, American Psychiatric Press, Inc., Washington DC: 1983, p.25

[143] Chisholm, G Brock, "The Re-establishment of Peacetime Society – The William Alanson White Memorial Lectures, Second Series', *Psychiatry: Journal of the Biology and the Pathology of Interpersonal Relations*, February 1946, p.9

escaped from these moral chains". In terms reminiscent of Weishaupt and the Protocols, one of the most profound influencers of post-WW2 global psychiatry remarkably goes on to quote Satan in Genesis, declaring:

"We have swallowed all manner of poisonous certainties fed us by our parents, our Sunday and day school teachers, our politicians, our priests, our newspapers and others with a vested interest in controlling us. 'Thou shalt become as gods, knowing good and evil', good and evil with which to keep children under control, with which to prevent free thinking, with which to impose local and familial and national loyalties and with which to blind children to their glorious intellectual heritage....

If the race is to be freed from its crippling burden of good and evil, it must be psychiatrists who take the original responsibility."[144]

All the more incredible are Chisholm's words when the still smoking ashes of war-torn Europe rise as smouldering testament to the unhinging of society from traditional moral precepts. Chisholm defends his beliefs with the following hauntingly ironic words which are to prefigure the future: *"The pretence is made, as it has been made in relation to the findings of any extension of truth, that to do away with right and wrong would produce uncivilised people, immorality, lawlessness and social chaos."*[145]

And so, after the war, psychiatry moves into the current era, its modalities intact, its racist and eugenics philosophies undented; many of its most barbaric practitioners vaunted and honoured. The number of American psychiatrists increased tenfold in the forty years following World War 2.[146] The amount of government-funded research grew more than a hundred times during the same period. In fact, psychiatry would earn the distinction of being the only medical profession regularly to receive US federal funding for the education of its members, training grants increasing eightyfold from 1948 to 1972.[147]

And around the world, governments and their flocks remained somnolent; largely unaware of the wolf that had taken up residence in their midst.

---

[144] Chisholm, G Brock, op. cit. pp.7-9
[145] Ibid. p.9
[146] Torrey, E Fuller, *Nowhere to Go*, Harper & Row, New York: 1988, pp.163-164
[147] Ibid.

PSYCHIATRY
- THE TREATMENTS -

A Rape of the Soul

"Then something beat down and took hold of me and shook me like the end of the world. Whee-ee-ee it shrilled, through an air crackling with blue light, and with each flash a great jolt drubbed me till I thought my bones would break and the sap fly out like a split plant. I wondered what terrible thing it was that I had done."

- Sylvia Plath, *The Bell Jar*

"When I saw the patient's reaction, I thought to myself: This ought to be abolished!" – Ugo Cerletti, pioneer of electroshock[148]

"From the cases I have seen treated by shock therapy... I do not believe that we can scramble brains and expect to have anything left but scrambled brains." – Anonymous American psychiatrist (1942)[149]

Medical history reveals how 1st century Roman physicians used electric eels held against their patients' head as an early form of electroshock therapy for various conditions. The modern idea of using high-voltage raw electricity to 'cure' mental illness however was pioneered by Italian psychiatrist Ugo Cerletti, who marvelled at how pigs in slaughterhouses were stunned by electroshock, making it easier to slit their throats. But it was Lothar B Kalinowsky who, after witnessing his first 'shocking' of a patient as a student of Cerletti's, became its most passionate advocate, later introducing the terrifying procedure into France, Holland, the UK and the United States.[150] Kalinowsky would later admit being in possession of *"personal communications on [ECT] fatalities which remain unpublished because of understandable fear of lawsuits."*[151]

LEO ALEXANDER

US psychiatrist Leo Alexander studied psychiatry in Germany and Austria in the late 1920's. Completing his studies in Frankfurt during the time of Hitler's nationalistic rise to power, he became taken with

---

[148] Szasz, Thomas, *The Manufacture of Madness*, op. cit. p.31
[149] Quoted in Kolb, L & V Vogel, "The Use of Shock Therapy in 305 Mental Hospitals", *American Journal of Psychiatry*, 99:90-93, July 1942
[150] Abrams, Richard, "Interview with Lothar Kalinowsky MD", 8th October 1987, *Convulsive Therapy* 4 (1988)
[151] Kalinowsky, L, "Additional remarks on the danger of premedication in electric convulsive therapy", (letter to editor), *American Journal of Psychiatry*, 113:79-80, July 1956

psychiatry's eugenics and racist viewpoints prevailing at the time. Later, Alexander joined the American military as a psychiatric consultant to the Secretary of War. Alexander was chosen as an advisor to the Office of Chief Counsel for War Crimes in Nuremberg and was pointman in the prosecution of a number of Nazi psychiatrists involved in the early killings of mental defectives, and later Jews and other groups.

It was chiefly Alexander's dispassionate descriptions of the experiments carried out by Nazi doctors which helped many culpable psychiatrists escape justice and go on to become respected practitioners after the war. He was the first to analyse documents from Himmler's files on freezing experiments carried out on concentration camp victims at Dachau. Among a whole wealth of condemnatory evidence against Nazi psychiatry, Alexander had absolute evidence of the killing of children with gas and electricity at Grafnek and Hadamar centres in 1940 and 1941. Yet Alexander not only failed to condemn the barbarism, he was actively to practise some of it himself as head of US Electroshock Research in 1951-52. The Citizen's Commission on Human Rights reports:

"Alexander must have known that between 1939 and 1941, German psychiatrists responsible for the euthanasia programs had made a film called 'The Mentally Ill', in which electroshock and gassing procedures were discussed. Incredibly the film proves the 'scientific' incurability of the insane by electroshock and justifies gassing them to death as the only other valid option." [152]

Discovering that rapidly increasing the current caused contortions and spinal fractures in his own patients, Alexander, unmoved as ever, reports with customary banality:

"I produced painful, though otherwise fortunately harmless spinal fractures (2 of them multiple) in 3 patients in fairly rapid succession." [153]

FIXING THE GREMLINS?
Most citizens today will remark, "Electroshock? They banned that years ago, didn't they?" Unfortunately, no. Psychiatrists detest the word 'shock', in view of its distressing yet true connotations. The terms

---

[152] Röder et al, op. cit. p.62

[153] Alexander, Leo, "The suppression of the clonic phase in electrically induced convulsions in man", *Journal of Neuropathology and Experimental Neurology*, 11(2), April 1952, p.182

'electrotherapy', 'neuro-electric therapy', and 'electro-convulsive therapy' (ECT) are used today to give the banana republic torture-chamber procedure its requisite medical 'credibility'. But ECT, as we shall see, is not only as far from 'scientific' or 'medical' as it gets, it has also given rise to some of the most disturbing human rights abuses since the war.

The theory behind flooding the brain with overwhelming current and inducing grand mal seizures in the patient is to 'depattern anti-social behaviour', such as depression, violence, 'schizophrenia' or any other conduct deemed aberrant by the psychiatrist. Unable to rationalise the devastating effects of shock therapy upon their patients as plain, old-fashioned torture, psychiatrists such as Dr Abraham Myerson incredibly remark of their 'successes':

"The reduction of intelligence is an important factor in the curative process... The fact is that some of the very best cures that one gets are in those individuals whom one reduces almost to amentia [feeble-mindedness].*"* [154]

Myerson's idea of a 'cure' is standard among psychiatrists, who treat 'aberrant' behaviour with electroshock, insulin shock, psychotropic drugs and lobotomies (psychosurgery). 'Dangerous intelligence', as in 'the tortured genius', is something that has always fascinated psychiatry. Yet its methods are not designed to cure the underlying reasons why a person has begun to behave in an abnormal fashion – psychiatry freely admits it has no idea - but to stop them doing it. The rationale is that electrocuting the brain will cause it to 'forget' the problems with which it was previously preoccupied.

NO IDEA
Psychiatry has never made any pretence of knowing what causes what it terms 'mental illness'. Its goal has been to annihilate the symptoms and render the patient more controllable. Thus, even a patient reduced to a catatonic state of feeblemindedness through the catastrophic effects of ECT is hailed as 'cured', as long as they behave themselves in a more 'acceptable' fashion.

And it is here that we see the truly frightening and arbitrary nature of the 'science' of psychiatry. Who determines what is acceptable behaviour

---

[154] Myerson, Abraham, "Fatalities following electric convulsive therapy: a report of two cases with autopsy findings", *Trans. Amer. Neurol. Assoc.*, 68:39, June 1942

and what isn't? With the involuntary commitment laws that exist today, the psychiatrist becomes the jailer. Often members of the public deemed 'troublesome' and turned in to the local psychiatrist by even their own family can be incarcerated, drugged up, shocked at will and abandoned by their loved ones. Betrayed by the 'concerned' psychiatrist they believed was going to help them; railroaded into custodial care by the very justice system that should have protected their rights, frightened men, women and children are jettisoned by society into terrifying, medieval institutions all around the world, no longer even allowed to articulate their innocence or concerns. Having been branded 'of diminished responsibility', they no longer have a voice.

MEDIEVAL DUNGEON FARE

With the old ECT methods practised prior to the 1960's, at least 20 percent of electroshock victims suffered compression fractures to their spines, broken teeth, lacerated tongues, and broken bones. As a result of the powerful contractions induced by the shocks and subsequent medical complications, many died of their injuries. Yet, rather than abandoning ECT as torture, psychiatry simply switched to using muscle-relaxants and anaesthesia to prevent these 'unwanted' side-effects. Psychiatrist Dr Lee Coleman writes of the common after-effects of having the brain violently jarred by electricity:

"The changes one sees when electroshock is administered are completely consistent with any acute brain injury, such as a blow to the head from a hammer. In essence, what happens is that the individual is dazed, confused, and disoriented, and therefore cannot remember or appreciate current problems." [155]

Which, of course, is the whole point, according to ECT proponents. But the inherent violence of the treatment, and the unsettling notion that somehow this was indeed 'a rape of the soul' - an intimate violent moment with another human being - has caused a storm of controversy even within psychiatry. One American board certified anaesthesiologist, Dr Michael Chavin, would later, after assisting in 2,000 ECT procedures, not only turn his back in disgust on the treatment, but actively begin campaigning for the removal of ECT and other harmful psychiatric treatments from hospitals. He argues:

---

[155] Lee Coleman's introduction to Frank, Leonard, *The History of Shock Treatment*, San Francisco, CA: 1978, p.xiii

"Why is ECT continually dogged by controversy? What is the real origin and history of ECT? ....What really happens when the brain is subjected to hundreds of volts of raw electricity? Who profits from ECT? ....Deceived by psychiatry's propaganda machine, the majority are content to leave it up to the 'experts'. Whilst openly admitting that they have no idea of how ECT 'works', psychiatrists have no trouble in arrogantly assuming the mantle of 'expert'.

Having personally contributed to the horrors attendant to ECT, I have experienced the anguish involved in confronting the consequences of my own lack of awareness.... I eventually became convinced that the only time psychiatrists would admit harm from ECT would be if the patient was electrocuted on the table while the procedure was videotaped and observed by a United Nations Task Force." [156]

GETTING WIRED

The patient goes without food and drink for four hours prior to the procedure. Thirty minutes prior to shocking, the patient is given Atropine or Robinol, drugs which reduce secretions of saliva in the mouth and air passages, lowering the risks of suffocation and other problems, should the patient involuntarily swallow their own saliva.

The patient is then strapped to a bed and a jelly applied to the head, as with victims of America's electric chair, to facilitate the transmission of current into the target area. A defibrillator stands nearby on a cart (unlike with the American electric chair), should the patient suffer a cardiac arrest as a result of the electrocution. Immediately prior to the shock, the patient is given an anaesthetic and slips into unconsciousness. A muscle relaxant is given, almost completely shutting down muscular activity in the body. The patient is then placed on an artificial respirator until their breathing resumes unassisted after the electrocution is administered. A rubber gag is placed into the mouth to prevent the biting of the tongue and splintering of the teeth due to the severe autonomic reactions induced by the shock. A band is fitted around the patient's head, containing electrodes which are positioned over the targeted areas of the brain.

A button is pressed. Between 180 and 460 volts of raw electricity are blasted into the brain from temple to temple (bi-lateral ECT). Overcome by the assault, the brain convulses in a grand mal seizure of long duration.

---

[156] Chavin, Michael, "The Shocking Truth about ECT", *Psychiatry Destroys Minds*, CCHR, Los Angeles: 2002

105

Since the patient has been drugged, the body's reaction to the shock is muted. The psychiatrist watches for a curling of the toes to gauge the 'success' of the procedure. If toe-curling is not immediately evident, successive shocks can be administered until the treatment has 'worked'.

Dr Michael Chavin: *"There is a shock-wave through the brain, causing the brain to discharge energy in a very chaotic type of state. And this increases metabolism to a very high level, which deprives the brain of oxygen and can actually destroy brain cells."*[157]

Neurologist Dr John Friedberg warns: *"The muscle paralyser can cause prolonged failure to breathe and cardiac shock. The paralysis may also intensify the horror of the patient's experience. While barbiturates make for a smoother trip into unconsciousness, they also increase the chance of death by choking."* [158]

ECT SIDE-EFFECTS

ECT has also been found to raise blood pressure by as much as 200%, overwhelming the brain's usual pressure regulatory systems and causing ruptures and lesions in small and large blood vessels. This haemorrhaging is often the cause of death from ECT. One of the most fundamental aspects to electroshock is that it disturbs and damages the blood-brain barrier, compromising the brain's ability to isolate itself from toxins and foreign substances. The swelling of the brain can also result from invasion of fluids after the haemorrhaging and rupturing of blood vessels. Cellular activity in the brain is altered for days after each shock. Memory loss of varying degrees of severity is a permanent after-effect.[159]

Marilyn Rice was a US government economist who underwent ECT: *"I have lost the vast edifice of specialised knowledge that I had been adding to almost every day of my adult life. I have lost the pride and self-confidence (and income) that go with being an expert in one's field. I have lost the intellectual joy of utilising my mental capital. I have lost my value to society in that the work in which I was engaged was dependent upon my unique assemblage of knowledge. I have lost much of my*

---

[157] CCHR interview with Dr Michael Chavin, 1996

[158] Friedberg, John, "Let's stop blasting the brain", *Psychology Today*, August 1975

[159] Alpers, Bernard J & Joseph Hughes, "The brain changes in electrically induced convulsions in the human", *Journal of Neuropathy and Experimental Neuropathy*, January 1942, p.177; Friedberg, John, "Shock treatment, brain damage and memory loss: a neurological perspective", *American Journal of Psychiatry*, Vol.134, No.9, September 1977, p.1110

general education. I have lost personal memories that I would never willingly have given up – people I have met, places I have been, books I have read, plays I have seen." [160]

MAJOR INCOME

An electroshock session usually lasts between five and fifteen minutes. From this procedure alone, psychiatry in America reaps an estimated $3 billion each year.[161] Patients will often receive one shock a day, three times a week (at $1,000 a shock). Further courses of ECT are often scheduled due to lack of relief from whatever problem the psychiatrist believes his patient is combating. An article on the subject by *USA Today* on 6th December 1995 breaks down the earnings of US psychiatrists, the average for 1993 being $131,300. Repeated shock treatment of patients can increase a psychiatrist's income by $27,300.[162] Newspaper reports in 1993 indicate that as many as 110,000 Americans might be receiving electroshock treatments each year.[163]

TRAUMA-BASED MIND CONTROL –
MK-ULTRA, ARTICHOKE, BLUEBIRD AND MONARCH

Mind control experiments carried out by the CIA and other intelligence agencies around the world during the '50's and '60's broadened the possibilities of electroshock and drug-induced stupors for making the uncooperative ready and willing. Also examined at great length was the possibility of using trauma-based mind control to create suicidal assassins. This research, alluded to in CIA documents obtained under the Freedom of Information Act (FOIA), was to have a far-reaching impact on behavioural science.

Scientists became fascinated with the remote stimulation of the brain and how this affected a human's behaviour. Researcher Ron Patton writes in *Paranoia* 1994:

"Much of the preliminary experimentation concerning genetic engineering and behaviour modification was conducted by Dr Josef

---

[160] Rice, Marilyn, "The Rice Papers", *Madness Network News*, April 1975, pp.4-8

[161] *The Rights Tenet,* quoted by Dr Richard Hudson, St Mary's Hospital, evidence before Nov/Dec 1990 City Services Committee of San Francisco Board of Supervisor's Public Hearings on ECT

[162] Cauchon, Dennis, "Patients often aren't informed of full danger", *USA Today,* 6th December 1995

[163] Foderaero, Lisa W, "Electroshock Therapy for Depression Makes a Discreet Comeback", *International Herald Tribune*, 20th July 1993

Mengele at Auschwitz, where he analysed the effects of trauma-bonding, electroshock, eye-colouring, and 'twinning' upon his victims.

After WW2, the US Department of Defense (DOD) secretly imported many of the top German Nazi and Italian scientists and spies into the United States via South America and the Vatican ratlines. The codename for this operation was Project *PAPERCLIP*. One of the more prominent finds for the US was German General Reinhard Gehlen, Hitler's Chief of Intelligence against Russia. Upon arriving in Washington DC in 1945, Gehlen met extensively with President Truman, General William "Wild Bill" Donovan, Director of the Office of Strategic Services (OSS) and Allen Dulles, who would later become the head of the CIA. The objective of their brain-storming sessions was to reorganise the nominal American intelligence operation, transforming it into a highly efficient covert organisation. The culmination of their efforts produced the Central Intelligence Group in 1946, renamed the Central Intelligence Agency (CIA) in 1947.

The CIA decided to expand their efforts in the area of behaviour modification, with the advent of Project BLUEBIRD, approved by Director Allen Dulles in 1950. Its objectives were to: (1) discover a means of conditioning personnel to prevent unauthorised extraction of information from them by known means, (2) investigate the possibility of control of an individual by application of special interrogation techniques, (3) investigate memory enhancement and (4) establish defensive means for preventing hostile control of agency personnel. Project MK-ULTRA came into existence on April 13th 1953, along the lines proposed by Richard Helms, Deputy Director of Central Intelligence, with the rationale of establishing a 'special funding mechanism of extreme sensitivity'.

The US Office of Strategic Services (OSS), forerunner to the Central Intelligence Agency, was more than interested during World War 2 in finding a 'truth drug' for use during interrogations. Thus it was, that while Nazi doctors were experimenting on prisoners in Dachau with mescaline and other substances, American and British intelligence research was following similar paths, albeit without the mass brutality.

The CIA's infamous MK-ULTRA and MONARCH programs were spawned out of Mengele's 'research' on his prisoners in Auschwitz using electroshock, trauma- and drug-based mind control. Infliction of torture on a subject was found to produce a survival response by the brain in the form of a breakaway persona or 'alter', which could be programmed and given access codes, much like a computer file. The idea was to find a way to develop the perfect assassin using buried alters – create a subject who would assimilate into everyday life, who could years later be triggered to kill or maim by radio frequency implant stimulation or spoken codeword.

A CIA document dated December 1951 discusses the use of psychiatric electroshock to prepare subjects for just this type of activity:

"[blacked-out name] *is... an authority on electric shock. He is a professor at the* [blacked-out] *and, in addition, is a psychiatrist of considerable note.... [He] is, in addition, a fully cleared Agency consultant.*"

In the same document, the unnamed psychiatrist tells the CIA that a person can be reduced to a 'vegetable level' through the use of electroshock:

"*The standard electroshock machine could be used in two ways. One setting... produced the normal electric shock treatment (with convulsion) with amnesia after a number of treatments.... The other or lower setting of the machine produced a different type of shock.... When it was applied without convulsion, it had the effect of making a man talk....*" [164]

An accompanying document from the MK-ULTRA files discusses a planned assassination experiment to be carried out "*...on a prominent* [blacked-out] *politician or if necessary against an American official.*" [165]

Using techniques reminiscent of those employed by the Nazi psychiatrists the CIA was so keen to examine, it seems the US intelligence agency has an apparent willingness to murder its own country's officials. That this was not a surprise later to the US public is clearly seen with the numerous Hollywood movie plots of CIA assassins. Even the *Manchurian Candidate* introduced to a bewildered public the possibility of a Nazi-like US police state, complete with summary arrests, forceful incarcerations and the use of assassins remotely programmed by psychiatrists using trauma-based mind control. Gordon Thomas, author of *Journey into*

---

[164] Document obtained under FOIA from the CIA's MK-ULTRA program ARTICHOKE, dated January 1951.
[165] Ibid.

Madness – The True Story of Secret CIA Mind Control and Medical Abuse, writes in 1989:

"The Agency doctors would continue committing serious breaches of their sacred oath; would still, if need be, use treatment methods that were reckless and dangerous to life.... The [CIA's] director [would look] beyond the borders of the United States, to Canada, to Montreal, to Dr Ewen Cameron. The psychiatrist and his unsuspecting Canadian patients would be the Agency's flag bearers into the unknown world of influencing memory, changing personality, and disturbing the mind."

DONALD EWEN CAMERON

Psychiatrist Cameron received millions of dollars from CIA Director Allen Dulles through front organisations such as the Investigation of Human Ecology, over which Cameron presided. Experiments in mind control and euphemistically named 'basic programming' were conducted in Montreal, mostly at McGill University, St Mary's Hospital and Allan Memorial Institute.

Cameron pioneered 'psychic driving' (constant auditory repetition), drug-induced coma and the application of electroshock trauma forty times the intensity than was normally considered 'safe' for the purposes of alter programming. Many victims were drugged and kidnapped under guise of an 'alien abduction' or recruited through medical 'guinea-pig' programs.

CCHR reports: *"OPERATION KNOCKOUT, as part of MK-ULTRA, had the goal of conducting 'research to define mechanisms involved in the production of involuntary sleep and related unconscious states'.*[166]*Many of Cameron's victims were placed into a drug-induced stupor sometimes lasting as long as 90 days. A continuous audio tape played negative*

---

[166] Cameron, Deborah, "The CIA link to deep-sleep research", *Sydney Morning Herald*, 8th October 1988

messages to the patient 16 hours a day for several weeks. Patients received a shock to their legs at the end of the message. This was followed by 2 to 5 weeks of 'positive' messages run the same way. Politically correct messages, therefore, were implanted into the individual's mind to be unwittingly acted upon in the future." [167]

John Marks writes: "The frequent screams of patients (usually women) that echoed through the hospital did not deter Cameron or most of his associates in their attempts to 'depattern' their subjects completely. Other hospital patients report being petrified by the 'sleep rooms', where the treatments took place, and they would usually creep down the opposite side of the hall."

One patient, L McDonald, who was 23 years old when Cameron 'depatterned' him, recalled 25 years later: "I have no memory of existing prior to 1963, and the recollections I do have of events of the following years until 1966 are fuzzy and few.... My parents were introduced to me... I did not know them. [My five] children came back from wherever they had been living. I had no idea who they were." [168]

DOWNFALL

Cameron's complete indifference to the suffering of his patients - indeed his desire for total physical, mental and spiritual control over them - are typical character traits of almost all psychiatrists who have been prosecuted for crimes of rape, assault and murder. Ewen Cameron, lionised by his peers, became president of both the American Psychiatric Association and the World Psychiatric Association, and swore an oath to 'do no harm' to his patients. He has been conveniently left out of most psychiatric journals, probably due to MK-ULTRA being publicly exposed in 1980 through a class action lawsuit filed by eight Canadian survivors of Cameron's torture. On 5th October 1988, the CIA, the US Justice Department and the Canadian government settled out of court with the plaintiffs for the sum of $750,000. The deal was that the survivors would never discuss either the case or Dr Ewen Cameron in public again.

One such subject, Cameron dispassionately recorded, "... was prepared by both sensory isolation (35 days) and by repeated

---

[167] Citizens Commission on Human Rights report: "Psychiatry Destroys Minds", Los Angeles: 2002. p.17-18
[168] Burstow, B and D Weitz, *Shrink Resistant: The Struggle Against Psychiatry in Canada*, New Star Books, Vancouver: 1988, p.206-210

depatterning, and although she received 101 days of positive driving, no favourable results were obtained." The woman had originally consulted Cameron for assistance in getting through the menopause.

'NON-LETHAL'

Such goings-on behind the scenes are hard to believe for the man in the street, but documentation on ULTRA, MONARCH and other associated operations is extremely extensive and persistent. Many press articles, such as those listed below, have mentioned some aspect of these programs:

➢ A *London Sunday Times*, February 1978, article revealed that in a NATO conference on Stress Reduction, a Navy Lieutenant-Commander Thomas Narut, stationed in Naples, admitted to a training program for killers and assassins.
➢ *New Federalist* journalist Anton Chaitkin asked former CIA Director William Colby directly, *"What about MONARCH?"* Colby replied angrily, *"We stopped that between the late 1960's and the early 1970's."*
➢ *Washington Times*, 27th December 1988 page A-2, author Bill Gertz.
➢ *Defense News*, 11th-17th January 1993 page 29, author Barbara Opall.
➢ *Tactical Technology*, 3rd February 1993 pages 1-5 - *Russian Technology Used For Mind Control*
➢ *Aviation Week and Space Technology*, 24th May 1993 - *Army Prepares For Non-Lethal Combat*
➢ *Aviation Week and Space Technology*, 7th June 1993 - *Washington Outlook Still Under Wraps* (discusses the use of non-lethal, psychiatric assaults on David Koresh and his followers, such as the squeals of slaughtered rabbits being broadcasted into the Branch Davidian compound in Waco by US authorities).
➢ *Defense Electronics*, July 1993, page 17, author Mark Tapscott - *DOD Intel Agencies Look at Russian Mind Control Technology, Claims FBI Considered Testing on Koresh.*
➢ *Wall Street Journal*, 4th January 1993, pages A-1/4, author Thomas E Ricks hosts a lengthy article exploring the future battlefield use of non-lethal weapon systems and psychiatric derivatives.

COMING OUT OF THE CLOSET

Some agents and victims of mind control experimentation have been willing to talk. 1940's model Candy Jones testified to 12 years as a CIA asset involved in MK-ULTRA. Cathy O'Brien, who relates that her father entered her into MONARCH, testifies in her book, *Trance Formation of*

America, co-written by the shadowy, possibly compromised Mark Phillips, to her role as a drug-mule and prostitute for the power élite, compromising high-echelon government personnel with sexual favours. Paul Bonacci has testified to two decades of MONARCH programming and involvement in the 'Franklin Cover-Up', where young men were selected from Boy's Town, Nebraska, and removed to Offutt Air Force Base where Bonacci alleges they, like him, were subjected to intense trauma-based programming before being used for compromising sexual favours.

"God made me do it", *"My television told me to kill"*, *"I heard voices in my head"* are classic confessions from MONARCH victims. Aberrant behaviour bouts and periods of 'missing time' associated with ET ('alien') abductions are hallmarks of trauma-based mind control. Typically the perpetrator has been programmed to kill him/herself after the assassination has been performed. Many suspected MONARCHS are not taken alive. When the subject's past is scrutinised, it has been discovered that they have often been subjected to in-depth psychiatric examinations at an institution and subsequently demonstrated the symptoms of classic split personality - violent bouts of rage and selective amnesia.

Some agents and researchers suggest that the following may have been victims of the psychiatric programs ULTRA or MONARCH, or individually subjected to psychiatric assault through electroshock, psychotropic drugs or other, unspecific interferences: Sirhan-Sirhan (RFK murder) - Charles Manson (Tate murders) - John Hinckley, Jr. (Reagan attempted murder) - Mark Chapman (John Lennon murder) - David Koresh (Branch Davidians, Waco) - Tim McVeigh (Oklahoma City bombing) - John Salvi (US abortion doctor murder) - Martin Bryant (Tasmania mass murders) - Michael Ryan (Hungerford, UK mass murders) - Horrett Campbell (Wolverhampton, UK machete attack on school children and teacher) - Jim Jones (Jonestown mass murders).

ABUSE IN AUSTRALIA
DEEP SLEEP TREATMENT (DST)
"In the old days during electroshock, we used to break arms... legs and elbows." – Psychiatrist Dr Harry Bailey

In 1980's Australia, the infamous Harry Bailey and his psychiatric team were appalling their countrymen after their reign of terror was finally brought to light. Bailey pioneered Deep Sleep Treatment (DST) as a supposed means of ridding mental patients of their phobias. This lethal combination of severe drug therapy, combined with constant electroshock, was practised for 16 years at a private psychiatric hospital named Chelmsford in Sydney, New South Wales.

DST held the patient in a coma for up to three weeks with a combination of barbiturates, sedatives and other psychotropic drugs. ECT was blasted through the patient at least three times a week. Frequently patients were shocked daily or, in the case of psychiatrists failing to check their records, twice daily. Anaesthetics were never administered prior to the electroshocks.

About 5,000 patients were subjected to Bailey's barbarism. During testimony heard by the New South Wales Royal Commission, presided over by Justice J P Slattery:

"Mrs G Whitty was admitted to Chelmsford. She did not recall being physically examined by Dr Bailey at any time.... Mrs Whitty was put to bed and given a tablet. She said that although she was heavily sedated for most of the time, her constant convulsing and thrashing about kept bringing her out of sedation.

The witness remembered falling out of bed at one stage and Dr Bailey saying that she was too much of a 'wriggler'....[A] short time after that she recalled waking up in a straitjacket.

She only learned she had been given ECT a few months before she gave evidence." [169]

Bailey learned his techniques in psychiatric centres across Europe and the US during the late 1950's. Such methods were popular at the time during mind control experimentation performed by intelligence agencies. At least 48 patients died in the hands of Bailey and his staff during a sixteen-year period. The scandal predictably rocked the sensibilities of the Australian public, bringing the practices of psychiatry once more under the global spotlight of outrage.

The Graylands state psychiatric hospital in Western Australia also came to the public's attention in 2000. Over the previous 12 years, the proportions of suicides to admissions had trebled. The *Hartford Courant* had reported in 1998:

---

[169] Slattery, Justice J P, "Appendix 25, Dr Harry Bailey's staff lecture", *Report of the Royal Commission into Sleep Therapy*, Vol.12, pp.534, 539

"Slammed face-down on the floor, Roshelle Clabourne's arms were yanked across her chest, her wrists gripped from behind by a mental health aide..." [170]

CCHR reports that Roshelle later became one of the tragic victims of forcible psychiatric restraint: *"She was forcibly drugged, became suddenly still, blood trickled from the corner of her mouth as she lost control of her bodily functions. Her limp body was rolled into a blanket and dumped in a seclusion room. No one watched her die."*

POPULAR TORTURE
Electroshock has of course been wildly popular with repressive regimes around the world. The Chilean secret police routinely used a Page-Russell ECT machine to administer shocks to the arms, legs, head and genitals of their victims. Dr Sheila Cassidy, who made the 'mistake' of treating the bullet wound of a revolutionary recommended to her by a

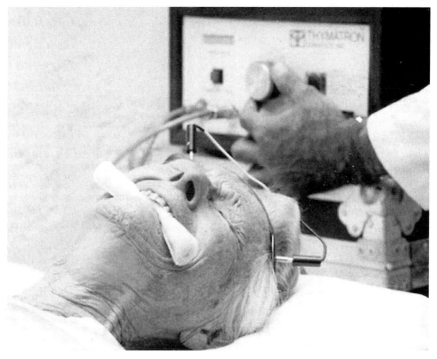

---

[170] Weiss, Eric M, "A Nationwide Pattern of Death", *The Hartford Courant*, www.courant.com/news/special/restraint/

priest, was arrested by Chilean authorities, tied naked to a bed, and repeatedly tortured with the machine for over an hour at a time. *"I don't want to talk about it anymore,"* Cassidy shudders.[171]

Brazil, Libya, Soviet Union, El Salvador, Morocco and Vietnam all have used electroshock tortures on their political victims. Iran also tortured most of the American embassy hostages with electricity. CIA doctors, who examined the released captives, later declared that only psychiatrists and psychologists would have had the expertise to do so.[172]

SOUTH AFRICAN APARTHEID

One nation that segregated race with disastrous results was South Africa. In 1924, psychologist Dr Hendrik Verwoerd earned his doctorate and commenced lecturing at Capetown's Stellenbosch University. Two years later, he furthered his studies in Berlin, Hamburg and Leipzig in Germany, then a hotbed of evolutionary, eugenicist and racist methodologies combined with white Aryan superiority. Verwoerd was taught that blacks were *"slothful, unintelligent, though motorically and physically capable people, who live in crime, poverty, and generally socially deteriorated conditions, and do so because of their genetically-based limited mental capacities."* [173]

Dr Verwoerd later became prime minister of South Africa, under whose tenure tens of thousands of black South Africans were kept in abandoned mining compounds and brutally abused by psychiatrists as part of the new apartheid (separate development) system Verwoerd introduced in 1948. From 1960 to 1965, the number of Africans incarcerated in mental institutions for trivial reasons increased by 500%. Contracted out as 'psychiatric patients' to work in factories and mines as part of their 'industrial therapy', psychiatry and its governors reaped huge financial rewards from this source of slave labour. Conditions in the camps were squalid, to say the least - a haven for disease. Most were forced to go without toilet paper, sheets, blankets, and adequate bathing and toilet facilities. Electroshock treatment was routinely administered with no anaesthetic. Chief government Dr J P Henning stated that *"It's simply too expensive, too slow and too risky. Blacks appear to be more susceptible to*

[171] Murche, John, "Shock Torture, Doctor Tells of Jail Horror", *Daily Mirror*, 31st December 1975

[172] Szasz, Thomas, *Journey into Madness*, op. cit. p.311

[173] Lerner, Richard A, *Final Solutions: Biology, Prejudice and Genocide*, The Pennsylvania State University Press, Pennsylvania, USA: 1992

the effects of anaesthetics and because we treat more Blacks than Whites, we would have to double our staff if we used anaesthetics." [174]

PSYCHIATRIC GENOCIDE IN THE BALKANS

Members of the Council of Europe signed a resolution in 1999 acknowledging that psychiatrist Jovan Raskovic was one of the chief architects of genocide in the Balkans. Raskovic's paradoxical brand of religious/nationalistic rhetoric, couched in Freudian terminology in his *Luda Zemla* (*A Mad Country*), succeeded in inflaming Serb hatred against the Balkan minorities.

Tellingly, Raskovic came clean to the *Vreme* and *Vjeskik* newspapers on 24th January 1992: *"I feel responsible because I made the preparations for this war, even if not the military preparations. If I hadn't created this emotional strain in the Serbian people, nothing would have happened. My party and I lit the fuse of Serbian nationalism not only in Croatia but everywhere else in Bosnia-Herzegovina.... We have driven this people and we have given it an identity. I have repeated again and again to this people that it comes from heaven, not earth."* [175]

Raskovic died later that year in 1992. He had allowed one of his psychiatric patients, Radovan Karadzic, another psychiatrist, to lead his Serbian Democratic Party, along with one of Karadzic's former patients, Slobodan Milosovic. In his book *The Tenth Circle of Hell*, Bosnian survivor Rezak Hukanovic writes that, like Hitler, these leading Serbs were willing to go all the way. Karadzic was responsible for implementing the 'Memorandum' – the systematic extermination of Croats and Muslims. *"And where on earth was the poisonous game conceived? In the head of that bloodthirsty lyricist, the mad psychiatrist from Sarajevo, Radovan Karadzic."* [176]

Although Milosevic was subsequently arrested and brought to the Hague to answer for war crimes, At the time of writing, Karadzic remains at large, often being seen wandering the streets of Pale. Like the Nazi psychiatrists after World War 2 before him, no real effort has ever been made to bring the Serbian leader to justice.

---

[174] "Mental Health Industry is Uncovered", *Peace and Freedom*, South Africa, January 1976
[175] "Bosnia: Ending the Religious Genocide", *The Crusader*, August 1993, pp.1,6
[176] Hukanovic, Rezac, *The Tenth Circle of Hell*, Basic Books, 1996

SHOCKING IN THE UK

In the UK, electroshock has been used on pregnant women. Even British children do not to escape:

"At 12, Jessica, from Bristol in the UK, was raped by three teenage boys who told her that they had left her pregnant. Terrified that this might be the case, Jessica started staring at her stomach and became obsessed with the idea that she was having a baby. She drank bleach to try and rid herself of it. Her feeling of self-worth was destroyed. She wouldn't eat, couldn't sleep and became withdrawn.

Although seen by consultants from an adolescent's unit, her condition did not improve. When she was 17, she stopped eating for 12 days. A psychiatrist, instead of addressing the problem of getting Jessica to eat, recommended she have electroshock. Her parents objected – the father had worked at an infirmary and witnessed electroshock being given. "I saw it as brutal and archaic," he said. Their objections were overruled by psychiatrists who had committed Jessica. A Mental Health Board doctor gave permission for her to be administered 16 electroshocks on consecutive days.

Jessica's health deteriorated rapidly. She was transferred to an adult psychiatric ward where she was placed on powerful, mind-altering drugs. The consultant psychiatrist suggested a lobotomy. Through the intervention of a group called MIND, the operation was prevented. Jessica is now 21." [177]

NEW ZEALAND - CLAMPING DOWN ON ABUSE

Mental health watchdog CCHR acted against the infamous Lake Alice hospital in New Zealand, ordering them through court order to desist from *"....subjecting children to ECT without anaesthetic for 'behaviour modification'. Children and adolescents had been given electric shocks to their genitals and legs, the same practice used to torture political prisoners. After a judicial hearing, the 'shock ward' was closed down and the ECT machines ordered removed."* [178]

---

[177] "They gave our child electroshock treatment – and we couldn't stop them", *Best* magazine, 31st October 1996, Issue 43/95, pp.50-51

[178] CCHR Australia: "Lake Alice – A Child's Nightmare", *Beating the Odds for Sixteen Years*, 1994; "Shock Equipment Taken from Unit", *The New Zealand Herald*, 14th May 1977

VIOLATIONS IN AMERICA

CCHR also monitored and helped end abuses occurring in US psychiatric institutions, such as the Camarillo and Metropolitan State hospitals in California. One 36-year-old man was found dead, shackled upside down in bed with leather restraints. A grandmother was discovered dead in a hospital closet two weeks after the staff informed the family that she had gone 'missing'.

JAPAN

In 1994 and 1998, psychiatric scandals hit Japan. Authorities had discovered that private psychiatric hospitals were forcefully imprisoning and restraining elderly patients against their will. In 2000, legislation was passed forbidding the use of restraints on the elderly unless in emergencies.[179]

A LAW UNTO ITSELF

Traditional medicine is scathing to its red-headed stepchild, psychiatry. A California family physician for 17 years, Dr Megan Shields says, *"The bottom line is that psychiatrists know nothing about the mind, treat the individual as no more than an organ in the head (the brain), and have about as much interest in spirituality, standard medicine and curing as an executioner would have in saving lives."* [180]

Dr Lee Coleman observes that *"... the brain, for a while, is so injured that the patient is too confused to know or remember what was troubling him.... When the brain begins to recover... the problems usually return, since electricity has done nothing to resolve them."* [181]

Psychiatrist Dr Thomas Szasz remarks in *Cruel Compassion*, *"The young and the old are defenceless against relatives who want to get rid of them by casting them in the role of mental patient, and against psychiatrists whose livelihood depends on defining them as mentally ill."* [182]

---

[179] Regulation 39, Health & Welfare Ministry, 31st March 1999

[180] Citizens Commission on Human Rights report: "Psychiatry Destroys Minds", Los Angeles: p.34

[181] Coleman, Lee, "Introduction", *The Case Against ECT*, National Research Office, Los Angeles: 1977

[182] Szasz, Thomas, *Cruel Compassion*, John Wiley & Sons, New York: 1994, p.175

Remarking on the tremendous earning potential through insurance schemes and private treatment of holding a patient for repeated 'therapy' over a protracted period of time, another whistleblowing psychiatrist notes: *"The psychiatric chains have been doing everything they can to keep people for an unnecessary long period for no medical reason. We think that between 40% and 70% of the people now in psychiatric hospital don't need to be there."* [183]

Electroshock is just one weapon of an insidious arsenal brought to bear against 'mental' conditions psychiatry itself, as we shall see, has arbitrarily invented. Other menacing methods are also used, quietly behind the scenes. Destroying the mind of the hapless victim, piece by piece, memory by memory, in horribly compelling scenes more befitting the sickest of horror movies than a supposedly benevolent medical 'science', psychiatry and its modalities are forever today sold to the world as the answer to all our mental turmoils.

---

[183] Ibid.

Cutting the White

The term 'psychosurgery' can still instil horror. Cutting into the brain in order to render the patient 'more docile and compliant', a procedure often combined with electroshock, takes many back to Ken Kesey's landmark 1970's anti-psychiatry movie, *One Flew Over the Cuckoo's Nest*, starring Jack Nicholson. Later, audiences would shiver in titillation at the awful scene in *Hannibal*, where murderous psychiatrist Hannibal Lecter, played by Anthony Hopkins, excises part of Ray Liotta's brain and sizzles it in a frying pan before wolfing it down.

Gottlieb Burckhardt, a Swiss asylum superintendent, carried out what was thought to be the first psycho (brain) surgery, removing part of his patients' cerebral tissue in order to render them more controllable. Out of the six initial patients, one died, while the others suffered repeated and devastating bouts of epilepsy, paralysis and the inability to speak or understand words (aphasia). Yet Burckhart deemed the outcome of his surgeries a success, since the patients were indeed far more controllable. He stopped performing the operations after severe criticism from his peers.[184]

But it was Egas Moniz, a Portuguese neurologist, who was to open a new and shameful chapter in the history of psychiatry. Attending the Second Neurological Congress in London in 1935, Moniz learned of two chimpanzees which had had their frontal lobes removed in an experiment. After the chimps recovered from the operation, they exhibited no alarm or concern with matters about which they had previously been preoccupied.

Less than two months after the conference, Moniz had already performed not one, but 20 of his own pre-frontal lobotomy operations. Using a tool he had made himself, dubbed the 'leucotome', he probed into the white matter of the brain's frontal lobes before pressing a plunger on the instrument. A loop protruding from the end of the leucotome encircled the target area. The instrument was then turned, coring a section of the patient's cerebral tissue.[185]

---

[184] Kiloh, L G, et al, *Physical Treatments in Psychiatry*, Blackwell Scientific Publications, London: 1988, p.277
[185] Isaac, Rael Jean & Virginia C Armat, *Madness in the Streets*, The Free Press, New York: 1990, p.178

Moniz claimed that his operations, which involved the cutting of the patient's frontal lobes (lit: *lobotomy*), were a success. Such a subjective view of his own work seemed never to have been questioned by his psychiatric peers, who accepted his assertions that a third of Moniz's patients were cured, a third improved, while a third remained unchanged.[186] Coining the term *psychosurgery*, thus lending a requisite veneer of medical respectability to the new 'science', Moniz's work was promoting a 'medical' procedure that had absolutely no scientific underpinning to justify its later widespread use. Nevertheless his work was quickly supported by the worldwide psychiatric community as being the new 'cutting edge' procedure to 'cure' mental patients by rendering their symptoms more controllable.

Naturally, psychiatry touted the procedure as 'safe', and even that it was supported by the very patients who underwent 'leucotomy' (*leuco*: 'white'; *tomos*: 'cut'). It is perhaps ironic that Moniz was later shot and permanently paralysed by one of his leucotomised patients in 1944. Not widely known however is that twelve years later, another of his patients found and attacked the immobile Moniz, this time ending the controversial physician's life.[187]

WALTER FREEMAN AND JAMES WATTS

Psychosurgery was to garner its share of showmen. Within three months of the publication of Moniz's work, American psychiatrist and neurologist Walter Freeman joined fellow neurosurgeon James Watts to carry out the first brain operation in the United States. Researcher and CCHR US president Bruce Wiseman:

*"Freeman gave the surgery a new name – a name that, unbeknownst to him, would live in infamy: the frontal lobotomy. The patient was a woman who, before surgery, 'showed uncontrollable apprehension, was unable to sleep, laughed and wept hysterically.' She was held down while a drug was administered, rendering her unconscious. 'Four hours later after the anaesthetic had worn off,' wrote Freeman and Watts, 'her face presented a placid expression and she admitted that she felt much better....'"[188]

---

[186] Rodgers, Joann Ellison, *Psychosurgery*, HarperCollins, New York: 1992, p.12; *Frontiers of Psychiatry*, "The psychosurgical question", p.1
[187] Lapon, Lenny, *Mass Murderers in White Coats*, Psychiatric Genocide Research Institute, Springfield, Massachusetts: 1986, p.84
[188] Wiseman, Bruce, op. cit. p.160

It wasn't long however before the side-effects became apparent. Using their first operation as an excuse to copy the procedure far and wide, Freeman and Watts carried out 108 operations on a variety of mental patients exhibiting a wide cross-section of symptoms. Four died as a result of the procedure. Freeman began noticing *"frontal lobe syndrome"* - a catatonic, vegetative state where the patient demonstrated *"nonchalance"* and an *"inability to carry out tasks, and loss of social control."*[189]

As more and more of the patients who received Freeman and Watt's ministrations demonstrated this dull-eyed regression of their mental faculties, the two neurosurgeons came under increasing pressure to carry out damage control. Bruce Wiseman again:

"Freeman's idea of 'benefit' or 'improved' however was similar to Moniz's. Where others saw 'zombies', Freeman saw patients who were 'less anxious, less concerned about their inner experiences, and more responsive to the environment.' [190] *When the lobotomy was performed on patients in chronic pain, the psychiatrist thought it a success that they no longer cared or, as he put it, 'the patient was enabled to face disability and death with equanimity.'*

This is the key point, for it applies across the board to all psychiatric treatments today. When you read the numerous, self-serving newspaper quotes from psychiatric spokespeople claiming they can successfully control or cure or blunt depression, psychosis and numerous other ailments, remember the previous paragraph...."[191]

One of many adverse letters received by Freeman illustrates how the gloss was later applied:

24th March 1940

Frankly Dr Freeman, I don't know of any way that I might suggest to anyone to more effectively cause the deterioration of an entire family than that operation. Progressively since the operation, my father has been regressing towards childhood. He lost his business... dissipated the family

---

[189] Frankel, Glenn, "DC Neurosurgeon Pioneered 'Operation Icepick' Technique", *Washington Post*, 7th April 1980, p.A1
[190] Freeman, Walter, "Psychosurgery", *American Handbook of Psychiatry*, edited by Silvano Arieti, Vol.2, Basic Books, Inc., New York: 1959, p.1521
[191] Wiseman, Bruce, op. cit. p.160-161

savings… and made our home life practically an unbearable thing. Apparently for him the operation was a huge success, for he had no worries about the past or future and almost daily suggests that others see you about the operation.…"

Freeman's notes on the patient indicated that *"he became quite unruly and aggressive towards his family and clients, lost the rest of his business, was faced with lawsuits on account of financial irregularities as well as physical attacks. He turned his son out of his home, changed secretaries every few days, behaved in a very arbitrary way towards his clients, and turned completely against his wife who was ill of cancer."*

Freeman and Watts responded: *"From the standpoint of the patient's inner harmony, it cannot but be considered an overwhelming success. Here stands a man with his business ruined, his family alienated, facing criminal proceedings, and he insists that he never felt better in his life."*[192]

ROSEMARY KENNEDY
Rosemary Kennedy, sister of US President John F Kennedy, was a young lady in the wrong place at the wrong time. Suffering mild retardation, Rosemary received the best medical help her very wealthy family could buy. One magazine states: *"Eminent medical specialists were consulted and the advice was that the girl should undergo a 'certain form of neurosurgery.'"* [193] The Kennedy's money bought them Walter Freeman and his famous lobotomy. Years later Rosemary's mother Rose gave her verdict on the effect of Freeman's handiwork:

"The operation eliminated the violence and the convulsive seizures, but it also had the effect of leaving Rosemary permanently incapacitated. She lost everything that had been gained during the years by her own gallant efforts and our loving efforts for her. She had no possibility of ever again being able to function in a viable way in the world at large."[194]

Encouraged by the belief that collateral damage was eminently acceptable since their patients were in dire straits anyway, Freeman and Watts were busy refining their techniques. By 1948, they had carried out

---

[192] Case quoted in Scheflin, Alan W & Edward Opton, *The Mind Manipulators*, Paddington Press, New York: 1978, p.258; quoted in Wiseman, Bruce, op. cit.
[193] Porter, Martin, "Night of the Human Tomatoes", *High Times*, March 1979, p.64
[194] Porter, Martin, op. cit.

623 lobotomies with a 3% death rate. Using deeper and more accurately targeted cuts to the brain, the brain surgeons began switching from general anaesthetic to a shot of novocaine in the head, allowing the patient to remain conscious during the operation, and facilitating the surgeons to monitor the patient's reaction as they cut through their brain.[195]

IN WITH THE ICEPICK

Perhaps Freeman's most famous, or should we say *infamous* innovation was 'icepick' surgery. Wishing to simplify what was turning into a costly and complicated operation requiring anaesthetists, nurses, orderlies and expensive equipment, Freeman switched to an ordinary kitchen icepick. The first patient to undergo his new technique was a woman named Ellen, whom Freeman stunned unconscious with

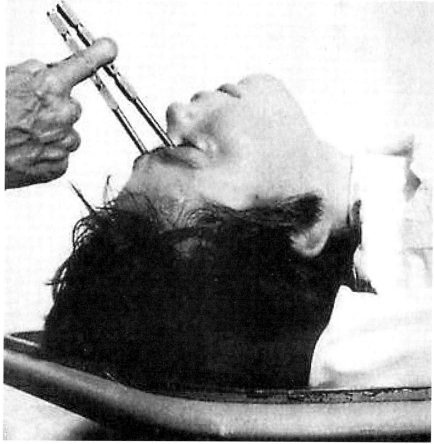

April 1980, p.A1

electroshock. Freeman pulled back one of her eyelids to expose the tear duct where the eye socket met the bridge of the nose. He placed the tip of the icepick against the thin bone. *"A light tap of the hammer is usually all that is needed to drive the point through the orbital plate,"* Freeman wrote. *"In other cases, however, the plate is so thick that the operator risks bending or breaking the instrument. Quite often there is a sudden give or even an audible crack as the... plate fractures."* [196]

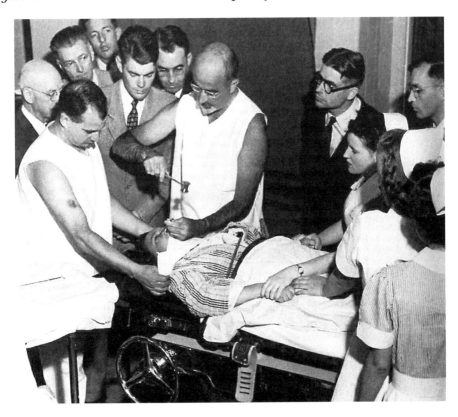

Freeman would hammer the icepick into the front portion of the brain and then swipe the instrument from side to side, carrying out the required injury to the lobes. The procedure was then carried out through the other eye socket. The patient almost always awoke with black eyes.

---

[196] Rodgers, Joann Ellison, *Psychosurgery*, op. cit. p.5

THE FREEMAN CIRCUS

Named the 'transorbital lobotomy', Walter Freeman travelled around America, demonstrating the procedure to psychiatrists. Boasting that surgeons were now no longer needed to perform this most vital of operations for the terminally retarded, Freeman's notoriety and press acclamation soared. His partner James Watts revolted, declaring that their original agreement had been only to perform lobotomies as a case of 'last resort'. But Walter had tasted the world stage and had become a media icon. An accomplished speaker and consummate showman, Freeman revelled in the praise of his peers and the renown of having revolutionised psychiatry. His icepick surgery motto was American folksy comfort melded with the indispensable service Freeman was graciously bestowing upon fellow humanity: *"Lobotomy gets them home."* [197]

Dubbed 'Operation Icepick', Freeman's five-state tour of America in 1952 was loved by the press for its protagonist's stage theatrics, posing with lights in front of a specially prepared backdrop, a golden icepick in hand, often performing on ten patients in a row, sometimes two at a time. [198] But Freeman's casual, almost celebrity mien angered many. His icepick surgery naturally touted controversy, even from the home stables.

"I was horrified when I saw it." American Psychiatric Association president Alan Stone. [199]

"It was awful. Ugh. I got sick. I couldn't watch it. None of us could very easily.... I had to walk out of the room. I don't have a very good answer as to why he wasn't stopped." Psychosurgeon Thomas Ballantine. [200]

So why wasn't Freeman stopped? *Psychosurgery* author Joann Rodgers: *"Nothing it seemed could stop the lobotomy juggernaut, or its apologists. Enthusiasm far outstripped suspiciously bloated results."* [201]

Even when talking up the horrendous results of his actions, Freeman was never at a loss for words:

---

[197] Frankel, Glenn, *The Washington Post*, op. cit.
[198] Porter, Martin, op. cit.
[199] Ibid.
[200] Ibid.
[201] Rodgers, Joann Ellison, *Psychosurgery*, op. cit. p.21

Loss of bowel and bladder control – (*"More troublesome to the family than the patient."*). Epileptic seizures in up to half the patients receiving lobotomies – (*"The seizures may begin soon after operation and come under control easily, or they may first appear five to ten years after operation."*). A predisposition to alcoholism – (*"The family has a responsibility to... prevent the development of a taste for alcohol."*)

Walter Freeman reasons: *"Isn't it true that when these poor devils stop suffering, it is through a loss of what you call psyche.... What happens to the psyche if it is not 'mercy-killed'?"* [202]

USES OF PSYCHOSURGERY

Lobotomies and other 'behaviour-controlling' surgeries, such as hypothalamotomies, are today mostly carried out away from the public spotlight. A study of 70 hypothalamotomies carried out on sex offenders to reduce their libido in Germany between 1962 and 1975 demonstrated that *"indications for surgery* [were] *based on questionable scientific and clinical grounds and practically* [excluded] *psychotherapeutic... aspects."* [203] Japan has used the same procedure to control aggressive or violent behaviour in its youth, as well as hyperactivity. Incredibly, reports show the Japanese doctors *guessing* that *"...the area we have been stimulating and electrocauterising probably involves* [either of two small brain sites].... *Therefore it is quite probable that destruction of the* [tissue fibre] *bundle would result in a decrease of... the expression of rage or aggression."*

A post-operative follow-up of these youngsters years later found that 13 of the 60 patients studied had died, variously of suicides, drownings and unknown causes. Refusing to accept that their brain ministrations could conceivably have had anything to do with this inordinately high death rate, and even concluding that their results indicated that surgical procedures for these disorders were promising, the doctors merely remonstrated:

"Since any cause of death does not seem directly related to the surgical intervention, this unusually high rate of death may reflect a relatively short life expectancy of those handicapped patients.... The

---

[202] Quoted in Scheflin, Alan W & Edward Opton, *The Mind Manipulators*, Paddington Press, New York: 1978, p.256
[203] Rodgers, Joann Ellison, *Psychosurgery*, op. cit. pp.52, 83

experiences of the present group of 29 children seem to support an early surgical intervention." [204]

SURGICAL QUACKERY

The move to solve the growing violence problem in society after the hedonistic explosion of the 1960's, and the subsequent effects of its drug abuse, prompted many in psychiatry to apply lobotomy, hypothalamotomy or amygdalotomy to excise the parts of the brain they believed would not cure the patient, but control their behaviour. It seems to have been of non-existent interest to these physicians that the violence, hyperactivity, aggression, hypersexuality, autism or other 'social deviations' could have altogether more simple and rational causes, as we will discover later. Psychiatry merely ploughed ahead and did what it thought it had to do.

In Czechoslovakia, a mental disease named 'hedonia' was coined to describe those unfortunates who disturbed the existing social order through excessive smoking, drinking or eating. One of these hedonists who underwent the knife was a six-year-old little boy. [205] Researchers Scheflin and Opton describe how, in an interview they arranged, an American psychosurgeon *"...told us that the four to five million children in the United States with 'varying degrees of mental retardation', hyperkinesis* [hyperactivity], *or autism are also good prospects for psychosurgery.* [The surgeon] *personally has operated on 'a great number' of retarded children and a few with autism."* [206]

THE HIDDEN SHAME

What goes on behind the walls of mental institutions today is something most of the public would rather not know. But who in government is speaking up for these unfortunates who find themselves cut off from the outside world, taken away from the loved ones who would rather not have the nuisance of them any more, incapacitated with mind-altering drugs, and then subjected to the controlled violence of quasi-medical procedures of no scientific benefit or merit?

Psychosurgery bans have only happened in nations where severe abuses have been brought to light and predictably shocked the public. Japan banned psychosurgery in the mid-1970's after various scandals. The

---

[204] Sano, K, & Y Mayanagi, "Posteromedial Hypothalamotomy in the Treatment of Violent, Aggressive Behaviour", *Acta Neurochirurgica*, Suppl. 44, 1988, pp.148, 150
[205] Scheflin, Alan W & Edward Opton, *The Mind Manipulators*, op. cit. p.274-275
[206] Ibid. p.273

state of Michigan banned psychosurgery after a 1972 court case. Psychosurgery is now banned in the US in Oregon and South Dakota. That psychosurgery, like electroshock, is a human rights abuse of the most pernicious order is clear when the authorities take matters into their own hands. According to US Senate testimony in 1974, California psychiatrists were let loose on certain violent inmates to see what could be done about them:

> *"California officials secretly amygdalotomised three prisoners, paying scant regard to legal and ethical issues of informed consent. This serious tampering with the human brain yielded no favourable results for reducing crime or violence. In fact, the prisoner reported by officials to be the most improved is still in prison. His old symptoms have returned, and he now suffers additionally from memory loss and other effects of the brain destruction."* [207]

Today, behind the scenes, the devastation continues all over the world. And after the devastation trudges the inevitable tide of psychiatric refugees, the broken and the wounded, their memories erased or severely impaired, not being able to recognise their children, their wives, their husbands. Years of education wiped out, skills destroyed, amnesia, an unsettling feeling that someone has invaded the very heart of their soul. The fear.

James is finding his recovery from psychosurgery and electroshock slow and painstaking. He told Credence researchers: *"The abiding memory I have is of the blue flashes and the chainsaw in my brain. Today, I still can't recognise the man they say is my dad. My wife left me when I asked who those children were. They were mine! I guess she had had about enough of me and my problems by then, and packed up and went back to her mom's in Wichita. I don't have any friends anymore, but I have my God. And I hope, in the fullness of time, He will be able to help me understand and forgive me for what I did that was so very wrong."* [208]

---

[207] "Individual Rights and the Federal Role in Behavior Modification, A Study Prepared by the Staff of the Subcommittee on Constitutional Rights of the Committee on the Judiciary", US Senate, November 1974, pp.326, 328
[208] Credence Research personal correspondence

Dream with Me for a Moment

"You live and learn. Well, at any rate, you live." - Douglas Adams

"Just because you are paranoid doesn't mean they aren't out to get you." - Patrick Murray

"And the dictator... will do well to encourage... the freedom to daydream under the influence of dope and movies and the radio. It will help to reconcile his subjects to the servitude which is their fate." – Aldous Huxley, *Brave New World*, 1932

The area of psychiatry that really worked for its expansion was in the realm of drug treatment. As we shall see, psychiatry can justifiably be charged with laying the foundations for today's runaway drug culture. In later years, the mental health industry would remain firmly unapologetic with regard to its role in popularising the recreational use of drugs, while continually failing to bring itself to condemn the habit, while simultaneously fostering drug dependency in its own patients, many of them children. Indeed, as we shall see, psychiatry remains one of the leading drug pushers in the world, hooking millions on its expensive and extremely lucrative medications. With its earning power through the pharmaceutical industry finally appreciated and welcomed by the mainstream chemical industry, psychiatry now has its place in medicine secured, even in the minds of most traditional physicians.

Psychiatry originally started out as a great embarrassment to traditional medicine, which repeatedly refused to bring the renegade practice into the fold. Later, electroshock and lobotomies, coupled with the sheer human rights abuses that were starkly evident to all but psychiatry itself, had kept the whispers susurrating around the corridors of medical officialdom. Psychiatry however was canny enough to recognise it had a public relations problem, even if it could not, incredibly, fully appreciate why it was happening. With the advent of America's National Institute of Mental Health (NIMH), inaugurated after World War 2 under Robert Felix, the mental health industry began to employ some well-needed political spin to add some spit and polish to its tarnished public persona.

Nothing helped more to integrate mental health into mainstream medicine, in the public's view, than when psychiatry began prescribing drugs to its patients to control their behaviour. This was 'real' medicine being prescribed after all. Since the inauguration of modern allopathic medicine, instituted so effectively under America's Abraham Flexner and John D Rockefeller in the early years of the 20th century, drug regulation, the training of doctors in institutions funded by the drug industry and the modern, drug-dominant health system have enjoyed an unparalleled financial and social success, which the allopathic system jealously guards to this day. Psychiatry remained outside this hallowed realm; viewed along with other alternative health 'charlatans' as unscientific and old-fashioned quackery. Yet World War 2 had demonstrated to the medical and government powers that human thought, behaviour and desire could be controlled using artificial means. Even after the war, as we have seen, the eugenics ideal lived on. Indeed, questions as to the whereabouts of many leading Nazi psychiatrists and doctors following the uncovering of unspeakable horrors in Europe were quietly buried or diverted, hardly earning any mention in the media of a post-World War 2 Europe, keen to put the traumas of the past behind it.

But after the war, psychiatry was truly to enter the drug arena, and thereby assure itself of massive funding and a mainstream social status as a reward for all its efforts. Now, straitjackets could be discarded in favour of a more mobile and profitable restraint – the use of drugs.

THE DRUG LANDSLIDE BEGINS
US President Howard Taft recognised the brutal impact of psychiatric drugs on society, remarking in 1910: *"The illicit sale* [of cocaine] *and the habitual use of it temporarily raises the power of the criminal to a point where in resisting arrest, there is no hesitation to murder. It is more appalling in its effect than any other habit-forming drug used in the United States."* [209]

Even as recently as the 1950's, society still traditionally frowned on mind-altering substances, disdaining those who took them as weak and addicts who could not help themselves. Bruce Wiseman comments that *"...this view of drugs may seem ancient, but it came from centuries of mankind's experience with them. After enough eyewitness accounts of fathers, sisters and acquaintances decaying, living the fate of the opium smoker, the morphine addict, the cocaine user – few needed further convincing."* [210] Interestingly, today there are those who frown upon

---

[209] "Drug Facts", *Executive News Service*, 1989
[210] Wiseman, Bruce, op. cit. p.192

recreational drug use while addicted themselves to pharmaceutical medication.

Back in the 1800's, bromides had been used to desensitise the central nervous system, assisting in calming the patient. Raw opium was considered too dangerous; its historical, addictive properties were widely known. The pathetic plight of the opium addict caused those familiar with the problem to develop approaches they believed would relieve the sufferer of their addiction. A new substance was brought forward and named 'morphine'. By 1870, physicians were complaining that morphine itself was horrendously addictive and was beginning to cause more problems than the opium addiction it was expected to cure.[211]

In 1898, a solution to the morphine problem was developed and hailed as the non-addictive way forward. The new substance was called 'heroin'. Like laudanum before it, heroin, during the next decade, gained its now-famous notorious reputation for its soft-cushioning, other-worldly, central nervous system and mental effects, while simultaneously locking the patient's mental faculties and dependence into its golden brown embrace. Worse still, heroin, so powerful and thus able to be diluted for greater profit and illicitly distributed to those in need, became the drug of choice for unscrupulous dealers who peddled the narcotic and built their businesses on the misfortune of others.

The dawning of a new and uncontrollable drug problem breeding crime and violence was a new experience for western societies, who found themselves powerless in knowing what to do to combat the scourge. Once discovered, it became almost impossible to extirpate the demand for the insidious new substances, which offered their devotees an alluring escape from the pain and drudgeries of normal life. Psychiatry too was failing to provide an answer, attempting from the outset to pathologise the 'new disease of addiction', and trying to cure addicts of their affliction through the use of their electroshock and lobotomy procedures.

Barbiturates too were already in circulation, able powerfully to sedate the suffering patient, rendering them more amenable to control. Chloroform also had, for half a century, provided the means to 'knock a patient out', thus removing the horror of having to endure operations fully

---

[211] Kleber, Herbert D, "Detoxification from Narcotics", *Substance Abuse: Clinical Problems and Perspectives,* edited by Joyce Lowinson MD and Pedro Ruiz MD, Williams & Wilkins, Baltimore and London: 1981, p.318

conscious. In the 1920's, it became possible to synthesise barbiturates and provide the burgeoning drugs market with a constant, reliable, *regulated* supply of the new product. The 1930's saw the advent too of the stimulant amphetamines, with the American Medical Association even stating that with Benzedrine ('bennies') *"...no serious reactions had been reported"*, and that the public could, under strict supervision of their physician, of course, take the drug recreationally to create *"a sense of increased energy or capacity for work, or a feeling of exhilaration."*[212]

Lester Grinspoon MD articulates in a 1977 report how the medical system was keen to promote their new products to the public as 'safe and effective', with no appreciable downsides:

"Of all the myths surrounding the amphetamines, that of their alleged non-addictiveness is the most transparent, although when they were first introduced, they were hailed as having little or no addictive potential. This is not surprising, as the medical establishment originally guaranteed as non-addictive almost every drug known to cause addiction.... Cases of addiction were reported almost immediately, but the drug industry was so successful in reinforcing and sustaining early medical enthusiasm, that as late as 1958, C D Leake could categorically state that 'no clear case of addiction to amphetamines has been reported.'" [213]

'DOLOPHINE'
World War 2 Nazi Germany, with its unrestricted and well-funded drug research, produced dolophine, named after its Führer. In the aftermath of the war, this drug was renamed 'methadone'. Psychiatrist Marie Nyswander was one of many enthusiastically promoting methadone as the non-addictive solution to heroin. However, by 1963, Nyswander and fellow psychiatrist Vincent Dole, of the Rockefeller Institute, were admitting methadone addiction in their patients, but proffered that it could replace heroin addiction for life.[214]

Dr Michael Smith, of the Lincoln Detox Program in New York, explains how the 'cure' soon became the new problem: *"Withdrawal from methadone is a long, drawn-out, brutal experience. There is not a two-to-*

---

[212] Grinspoon, Lester & James B Bakalar, "The Amphetamines: Medical Uses and Health Hazards", *Psychiatric Annals,* August, 1977, p.9
[213] Ibid.
[214] "The Nightmare of Methadone", *Freedom*, Vol.21, October 1988, pp.20-23

five-day crisis of vomiting and tremors, as with heroin. These and other frightening symptoms occur for weeks and usually months on end." [215]

Not surprisingly, methadone continued to be touted after the war as the permanent replacement to heroin. By the 1970's, methadone maintenance programs were treating more than 75,000 patients across the United States. In 1987, *The Columbus Dispatch* was reporting that less than 1% of methadone junkies were able to stop using the drug. [216]

MUGGINGS ANDS MONEY
Clinics themselves became the cause of the problem. By the mid-1970's, Nyswander and Dole were themselves admitting the failure of their methadone program. A 1987 article in the *Journal of Psychiatric Drugs* declared: *"Approximately half of those who were now paying for [methadone] maintenance reported resorting to crime to pay their clinic fees. As one client described the situation: 'The clinic has now become my drug dealer. I am committing crimes to pay for an addictive drug [methadone]. It's really not much different than the street."* [217]

Predictably, psychiatry was to pioneer another drug to cure the methadone problem. This time 'ibogaine' became the hope for an end to the addictions, which psychiatry itself had brokered. However ibogaine's notorious reputation gained it a Class 1 regulation (dangerous and of no medical value) and treatment with it was outlawed in the United States. Bruce Wiseman sums up:

"The lessons of heroin and methadone have been poorly learned by our mental health experts. Most drug addicts already feel they are in a netherworld from which there may be no return and, so far, these experts and their experimental cures have only led them deeper into it." [218]

MASSIVE MARKETS = MASSIVE REVENUES
The explosion of pharmaceutical drug use for mental disorders has fuelled a huge expansion in drug sales globally. Billions of dollars are

---

[215] Ibid.

[216] Belew, Ray, *The Columbus Dispatch*, "Methadone Victory Rate: 1 Percent", 2nd July, 1987, p. 1A

[217] Rosenbaum, Marsha, et al, "Money for Methadone: Preliminary Findings from a Study of Alameda County's New maintenance Policy", *Journal of Psychiatric Drugs*, Vol. 19, January-March, 1987, p.40

[218] Wiseman, Bruce, op. cit. p.218

spent annually in North America alone to treat the 'mentally ill'. These medications have become among the most expensive costs of the US mental healthcare system. The elderly especially have struggled with the rising cost of prescription drugs in Canada, prompting both candidates and their parties in the year 2000 elections to address the issue of the elderly being unable to pay for their medications.[219]

IMS Health US stated in its March 2001 annual report that psychotropic medication sales increased by 21% over the previous 12 months. Sales of medications relating to treatment of mental illness were second throughout the global market.[220]

An IMS Canada Report for the province of British Columbia in 1997 indicated a 66% increase from 1992–1996 in the number of psychiatric prescriptions issued.[221] A recent US study showed that the number of 2-4 year olds on psychiatric drugs such as Ritalin and Prozac soared 50% between 1991-1995.[222]

DRUGS AND CRIME
Given that psychotropic drug use for mental patients began in earnest in the 1960's concurrently with the releasing of psychiatric drugs, such as methadone, heroin, LSD and Thorazine into Crowley's drug-fuelled, sexually 'liberated' society for 'recreational purposes', we can get a clear picture of what psychiatry has really done for the world if we analyse social statistics coming out of the United States during this period.

Between 1960 and 1992, the US violent crime rate known to police went from around 105 violent crimes per 100,000 to around 760/100,000. During the same period, the aggravated assault rate known to police jumped from 80/100,000 to 440/100,000. The forcible rape rate known to police went from 10/100,000 to 43/100,000. Arrests for drug abuse violations among African Americans soared from 220/100,000 to a

---

[219] 'A Framework for Reform", A report of the President's Advisory Council on Health, December 2001. www.gov.ab.ca/home/health_first/
[220] IMS Health: World Drug Purchases – Retail Pharmacies, Drug Monitor, 2 Months to March 2001
[221] "Increase in Psychotherapeutic Prescriptions in BC", *Vancouver Sun*, 7th June 1997
[222] Zito, J M, et al, "Trends in the prescribing of psychotropic medications to preschoolers", *Journal of the American Medical Association*, 283, pp.1025-1030

peak of 2,400/100,000 in 1990. Those for Caucasians rose from 50/100,000 to 400/100,000 in 1992.[223]

A NEW UTOPIA?

Drugs which produce altered mental states of any kind have always instinctively appalled ordinary citizens, symbolising weakness in the person taking the drugs, a loss of control over one's most basic social responsibilities, and embarkation upon a spiral of addiction often leading to death. That drugs producing these effects could simultaneously be viewed by other, more influential groups within society as a major evolutionary step in the consciousness development of mankind seems, at first glance, dismissible and fantastic. But are we truly surprised when research psychopharmacologist Ronald Siegel of the University of California Los Angeles' Department of Behavioural Sciences asks us in 1990 to:

"Dream with me for a moment. What would be wrong if we had perfectly safe drugs? I mean drugs that delivered the same effects as our most popular ones, but never caused dependency, disease, dysfunction, or death? Imagine an alcohol-type drug that never caused addiction, liver disease, hangovers, driving under the influence, or workplace problems. Would you care for a cigarette that is as enjoyable as marijuana or tobacco, but as harmless as clean air? How about a pain-killer as good as morphine but safer than aspirin; a stimulant more appealing than cocaine and less harmful than caffeine; a tranquilizer less addicting than Valium and more enjoyable than a martini; or a user-friendly hallucinogen that is as benign as a movie?" [224]

Siegel argues that for man to be truly happy, he must satiate his four desires: hunger, thirst, lust and, predictably, the need to become intoxicated.[225] However one views the opinions of the influential Siegel (to which he is, of course, entitled), one must decide what is to be made of the 10 million Americans who take tranquillisers each year, and the millions elsewhere in the world who are hooked on benzodiazapines and other 'popular' medications people like Siegel are pushing.

---

[223] Sourcebook of Criminal Justice Statistics, US Department of Justice.
[224] Siegel, Ronald, Ph.D, *Intoxication*, Pocket Books, New York: 1989, p. x
[225] Ibid. p. viii

THE GHOST OF ALEISTER CROWLEY

During the researching of this book, it seemed that the influence of the occult was never too distant from psychiatry and the world of institutional and social drug-taking. Traditionalists will point to the enigmatic Book of Revelation which declares that in the 'last days' *"...By their sorceries* [Greek: *pharmakia*] *did the merchants* [big business?] *deceive the whole Earth."* (Rev 18) Presumably, at the time these verses were written, drug abuse was a problem even in these earlier cultures. The implication biblically is that drug-taking induces altered states and precipitates contact with demons. As we will see in the next chapters, the drug and Luciferian legacy left by arch-wizard Aleister Crowley, dubbed 'the patron saint of rock stars', was to produce testimony after testimony of what appears at first sight to be exactly this type of problem.

Crowley, who advocated constant drug abuse as a means of 'expanding self', could easily have been dismissed as an eccentric 'Hooray Henry', were it not for the fact that, after his death in 1947, holed up in a squalid bedsit in Hastings, England, his ideas and procedures were given a lurid immortality by the pop music culture which posthumously adopted him. Crowley wrote under the influence of his spirit-guide, which he later identifies as Satan: *"I am the Snake that giveth Knowledge and Delight and bright glory and stirs the hearts of men with drunkenness. To worship me take wine and strange drugs whereof I will tell my prophet and be drunk thereof!"* [226]

A UTOPIA OF COTTON WOOL

More recently, psychiatrist Seymour Rosenblatt in 1981 was prepared to visualise the next step in drug-taking evolution:

"Consider some of the possibilities currently being promoted by serious scientists: In the next twenty years [i.e., by the year 2001], it has been conjectured, we will be able to control people's feelings and emotions. Madness will go the way of smallpox, and mental institutions will become as rare as monasteries. Everyone will be able to get a night's sleep. Senility will be arrested by a pill or injection. Our memories will be extended beyond their present capacities, and both drug addiction and alcoholism will become things of the past.

---

[226] Crowley, Aleister, *The Book of the Law*, Samuel Weiser Inc., 1989

Sex offenders will be controlled by medication. Our system of penology will be in the purview of chemistry. Steel bars will be replaced by pharmacological agents, leaving criminals to roam free but restricted from harming people.

We will have jamais vu [never seen] drugs that create feelings of novelty and déjà vu [already seen] drugs to breed familiarity. Both boredom and anxiety will be alleviated, and our sex lives will be enhanced and intensified.

Blood cells will be harnessed to become the psychiatrist's allies. They will become like beasts of burden, hauling drugs throughout our bodies. There will be no side-effects, no nausea, no liver damage.

Finally we shall emerge into a drug-free society in which genetic engineering precludes mental illness. The substances produced by our biochemists will exactly match those endowed to us by nature." [227]

Well, here we are, Rosenblatt's twenty years on. What's wrong with his picture, with the benefit of hindsight? Can we not see the lie to one beatific view of man's near future? The drug carnage we face today, if one re-reads Rosenblatt's envisioned utopia, is as shocking as it is condemnatory.

THE LIQUID LOBOTOMY

Nazi-occupied Paris saw the development of a new drug to treat allergies. Soon researchers found that the drug "produced a previously unknown type of central nervous system effect." After the war, French scientists found that they could engineer an offshoot of this drug which could produce "maximum behavioural disruption." French psychiatrist C Quarti tried the drug on herself. She later recorded her experiences one hour after taking it: *"I began to have the impression that I was becoming weaker. That I was dying. It was very painful and agonising."* An hour after that: *"I felt incapable of being angry about anything."* [228]

The new drug reached America in 1954 and was marketed by Smith, Klein and French. It was known as 'Thorazine'.

---

[227] Rosenblatt, Seymour MD & Reynolds Dodson, GP *Beyond Valium – The Brave New World of Psychochemistry*, Putnam's, New York: 1981, pp.18-19
[228] "Thorazine Therapy", *Dendron Monthly News*, August 1988, issue 7

Bill Mandel, a *San Francisco Examiner* columnist, decided to find out what a day's dose (50mg) of Thorazine would do: *"Simply put, Thorazine made me stupid. Because Thorazine and related drugs are called 'liquid lobotomy' in the mental health business, I'd expected a great grey cloud to descend over my faculties. There was no great grey cloud, just small, unsettling patches of fog.*

My mental gears slipped. I had no intellectual traction. It was difficult, for example, to remember simple words. I'd start to describe something and find myself unable to remember such terms as 'screwdriver' and 'volume'."[229]

Significantly, a 1977 California study revealed that 29 patients in four state hospitals were being prescribed in excess of 800mg a day, 16 times the amount experienced by Bill Mandel.[230] One can but imagine the massive debilitating effects the drug would have had on its recipients.

CHEMICAL STRAITJACKETS

More and more, drugs have come to be viewed as chemical straitjackets in institutions, prisons, nurseries, old people's homes and now in open society. Such was psychiatry's growing faith in drugs that in 1963, America saw the implementation of the Community Mental Health Centers Act, which saw psychiatric patients 'deinstitutionalised' and turned onto the streets, drugged up and more than a few homeless. Psychiatrist Dr Thomas Szasz remarks: *"The insane person could now be controlled with a chemical, instead of a mechanical straitjacket. The restraint could be put in him, instead of on him."*[231]

Within twenty years, the program showed itself to be an unqualified failure. Many discharged patients were unable to cope with the harsh rigours of life on the streets and would turn to crime, violence and street drug addiction. By 1991, the *New York Times* was calling 'deinstitutionalisation' *"...a cruel embarrassment, a reform gone terribly wrong."*[232]

---

[229] Wiseman, Bruce, op. cit. p.197
[230] "Dr Caligari's Psychiatric Drugs", Network Against Psychiatric Assault, Berkeley, CA: 1987, p.20
[231] Szasz, Thomas, *Cruel Compassion*, John Wiley & Sons, New York: 1994, p.166
[232] Sharkey, Joe, *Bedlam, Greed, Profiteering, and Fraud in a Mental Health System Gone Crazy*, St Martin's Press, New York: 1994, p.177

Today, many cities around the world, which adopted their own versions of deinstitutionalisation, have been paying the social penalty for this catastrophic wrong turn. Few administrations are willing to shoulder the unpopular and costly responsibility of putting such a difficult problem right. And so the abuse continues. The public sees a deranged person on the street, believing them to be insane, or 'not right in the head', yet how many of these unfortunates are simply doped up with drugs that have been prescribed 'to keep them out of trouble'?

The use of psychiatric drugs to make the elderly more manageable in care homes is of course commonplace. A 1986 study of 2,000 US pharmacies discovered that 76% of prescriptions written for nursing home residents over 65 were tranquillisers. 60% of these called for heavy tranquillisers such as Thorazine.[233] This is all the more appalling when one learns that 73,000 US elderly die every year from adverse drug reactions, interactions and medication errors.[234]

Seen as more socially acceptable, drugs replaced the need for applying the high-profile and reputation-destroying electroshock and psychosurgical alternatives to control the custodial cases. A global paradigm shift had occurred in society with the advent of new psychotropic substances. Gone now was the centuries-old, moral barrier that prevented society from solving its problems with mind-bending drugs. Now it was OK to prescribe psychotropics to patients with a free conscience. After all, this was cutting-edge medicine. And the patients had been diagnosed 'mentally ill' by professionals.

OVER THE RAINBOW
At the same time Thorazine was being trumpeted to the world as the answer to man's cerebral woes, another substance was being investigated in a laboratory. The compound was first synthesised by Swiss chemist Albert Hoffman of Sandoz Laboratories in 1938, who was studying the hallucinogenic properties of the rye fungus 'ergot'. Hoffman's

---

[233] Masterson, Mike & Chuck Cook, "Mentally sound given psychiatric drugs", *The Arizona Republic*, 26th June 1988
[234] *Journal of the American Medical Association*, Vol. 284, 26th July 2000, publishes collective data for iatrogenic death in the US; also Kohn L, ed, Corrigan J, ed, Donaldson M, ed. "To Err Is Human: Building a Safer Health System", Washington, DC: National Academy Press; 1999. This report highlights 106,000 deaths in the US brought about by 'non-error, negative effects of drugs' – in other words, correct drug prescribing.

revolutionary new kaleidoscopic trip was to skew the perceptions of an entire generation to come.

Ergot had been investigated for its role in the medieval mass delusions, referred to as 'St Anthony's Fire', which would periodically blanket unsuspecting villages and towns, and madness would reign for several days. In Salem, Massachusetts, the famous 'bewitching' episodes resulted in the lynchings and deaths of 'witches', who had apparently caused the episodes with their vindictive spells. Was this another example of ergot poisoning?

After some non-conclusive testing, Hoffman shelved his substance, until in 1943, he accidentally absorbed a minute dose through his fingertips:

"Soon [I] felt a remarkable but not unpleasant state of intoxication, characterised by an intense stimulation of the imagination and an altered state of awareness of the world.... As I lay in a dazed condition with eyes closed, there surged up from me a succession of fantastic, rapidly changing imagery of a striking reality and depth, alternating with a vivid, kaleidoscopic play of colours. This condition gradually passed off after about three hours." [235]

Hoffman named the 25th permutation of the series 'lysergic acid diethylamide', or LSD-25.

Werner Stoll, president of Sandoz, was the first to consider the compound for psychiatric use, even the compound was already known to produce 'a transitory psychotic disturbance' in normal subjects. [236] It wasn't long before psychiatrists were obtaining samples of the drug for their own experimentation, combining psychoanalysis with LSD to get their patients to 'open up'. [237] The CIA too began to take an interest in *"...psychiatric reports suggesting that LSD could break down familiar behaviour patterns, for this raised the possibility of reprogramming or brainwashing."* [238]

---

[235] Lee, Martin A & Bruce Shlain, *Acid Dreams, The CIA, LSD and the Sixities Rebellion*, Grove Press, New York: 1985, p. xiv
[236] Ibid, p.20
[237] Ibid.
[238] Ibid.

Extensive funding was made available by the Agency to these psychiatric researchers to continue their work. One institution involved was the federal Addiction Research Center in Lexington, Kentucky. Under the guidance of Dr Harris Isbell, inmates were offered the choice of reduced custodial sentences or 'recreational' drugs. Most chose Isbell's drugs, expecting to get the usual heroin or morphine. What none realised was that Isbell was also giving them the highly experimental LSD. According to John Marks, author of *The Search for the Manchurian Candidate*, Isbell kept seven men on LSD trips for 77 days straight. One teenager reported later that he had tried the drug just once and had hallucinated and suffered with nightmarish, demonic visions for 17 hours. Isbell is also reported to have tested other unproven drugs from the CIA and National Institute for Mental Health upon inmates ignorant of the name or probable side-effects of the chemicals.[239] The later head of the National Institute of Mental Health, Robert Felix, had, perhaps coincidentally, served at the Lexington research centre before the war.

Canada's Dr Ewen Cameron, former President of the American Psychiatric Association, was particularly taken with the potential of 'acid', regularly using LSD, in combination with electroshock, in his attempts to 'depattern' his paying patients. Cameron had ironically been one of the psychiatric consultants working for the Nuremberg war tribunal and its much-publicised new Nuremberg Code, which he would later cynically violate with his bizarre and dangerous mind-control experimentations.

The Eli Lilly Company, manufacturer of today's Prozac, allegedly obtained the formula for LSD with the help of the CIA and boasted that the drug would soon be available in tonnage quantities. LSD, according to researcher Beverly Eakman, became something of a lark for CIA staff:

"At one dinner for Agency colleagues, Dr Sidney Gottlieb, head of MK-ULTRA, is said to have announced to the guests that he had slipped something special in the dessert. One of those guests, Dr Frank Olsen, had to be hospitalized and hurled himself from his hospital window. A 1954 memo surfaced from the internal security department quite seriously requesting that Agency staff stop putting LSD in the punch bowl at the office Christmas party." [240]

---

[239] Marks, John, *The Search For The Manchurian Candidate*, Time Books, New York: 1979, p.63
[240] Eakman, Beverly, *Cloning of the American Mind*, op. cit. p.226

UCLA psychiatrist Louis Jolyon 'Jolly' West was hired by the CIA as part of MK-ULTRA. West was to become notorious with his own experimentation, earning the infamous reputation of being the only person to kill an elephant with LSD.

But it was in the realm of open society that LSD, along with other psychiatric drugs, would have their most devastating and lasting impact. When Harvard psychologist and pop-culture guru Timothy Leary, a devoted follower of the infamous Crowley, publicised his own use of LSD with drug mystic Aldous Huxley in the early 1960's to expand 'self' and reign as one with the universe, an endlessly curious, 'newly-liberated' society listened with rapt fascination as Leary invited them to *"tune in, turn on and drop out."* LSD became a favourite in the arts. Pop artists such as Donovan, Paul McCartney, Keith Richards, Eric Clapton and others were introduced to the drug. Key musical events, later popularised around the world, were flooded with LSD. Among the crowds at the 1967 Monterey California Pop Festival and 1969's Woodstock, the pushers went quietly about their work, enthusiastically urging their customers to 'live life to the full' and 'trip out'. *Life* magazine even ran articles promoting LSD after the magazine's publisher, Henry Luce, experimented with the drug. One March 1963 article had even claimed LSD was *"...derived from a natural product."*

ALDOUS HUXLEY

Aldous Huxley, who had 'obtained' a professorship at the Massachusetts Institute of Technology (MIT), wrote prolifically of his trip experiences on LSD. Huxley's hallucinogenic experiences with Dr Humphrey Osmond became the basis of the former's book, *The Doors of Perception*, believed to have been the inspiration behind the name of Jim Morrison's band 'The Doors'. Huxley later tripped with former US Treasury Agent and Mafia confidante Alfred 'Cappy' Hubbard. Their experiences were reported in Huxley's widely acclaimed *Heaven and Hell*. Hubbard had obtained 6,000 bottles of LSD from Sandoz Laboratories which he handed out to friends and family members. One bottle ended up with Los Angeles psychiatrist Dr Oscar Janiger, who found a great reception for it with the Hollywood set.

144

The drug experiences Huxley, Crowley, Jung and other 'mystics' had described were popularised in cheap paperback editions of their works which found their way into the countercultures of Berkeley and Stanford Universities and into the hippie communes all over the world. In spite of Huxley perishing while 'tripping' in 1963, the new drug culture had arrived to stay. And psychiatry had been the one to introduce it.

PSYCHIATRY
- THE SOCIAL IMPACT -

Brilliant Cure But We Lost the Patient
The Psychiatric Assault on Hollywood and the Famous

Psychiatry's philosophies and treatments were to wreak their far-reaching effects in the areas of pop-culture, mass entertainment, media, religion and the family. Hollywood and the arts industry became rapidly infected and seduced with the new 'mental health' ethos, which brought with it its rebellion against law, order and religion. Language later found itself peppered with 'getting my head together', 'doing my head in', 'love and peace, dude', 'freaking out', 'far out, man' and 'chill'.

In the early decades of the 20th century, Los Angeles storefronts, Hollywood parlours and Santa Monica boardwalk shacks advertised psychoanalysis and tarot readings. Hollywood was getting spiritual, but quite what spirit it was getting was not to become immediately apparent.

Freud's sexual philosophies and Freud himself achieved cult status among the film-set, Samuel Goldwyn from Metro-Goldwyn-Meyer (MGM) even tediously sailing to Europe in 1924 in an attempt to persuade Freud to assist in creating 'a really great love story'. Freud declined.

CCHR reports: *"As early as 1922, we see an actor resembling a psychiatrist setting up key scenes in 'The Man Who Saw Tomorrow', a silent film in which the hero goes to a psychiatrist/mesmerist to find out which of two women he should marry. 'The Case of Becky' (1921) involved a 'nerve specialist' and 'One Glorious Day' has Will Rogers playing a 'mild-mannered psychology professor'. By 1925, there was a popular song entitled, 'Don't Tell Me What You Did Last Night, for I've Been Reading Freud.'"* [241]

The clever goal pursued by psychiatry was to increase its government funding and reputation with the public through positive portrayals of its 'philosophies' on the silver screen. In 1916, psychologist Hugo Münsterberg had penned *The Photoplay: A Psychological Study*, which clearly articulated psychiatry's newly discovered passion for the possibilities of the entertainment industry.

By 1940, the psychiatrist's many portrayals in movies had elevated the 'shrink' to a god-like status in the eyes of the public. Always the pipe-

---

[241] CCHR, *Psychiatry – Manipulating Creativity*, Los Angeles: 2002, p.7

149

smoking benevolent 'father', bestowing wisdom and chemicals into the ears and mouths of his 'children', the psychiatrist was in his element. The more extreme psychiatric treatments, such as Walter Freeman's famous icepick and the infamous Nazi electroshock, were all but absent from a Saturday night's cinema and TV fare. And the strategy was wildly successful. National Institutes of Health (NIH) grants for psychiatric research alone in America rocketed from under $10 million in 1957 to around $50 million by 1963 - an increase of 580% in just six years. Between 1963 and 1995, the funding exploded almost 900% from $60 million to just under $1 billion.

In 1939, *Blind Alley* portrayed a Dr Shelby remonstrating on the thin line between sanity and madness. The year before, *Carefree* had explored the sexual connection between the psychiatrist and his patient, with Fred Astaire playing the dancing doctor who falls for his patient, Ginger Rogers. Later movies, such as Elia Kazan's *Splendour in the Grass* (witty, omniscient psychiatrist helps Natalie Wood to 'get her head together'), and, of course, John Huston's *Freud*, starring Montgomery Clift, served almost to present the analyst as the saviour of mankind. *Pressure Point, David and Lisa* and *Tender is the Night* all propagated the psychiatrist as the authoritative voice of balance and reason. But the damage was already being wrought behind the scenes.

MARILYN MONROE
A young Norma Jean, caught up in the web of drugs and film industry pressures, turned to psychiatry to alleviate her problems. One of Marilyn's psychiatrists was Dr Marianne Kris, who received Monroe five days a week for therapy. Kris later prescribed the actress the powerful barbiturates that would eventually kill her. After a particularly nasty session, Kris committed Marilyn Monroe to a mental institution, where she was locked in a padded cell for two days. Monroe pounded the door hysterically until her hands bled. After her release, she fired Kris.

Dr Ralph Greenson was Monroe's psychiatrist in the final years. Still ensuring the actress remained on her barbiturates, Greenson increasingly began to take over the starlet's life, severing her connections with friends, and even her husband, baseball star Joe DiMaggio. The pretext was that familiarity would cause set-backs and prejudice the actress's recovery from the schizophrenia Greenson was publicly diagnosing as the reason for the starlet's absences. Towards the end, there is evidence Monroe had begun to realise the catastrophic effects the Svengalian Greenson was having on her life. She had made 23 films in the seven years prior to commencing therapy. Thereafter, she would complete a mere six films in the final seven years of her life. On 4th August 1962, after a six-hour therapy session with Dr Greenson, Marilyn Monroe was found by her housekeeper Eunice Murray, naked and sprawled across her silk sheets. Death had been delivered from Greenson's barbiturate bottle on her nightstand at the age of 36.

ROBERT WALKER

Hollywood star Robert Walker suffered from depression and heavy drinking following his separation from actress Jennifer Jones. In 1948, Walker was arrested for drunk and disorderly conduct and was given an ultimatum by MGM Studios head of production, Dora Schary. Submit to psychiatric therapy, or be fired.

After a short spell in the Menninger private psychiatric hospital, Walker took up treatment with Hollywood's 'psychiatrist to the stars', Frederick Hacker. On 28th August 1951, Walker went into shock and died after taking barbiturates while intoxicated.

VIVIEN LEIGH

Hollywood actress Vivienne Leigh's hysterical outbursts were well known in the industry. After filming of *Elephant Walk* in Ceylon was constantly interrupted by Leigh's frequent losses of control, wanderings in the night and hallucinations (widely believed to be caused by a combination of her TB medication and heavy drinking), her husband, film legend Laurence Olivier, became concerned for her mental well-being, and repeatedly pleaded with the actress to 'seek help'.

Vivien was persuaded to be flown to England for 'treatment' at the Netheren psychiatric hospital. Her treatments included being packed in ice, a diet of raw eggs and repeated electroshocks. Olivier naturally noticed her change in personality. While being treated on location as an outpatient in Warsaw, she performed with a splitting headache. Burn marks from the electroshock were visible on her head.

Oliver finally divorced her in despair in 1960. Even though it was widely recognised that physical illness can produce psychiatric-like symptoms, Vivien Leigh's long-running tuberculosis was relegated in favour of her psychiatrists continuing to diagnose the Hollywood star with various mental disorders. On 7th July 1967, after her TB had spread untreated to both lungs, Leigh was found lying on the floor. Choking on her own liquid, she had drowned.

ERNEST HEMMINGWAY

Believed to be another inevitably 'mentally tortured' genius, Pulitzer and Nobel Prize-winning author Ernest Hemmingway was given over 20 electroshocks by his psychiatrists to cure him of his 'mental illness'. After being released, Hemmingway was traumatised and extremely bitter:

"What these shock doctors don't know is about writers and such.... They should make all psychiatrists take a course in creative writing so they know about writers.... Well, what is the sense of ruining my head and erasing my memory, which is my capital, and putting me out of business? It was a brilliant cure, but we lost the patient...."[242]

In July 1961, just two days after leaving the famous Mayo psychiatric clinic, Papa Hemmingway put a shotgun barrel to his head and pulled the trigger.[243]

FRANCES FARMER

'Bad' Hollywood starlet Frances Farmer was always in trouble. High-spirited, rebellious, passionate and magnetically beautiful, Farmer was typical of many stars of that era who lived life in the fast lane. After her marriage to actor Leif Erickson failed, Farmer became increasingly unable to cope with her hectic schedule, turning to psychiatric amphetamines such as Benzedrine. Her constant drinking and fights soon landed her in court. After starring in the prophetically named *No Escape* in 1943, she was involved in a drunken brawl and arrested. Frances was placed into the custody of psychiatrist Thomas H Leonard, with whom she failed to co-operate. Leonard diagnosed her as *"suffering from manic-depressive psychosis – probably the forerunner of a definite dementia praecox"* – a diagnosis later described by doctors as 'pure gibberish'.

Farmer was transferred to the screen actor's sanitarium at La Crescenta, California, and subjected to a living nightmare under

---

[242] Hotchner, A E, *Papa Hemmingway*, Random House, New York: 1966, p.308-344
[243] Ibid.

psychiatric care. The Hollywood starlet was given at least 90 insulin shocks, finally escaping from the institution in terror. Her mother later signed a complaint against her and she was re-committed into custodial care in March 1944. At West Washington State hospital in Steilacoom, her psychiatrists gave her repeated ice baths and electroshock sessions in an effort to break her will. Finally, the subdued starlet was declared 'cured' and discharged.

Returning home disoriented and terrified, Farmer repeatedly ran away, believing she was going to be re-institutionalised. Her psychiatrists, stung by the media coverage Frances' escapes and failed rehabilitation were generating, contacted Farmer's mother and the actress was once more returned to Steilacoom and re-committed. Mental watchdog The Citizen's Commission on Human Rights (CCHR) reports:

"Conditions [in Steilacoom] *were barbaric. Both criminals and the mentally retarded were crowded together, their meals thrown on the floor to be fought over. Farmer was subjected to regular and continuous electroshock. In addition, she was prostituted to soldiers from the local military base and raped and abused by the orderlies. One of the most vivid recollections of some veterans of the institution would be the sight of Frances Farmer being held down by the orderlies and raped by drunken gangs of soldiers. She was also used as an experimental subject for drugs such as Thorazine, Stelazine, Mellaril and Proxilin."* [244]

One of the last psychiatrists to visit Farmer was Dr Walter Freeman. Farmer's biographer William Arnold describes what happened:

---

[244] *Psychiatry – Manipulating Creativity*, CCHR booklet, Los Angeles: 2002, p.35

"The tormented actress was held before him. He put electrodes to her temples and gave her electroshock until she passed out. Then he lifted her left eyelid and plunged the icepick-shaped instrument under her eyeball and into her brain. [After doing a number of other patients, Freeman left. William Keller, the superintendent of the hospital, had walked out, sickened]. *An hour later, Keller returned to the operating theatre and found everyone gone. He walked into the anteroom and looked at the post-operative patients resting on cots. One woman was silently weeping and several others were staring blankly at the ceiling. Near one end of the row of patients was Frances Farmer. She would no longer exhibit the restless, impatient mind and the erratic, creative impulses of a difficult and complex artist. She would no longer resist authority or provoke controversy. She would no longer be a threat to anyone."* [245]

The movie *Frances* was made of her life in 1982, starring another leading Hollywood actress, Jessica Lange. Frances Farmer died at the age of 57, broken, tortured and destitute.

JUDY GARLAND

Instantly recognised for her undeniable star quality and beautiful singing voice, the angelic Judy was known to the whole world after *The Wizard of Oz*. In Gerald Frank's biography, *Judy*, we learn that Garland was bound by a clause in her contract which stated that should her singing voice fail, or her body-shape change inordinately, she could be suspended without pay.

It wasn't long before the starlet was acquainting herself with psychiatric drugs such as Benzedrine and Phenobarbital to control her appetite and weight. As demand for her talents grew, Garland often couldn't sleep. The side-effects of her medications soon became apparent. Swinging like a pendulum between exhaustion and high anxiety, Garland was soon on a 'cocktail' of downers and uppers to assist her in fulfilling the demands of her acting schedule.

Judy had read Freud and consulted with famous psychiatrist Karl Menninger who told her 'she had problems; they could become serious, she needed help.' Menninger was one of a group of psychiatrists who were attracted to Hollywood actors and actresses for the renown, the referrals they could garner, and of course, the big pay cheques. Garland fell into the

---

[245] Arnold, William, *Shadowland*, McGraw-Hill Book Co., New York: 1978, as quoted in *Psychosurgery*, by Joann Rodgers, p.39

hands of 'psychiatrist to the stars', Frederick Hacker, who had 'treated' Robert Walker.

Hooked on Dexedrine and Seconals, experiencing hallucinations, shortness of breath and, later, suicidal tendencies, Garland used barbiturates as tranquillisers and amphetamines as stimulants. Gradually, the drugs and the pressure began to take their physical toll. Caught up in the frightening spiral of the cure becoming the sickness, becoming the cure, becoming the sickness, Judy committed herself to a psychiatric institution under advice from Hacker.

In 1949, not even yet 27 years old, Garland was given repeated electroshocks, later becoming a patient at the Peter Bent Brigham Hospital to recuperate. Despite a fabulous comeback to the theatre in 1951 in New York, Garland was stung by media speculation about her ballooning weight. Once again she turned to amphetamines to control her appetite.

By the end of the 1950's, Garland was in serious trouble and returned to hospital. She was placed on Thorazine, Valium and Ritalin. By 1968, she was hallucinating and suffering from rage, anxiety, suicidal tendencies, disturbed thinking and perception distortions. By the time Judy performed on stage for the final time the following year in Greenwich Village, New York, she was taking up to 40 Ritalin tablets a day and drinking heavily. On 21st June 1969, six days later, the tormented starlet died of a drugs overdose in a London hotel.

LENA ZAVARONI

The famous British child star had been struggling with anorexia for 22 years. In September 1999, after years of psychotherapy, anti-depressants and electroshock treatment had failed, she was admitted to the University Hospital of Wales at Cardiff for a lobotomy. In spite of warnings that the discredited operation could destroy her intellect, erase parts of her memory and change her character, Lena and her family persuaded themselves that it was for the best. After all, Britain's most skilled 'brain surgeons' would be presiding. Bob Burrows, a spokesman for the hospital, pointed out to the *London Times* that the operation was performed using the latest cutting-edge technology:

"We are one of the UK's premier teaching hospitals and at the leading edge of research and medical technology. Miss Zavaroni came to

Cardiff because we are one of the few centres in the world that carry out this operation." [246]

Lena died of a chest infection two weeks after the operation. She weighed just 49 lbs.

TUNING THE PUBLIC LIKE A STRADIVARIUS

Undeniably, Hollywood has been a key influence in the re-education of the public's perceptions of fear, sex, religion, morals accountability and horror – with predictably atrocious results. After the Cuban missile crisis, the 1960's saw an explosion of movies pushing an 'apocalypse'. The public of course has been familiarised with nuclear Armageddon ever since American children were taught how to 'duck and cover' in their classroom during the 1950's and '60's in case of a Russian missile strike. Popular trash-fiction both in the movies and on bookstore shelves has since painted various scenarios involving wide-eyed, often religious 'paranoid' extremists brought to their own point of mental critical mass, flicking off the nuclear safeties in leather-bound briefcases and setting the timer with those flashing, red digits. Pigeons clatter out of a crowded city park. Children lick their ice-creams. The eyeball-searing flash. Forty city blocks vaporise in the space of a passing moment.

Since the break-up of the Soviet Union, fissionable material from that nation's nuclear stockpiles, we are told, has apparently 'gone missing' over the years, bringing on the likelihood of weapons of mass destruction falling into the hands of minority elements. The movie-going public is already conditioned to accept this as a grim 'reality', through movies such as *Broken Arrow, True Lies, Melt Down* and *Peacemaker*. The world's predicament vis à vis nuclear terrorism is amply described by a character in the latter movie, who intones: *"I'm not frightened by the man who wants ten nuclear weapons, I'm terrified by the man who only wants one."*

Has this fostered an attitude of 'Let's Live For Today, for Tomorrow We Die' in our societies? Do we believe that the world is going to hell in a hand-basket? Can Big Government and its envoys possibly save us from Middle East catastrophe or thermonuclear annihilation?

---

[246] Bale, Joanna, "Zavaroni had lobotomy to cure anorexia", *The Times,* London: 4th October 1999

PROTOCOL #9 (EXTRACT) EXPOSED 1905

It is from us that the all-engulfing terror proceeds. We have in our service persons of all opinions, doctrines, restorating monarchists, demagogues, socialists, communists, and utopian dreamers of every kind. We have harnessed them all to the task: each one of them on his own account is boring away at the last remnants of authority, is striving to overthrow all established form of order. By these acts all States are in torture; they exhort to tranquillity, are ready to sacrifice everything for peace. But we will not give them peace until they openly acknowledge our international Super-Government, and with submissiveness.

If psychiatry is really trying to safeguard our mental health by removing all vestiges of 'stress', then why are the movie censor boards so transparently incompetent?

SILENT WEAPONS ASSAULTS ON GOVERNMENTS
Protocol #14 (extract) Exposed 1905

<u>*In countries known as progressive and enlightened we have created a senseless, filthy abominable literature*</u> [tabloid newspapers, gossip magazines, movies and pop-pornography].... *Our philosophers will discuss all the shortcomings of the various beliefs of the goyim, but no one will ever bring under discussion our faith from its true point of view* [Luciferianism], *since this will be fully learned by none save ours, who will never dare betray its secrets.*

Bruce Wiseman: *"As* [my] *book is being written, we took a sampling of subject matter from the week's television schedule:*
> - *Beverly Hills 90210: 'Donna and Kelly scour the campus for men to pose for their calendar; Steve learns the fraternity president is gay.'*
> - *Babylon 5: A Centauri slave seduces Londo for information that could destroy him.'*
> - *In the Heat of the Night: 'Bubba races to Atlanta to care for his nephew, who has overdosed on drugs.'*
> - *Melrose Place: 'Sydney takes over jailed Lauren's escort business....'"*[247]

A sampling by this author of the current week's TV fare in the UK reveals a startling conglomeration you wouldn't believe unless you read it. A documentary on live sex acts occurring in Ibiza nightclubs, young female

---

[247] Wiseman, Bruce, op. cit. p.22

holidaymakers taking part while their admiring mothers look on. Drunken brawls and gratuitous violence at British and European football matches. A British father rapes his own daughter and then murders her. The *Sopranos*, where a troubled Mafiosi visits his sexually alluring psychiatrist in between frank psychotic episodes, during which people die messily. And, of course, *Buffy The Vampire Slayer*, featuring demons, ghouls, decapitations and schoolgirls in short skirts and little white socks.

BLOCKBUSTER DEMONS

A trip down to the local video store, and the clerk advises us of some of their best-selling videos of all time: *Communion,* by Whitley Streiber, a best-selling book and popular movie, detailing a number of harrowing abduction accounts apparently involving Streiber and depraved extraterrestrials. Streiber in an interview gives an interesting description of his experiences at the mercy of one of his 'highly advanced' tormentors:

"Increasingly I felt as if I were entering a struggle for my soul, my essence, or whatever part of me might have reference to the eternal. There are worse things than death, I suspected. And I was beginning to get the distinct impression that one of them had taken an interest in me. So far the word 'demon' had never been spoken among the scientists and doctors who were working with me. And why should it have been? We were beyond such things. We were a group of atheists and agnostics, far too sophisticated to be concerned with such archaic ideas as demons and angels.

... I felt an absolutely indescribable sense of menace. It was hell on Earth to be there, and yet I couldn't move, couldn't cry out and get away. I lay as still as death, suffering inner agonies. Whatever was there seemed so monstrously ugly, so filthy and dark and sinister. Of course they were demons. They had to be. And they were here and I couldn't get away. I couldn't save my poor family. I still remember that thing crouching there, so terribly ugly, its arms and legs like the limbs of a great insect, its eyes glaring at me." [248]

ATTRACTIVE MEAT

How many parents around the world now share the worries of anxious mum, Yasmin Alibhai-Brown?

---

[248] Streiber, Whitley, *Communion*, Beech Tree, William Morrow, New York: 1987

"My daughter turns nine next month and all I feel is foreboding... a pulsating, loud panic which seems to be driving out pleasure.... The awesome changes in her face, body, language and personality, the anticipation of a spring birthday party and the relief that we have spent another year together – all reasons to be grateful – seem unable to divert me away from the persistent, thumping fear that my daughter, incredibly innocent still, is about to enter an increasingly sordid popular culture.

Powerful, immoral people will manipulate her desires and appetites and turn her into a needy, restless little soul who will be made to feel she is nothing unless she looks like Britney [Spears]. Not long after that, I imagine, she will be persuaded, by her also brainwashed peers, that there is something wrong with her if she hasn't had sex or if lusty boys don't find her attractive enough meat.

What kind of campaign needs to be directed at those advertisers, broadcasters, celeb peddlers, newspapers, magazines, pop stars and others who have made this carnal hell for our young ones, and who still insist that none of this has anything to do with them?" [249]

HOLLYWOOD BEHAVING BADLY

Thousands of entertainment productions released each year promote rebellion against the family order, apostasy, worldliness, rebellion against religion and, ultimately, through the worship of violence, sex and disobedience, rebellion against structured society. Some serials in the UK for example, which continually focus on these themes are 'serial' offenders: *Eastenders, Brookside, Neighbours, Friends, Buffy the Vampire Slayer, Men Behaving Badly, Father Ted, Married with Children, Absolutely Fabulous*, and so on. How about *Star Trek?* For example, the episode when Kirk and his intrepid crew go off in search of God and ultimately find him as they gaze up at a projection of themselves?

Films like the *Lion King, Mad Max, the Terminator, the Devil's Advocate* and *Beauty and the Beast* are all about teaching children to accept the 'morality of violence' and to 'love the beautiful side of evil'. The poster of *Beauty and the Beast* depicts a devil figure holding out a rose. The poster for Al Pacino's *The Devil's Advocate* has the caption, *"Evil Has Its Winning Ways."*

---

[249] Alibhai-Brown, Yasmin, "The powerful and immoral people who want to brainwash my lovely daughter", *Daily Mail*, 19th March 2002, p.12

In the movie *The Silence of the Lambs*, cannibalistic psychiatrist, Hannibal Lecter, portrayed by Anthony Hopkins, astutely admonishes Jodie Foster's FBI officer Clarice Starling for pathologising his wickedness: *"Nothing happened to me, Officer Starling. I happened. You can't reduce me to a set of influences. You've given up good and evil for behaviourism, Officer Starling. You've got everyone in moral dignity pants – nothing is ever anybody's fault. Look at me, Officer Starling. Can you stand to say I'm evil?"*

In his book *The Death of Satan*, author Andrew Delbanco addresses the issue of the 'un-naming of evil' with a change of vocabulary. Vance Packard, the author of numerous works on subliminal advertising, makes the observation in his book *Hidden Persuaders* that, in order to gain the moral/political/philosophical high ground in a given debate, your chances of gaining that ground are improved considerably by pre-empting the opening vocabulary. Delbanco discusses that, until quite recently, society had a clearly defined idea of 'moral evil'. Today, the words 'moral', 'sin', 'ethics' and 'evil' are constantly sneered at, and thus have all but disappeared from the language. Yet never has 'evil' been more abundant and ubiquitous in our cultures. The problem is, as Delbano writes, *"...we feel something that our culture no longer gives us the vocabulary to express."*

Examples of films and programs featuring themes which describe the destruction of the family and nation, as well as rebellion against traditional morality are: *Cape Fear* (with all those Bible quotes tattooed on the arms of de Niro's psychopathic killer), *Pulp Fiction, From Dusk Till Dawn,* and all 'Zoo Media' (the 'talk' shows of Jerry Springer, Oprah, Ricki Lake, Geraldo, etc.) Walk through a video shop and see for yourself the onslaught that is coming against you and your children.

Other films push religious 'Messiah' themes, such as *The Day the Earth Stood Still* (the ET is handsome and his name is Carpenter [Jesus]), *ET* (Grays as gods), and television series such as *V* and *The Intruders* (mate with a reptile and produce a magical child who'll save the world) play against Streiber's *Communion* (these things are nasty, but you can't help but love them) and *Fire From the Sky* (these things are nasty, and you can't help but fear them)." [250]

---

[250] Wallace, Wendy, *Four Horsemen of the Apocalypse*, op. cit.

In 1976, the number of reported child abuse cases in America was 670,000. By the early '90's, this figure had risen to nearly 3 million. Trashy teen magazines and social-climber periodicals across the world deify sex, promiscuity, adultery, drunkenness and the occult. Drug abuse is now so widespread in the world's cities and towns that when the Metropolitan Police in London randomly searched a large cross-section of club-goers in the King's Cross area in July 1998, 100% of them were found to be carrying, or under the influence of illegal drugs.

Undeniably, we in the western world have been spoiled by 50 years of uninterrupted peace and prosperity, having turned a de-sensitised, blind eye to just about every atrocity man is capable of committing, including Bosnia, Cambodia and the barbaric Rwanda, where 1 million are slaughtered in 100 days with machetes and other agricultural implements under the watchful eye of the UN.

We have become a nation of victims, whiners, sex-obsessed porn consumers, lottery addicts, materialistic sluggards, Jerry Springer worshippers and cry-baby vacillators with a collective attention-span of a laboratory amoeba. 25% of the movies rented in the US in 1998 were pornographic. *Christ for Nations Magazine* reports that *"In Washington D.C., within blocks of the Department of Justice, there are 37 'adult' bookstores, 8 X-rated theatres and 15 topless bars."* A published Pentagon telephone audit showed that $300,000 of taxpayers' money had been spent on 1(900) sex lines.

And while the polluting of the arts continues unabashed, in the name of free expression and the First Amendment, so does the torturing of its leading figures.

LIFESTYLES OF THE RICH AND FAMOUS

Many of the famous have owned up to needing drugs to get by. Singer Del Shannon (Charles Westover) thought the Prozac prescribed to him by his psychiatrist would *"...help me over the hump I'm in."* His wife LeAnne *"...watched him turn into somebody who was agitated, pacing, had trembling hands, insomnia and couldn't function."* On 8th February 1990, after taking Prozac for just 15 days, Charles Westover shot himself in the head with a .22 calibre rifle.

Princess Diana and Sarah Ferguson both admitted using the 'liquid sunshine' drug, Prozac, Diana becoming the subject of huge media speculation over her drug use. Royal author Andrew Morton's

161

controversial book, *Diana: Her New Life*, detailed her catastrophic mood-swings and alleged suicide attempt on board a royal flight, where she had attempted to slash her arms, smearing blood over the walls and seats before being restrained.[251]

Lady Brocket, Libby Purves, Al Pacino, Roseanne Barr and Mariella Frostrup are a few among many who have been some-time users of Prozac. INXS pop-frontman Michael Hutchence died in November 1997 in an apparent hanging suicide. His song-writing partner, Andrew Farriss, attributed the death to Prozac and alcohol. The actor and comedian Chris Farley died aged 33 after a four-day alcohol and drug binge. Prozac was present in his blood. Don Simpson, co-producer of Hollywood blockbusters such as *Beverly Hills Cop, Top Gun* and *Crimson Tide*, died in 1996 aged 52. Police searching Simpson's Bel Air estate in Los Angeles discovered thousands of tablets and pills lined up neatly in alphabetical order in his bedroom closet. They later discovered that Simpson had obtained over 15,000 psychiatric amphetamines, tranquillisers and sedatives from 15 doctors and 8 pharmacies. Steve Simmons, a senior investigator for the California Medical Board, stated:

"Everybody understands how lethal street drugs like heroin are, but it takes a prescription overdose by someone famous like Don Simpson to drive home the fact that pharmaceutical medications are just as deadly."[252]

POPULAR LITERATURE?

Elizabeth Wurtzel's book, *Bitch*, is one example among thousands of how popular literature continues to propagate the social revolt we are examining. The author's celebration of a life devoid of traditional values becomes a lament to spiritual abandonment and bondage. In *The London Times*, James Crowley (no relation) commences his review of Wurtzel's book as follows:

"...If she has a thesis, it is that women can find freedom only through aggressive self-assertion ['Girl Power']*, by wilfully flouting convention, by being entirely bad even. 'I intend to scream, shout... throw tantrums and confess intimate details about my life,' she writes. 'I intend to do what I want to do and be what I want to be and answer only to myself.' Can she be serious?"*

---

[251] "Di's Hooked on the Happy Drug", *Daily Record*, 7th November 1994, p.26
[252] "Buying Off the Drug Traffic Cop", *Freedom*, Vol.30, Issue 1, Los Angeles, CA

Crowley goes on to explain the downside to Wurtzel's rebellion: *"Wurtzel has certainly embraced the dark side. 'Prozac Nation'* [her previous novel] *told of her battles with depression and drug abuse, of her suicide attempt and chaotic sexuality and of the misery of a Manhattan childhood marred by her parents' messy divorce.... Over lunch, Wurtzel told me that she was indeed miserable. Her twenties were, in effect, a chain of successes, a staff job on* The New Yorker *magazine, a best-selling book that defined the spirit of the age, fame and wealth* [traditionally Lucifer]. *'I have so much good fortune, and everything is so glorious, yet there's this shadow hanging over me. I just can't keep hold of this good feeling.'"*[253]

THE DOUBLE MIND – NON-ACCOUNTABILITY

We are a society that can moralise about rape, murder and sex abuse when we read about them in the newspapers, but have no problem accommodating the latest Quentin Tarantino rape, demon, murder and sex abuse movie advertised on the very next page. England wept like babies during the serial run of the program *Hearts of Gold*, seeing all those ordinary folk doing good deeds for one another, dissolving the nation into sentimental, sticky goo. But how long did the magic last? The following day it was 'Hearts of Lead' as we cussed out the kids, gobbled down the porridge and carved up the grannies on our mad dash into work.

The double mind is a form of collective social insanity avidly pushed by psychiatry through its beliefs. Once again, at a time in history when we deem ourselves the most civilised, mankind has become the most bestial (Hitler, Stalin, Mao, Pol Pot). But this time there's all that technology to help us 'up' the body count. We allow our governments to murder whomever they term the 'bad guys', so long as the case presented to us between football games is even half-convincing. Clinton smart-bombs an aspirin factory in Sudan to get the world off Monica Lewinsky. Saddam was our friend against the beastly Ayatollah in the Iran/Iraq war, but then becomes a beast himself in Desert Storm. Our consciences are never seared since the action is so remote we can take that remote and turn off the evidence when it threatens to upset our delicate dispositions. All we have to do to be free of the bad stuff is walk away from the TV, put the cat out, kiss little Tommy goodnight and turn off the bedroom light.

---

[253] *The London Times*, 21st May 1998

VIOLENCE AND TV

Television today is our staple source of information – and oh, how it educates us. The all-pervasive MTV videodrome beacons our children with 24 hours of near naked, sexual sado-masochism. By the time a child is 16, he will have seen 300,000 acts of gratuitous violence, torture, mutilation, suicide and murder on television and at the cinema. The Comedy Channel has us laughing at euthanasia, adultery, religion, blasphemy and death in a way that makes it all funnier than hell. Hollywood has taught us how to enjoy the 'buzz' of sin without the aggravation of accountability, in much the same way Richard McDonald showed us how to enjoy a Big Mac without the aggravation of the abattoir.

After being presented with five volumes of scientific data showing that sex and violence shown on TV and film had a significant affect on society, ABC executives issued a statement denying that televised imagery affected real-world behaviour in any way. Film critic Michael Medved responds, *"Now if ABC TV believes that, then it better start refunding billions of dollars in advertising revenues. Because if televised imagery does not affect real-world behaviour in any way, what are they doing selling ad time?"* [254]

Once again, we see the double mind. How about the following British tabloid editorial:

Wrecked Lives

"There's one thing at which we [Britain] *DO lead the world. And we should hang our heads in shame: Britain has the highest rate of unmarried teenage mothers - nine times worse than Japan. Why is Britain so different? Not because we don't teach children about contraception. Just the opposite – <u>we teach them too much and in the wrong way</u>.*

The more sexually aware our children become at too early an age, the more they are tempted. Tragically, it has become unfashionable to drum into children the word 'No'. We are paying the price in wrecked lives." [255]

---

[254] Medved, Michael, *Hollywood: License to Kill*, a video presentation, American Portrait Films, PO Box 19266 Cleveland, OH 44119 U.S.A. (800) 736-4567
[255] *The Sun*, 15th May 1998

And this from *The Sun* newspaper on page 8. Turn back five pages and you will see the daily, half-page photograph of a teenage girl stripped to the waist in a provocative pose, earning some pin-money as the latest 'model' to break onto the national scene. Is *The Sun* doing its bit to prevent our youth from being sexually tempted? Hardly. But such hypocritical rubbish passes us by without a blink.

There used to be a time when if we fell off our bike, we'd just pick ourselves up, dust down and carry on as if nothing had happened. Today when we get slam-dunked by some appalling stroke of 'fate' such as wanton debt, an illicit affair or a Prozac or Valium dependency, we slip into the 'victim' jacket and seek out the nearest shrink, support group, astrologer or Feng Shui advisor. And these are only too happy to oblige with the latest inside scoop, pocketing our money and reassuring us it's nothing WE did, it's just that society's a dog, the new moon's in the 11th house and the furniture's all in the wrong place.

The double mind. A mind profoundly at war with itself and ignorant even of that fact.

PROTOCOL #5 (EXTRACT) EXPOSED 1905
The principal object of our directorate consists of this: to debilitate the public mind by criticism; to lead it away from serious reflections calculated to arouse resistance; <u>to distract the forces of the mind towards this sham fight of empty eloquence.</u>

<u>*In order to put public opinion into our hands, we must bring it into a state of bewilderment by giving expression from all sides to so many contradictory opinions and for such length of time as will suffice to make the goyim lose their heads in the labyrinth and come to see that the best thing is to have no opinion of any kind…, which it is not given to the public to understand.*</u>

THE HUMAN TRINITY - ME, MYSELF AND I
And what of religion? Today our religion is the religion of the 'me' and our god is gold.[256] Once we had churches, now we have glass cathedral malls decked out with all the latest retail outlets to satisfy that inner spiritual yearning. Once we went to church on Sundays to worship with the family. Today on Sundays we take the family to worship at Nordstrom's, Top Shop and Harvey Nicks. Instead of being given a song

---

[256] Psalms 135:15-18

sheet at the door we are given a loyalty card application. Instead of lining up at the altar rail for communion, we queue impatiently at the check-out. Instead of leaving our sins at the feet of Christ, we heave our shopping into the trunk of our Chryslers. We worship our Harley Davidsons instead of our heavenly David's Son. Laughingly we celebrate our greed with our sons instead of ashamedly confessing it before THE Son. We cry in anger at the cost of spirits instead of weeping in thanks for what we cost the Spirit.

Most American four-year-olds think their name is Jesus H Christ. Most of our dogs think they are illegitimate. Most adults will tell you Genesis is an English rock band, hell a pharmacy sold out of Viagra and Deuteronomy one of those two-humped camels. When did 'slain in the spirit' become the new Smirnoff commercial? When did Los Angeles become the New Jer**USA**lem? Was it about the same time the world figured out a magician's wand was made of holly wood? Was it then that the new Magic Kingdom was created?

Today you no longer need to watch TV, you can date one; you no longer have to drink Coke, you can snort it; you no longer marry the heroine, you can free-base her. When we contemplate divorce, we're so hardened, our only definition of 'a crying shame' is a plane full of lawyers crashing and burning with two empty seats. Forget the kids. Our teenage boyz don't know whether to lead or follow on the dance-floor; our teenage gurlz are obscene and not heard. With divorce proceedings going out at $300 an hour and half their worldly estate, have married men come to the conclusion that the cheapest sex is the sex they can pay for?

By the way, does God really look like George Burns in a baseball cap, or was Darwin right and God is just a doG who evolved... backwards? Bill Gates, can you open the 2,000 Windows of your Internet heaven so I can sneak inside and have a Word? Rupert Murdoch, thank you for your digital TV revolution. Now we have a porn channel for every psalm:

THE TWENTY-THIRD CHANNEL
The TV is my shepherd,
I shall not want,
It makes me lie down on the sofa,
It leads me away from the faith,
It destroys my soul,
It leads me in the path of sex and violence
For the sponsor's sake (Psa 5:6; 11:5).

Yea, though I walk
In the shadow of Christian responsibilities,
There will be no interruption,
For the TV is with me,
Its cable and remote,
They comfort me.
It prepares a commercial for me
In the presence of all my worldliness.
It anoints my head with
Humanism and consumerism,
My coveting runneth over.
Surely laziness and ignorance
Shall follow me
All the days of my life.
And I shall dwell in the house
Watching TV forever.

THE BOULEVARD OF BROKEN DREAMS

But what of those fuelling the TV and film revolution? How many
Hollywood actors and actresses bought into Freud's sex and drugs magick,
and had their careers wrecked and lives destroyed as a result? Maybe
Sunset Boulevard could be lined with its own memorial plaques as a
tribute to the lives of those whose profligate careers helped to fuel the new
hedonism by dynamiting the pillars of society's moral temperance. Studio
chiefs, lawyers, financiers, and the bewildering list of ancillary workers in
the film industry, from directors to best boys, from cameramen to make-
up artists - so much creativity; so much desire to please the public and
make the shows with the greatest talents in the world. But how many of
these lives were wrecked and on the rocks after drugs, sex and rock 'n roll
herded them into the sheep-pens of psychiatry, which believed it could
control the 'creative insanity of the artist'?

This writer lived in Los Angeles for many years and saw firsthand,
through his friends, contacts and work assignments, the drug tortures and
emotional pressures many live with in the film industry. And always just
in the background, or around the next palm-treed corner in Beverly Hills,
Miracle Mile or West Hollywood, like barnacles attached to an ocean-
going liner, the ever-present industry of 'mental health advisors' cling on,
shiny plaques on doors, brows crinkled with the faint concern of the
consummate professional. Their prey, would-be actors and actresses
coming to town to make it big, folios stuffed full of bright celluloid and
happy faces, end up working menial jobs and scraping together what living
they can. More than a few end up drug and sex addicts in the pornographic

industry centred in Northridge, twenty-five miles to the north-west of Los Angeles.

Wonderful human beings who make up Hollywood, giants of their time, like the lives we have examined, are still somebody's son, someone's daughter. Over the years they have been forced to witness the shattering of their own innocence, the bankruptcy of their dreams, the destruction of their special talents and the systematic breaking of their health. Many died. Today, the mental mill is working as smoothly as ever. Today, as you read this, how many more regrettable 'mental' diagnoses will be made? How many more prescriptions are being scrawled out? How many more lives will be betrayed today by the very professionals who have offered them 'help' and set them on the path which will assure their destruction?

And what of the real sermon being preached into the world's living rooms today? The religion of apostasy and abandonment, as we shall see, *is* the core essence of Satanism. A newspaper cartoon depicts a man arriving in hell, faced with the devil and a TV. "Wow!" exclaims the man. "I didn't know there'd be TV down here."

The devil replies, "There's nothing but TV down here."

Gunning for the Young
The Psychiatric Assault on Pop-Culture

Easy access to moderately priced, 'street-cred' hallucinogenics and psychotropic substances, originally pioneered for use on the mentally ill, caused parents in the 1960's to watch with a powerless trepidation as their kids grew into teenagers. But there was definitely a spiritual element of rebellion too. Anxious fathers became aware that they were losing their children to another authority, one that allowed them to revolt and become part of a 'twilight' generation of semi-literate waifs hell-bent on disobedience, self-destruction and intoxication. Realising with despair that they were being viewed by their offspring as staid, old-fashioned and from another planet, parents paid their children's bail, lent them money expecting no repayment and fervently hoped they'd emerge again on the flip-side, like the astronauts around the dark side of the moon, after finishing with their angst-ridden teenage experimentation, free love and hurtful non-communication.

Parents adore their children and pray they won't hurt themselves. They put it down to a sign of the times. They rationalise that every teen has to go through this new phase: *"They'll grow out of it, let's just make sure they don't drink and drive and crunch up the family Ford."* But the surprising outcome of the 1960's was that this teenage 'counter-culture' soon became so much a part of everyday life that it became the mainstream, while those few paragon teens, who trod the straight and narrow of the old morality, themselves became déclassé.

The odds became stacked against the old concepts of 'doing good', 'abiding by the law' and 'righteousness living'. Around the world in the years that followed, MTV and VH1 would provide their teenagers with non-stop, 24-hour, mind-numbing, hypnotic rock and rap music, accompanied by videos ridiculing religion and morality, along with those who believed in and practised them. Madonna, the darling of world's teeny-bopper brigade, served up video after video of blasphemous imagery featuring half-naked bodies gyrating in sado-masochistic paraphernalia. In England, the cradle of the '60's spiritual rebellion, punk bands with no-hope names and aggressive attitude conditioned the impressionable into acid-fried, zombied carbon-copies of their favourite pop icons, with all the trappings, leather trimmings and body piercings to match. It wasn't the fifties anymore. A bricklayer from Manchester could now become the new pop prophet to millions.

ALEISTER CROWLEY'S POP MAJICK

It is perhaps the weighty irony of mortality that Aleister Crowley, ridiculed, pitied and largely ignored as a cranky eccentric while alive, posthumously became the 'patron saint' of rock stars, a demonic, legendary icon of the hedonistic society he had so accurately predicted in the 'channelled' pages of his *Book of the Law*. Modern music is literally peppered with accolades to Satan's right-hand man. Pseudo-Christian rocker Ozzy Osbourne who, in his chequered and meteoric rock career, is said to have bitten the head off a bat in front of an audience, defecated on stage and then eaten the proceeds, writes a hit song, entitled appropriately enough: *Mister Crowley*.

In an interview with *Hit Parade* magazine, Ozzy enlightens us: *"I don't know if I'm a medium for some outside source. Whatever it is, I do hope it's not what I think it is - Satan!"* [257]

Crowley shows up on album covers (Jim Morrison and the Beatles' Sergeant Pepper album), in lyrics, in eulogies; his catch-phrase for the New Age, *"Do what thou wilt shall be the whole of the law"*, is adopted by many teen role models, including TV psychologist Timothy Leary, John Lennon, Mercyful Fayth and funk star, Bobbie Brown. With this saying, Crowlianism espouses the Luciferian, Protocol philosophy of: 'your parents don't understand you. You have a right to live your life the way you choose. There is no right or wrong, just opinion. You are your own power. No restrictions, no holes barred, no obedience if it doesn't suit you.' Most of this rebellious attitude is familiar to parents; the very real, extra-dimensional, Luciferian energy driving it is not. For centuries, man recognised, through the religious model, that evil forces were constantly trying to gain the upper hand in their lives and that manifestations of what is described as 'demonic possession' were symptomatic of a rebellious society that had turned its back on God.[258] For many, certainly an extraordinary premise. But is this what is in fact occurring?

Doubtless rock and roll, gangsta rap and other modern music contain a spirit of rebellion; after all, this has always been part of their universal appeal to youngsters. Teenagers work hard at their naughtiness. They're proud of their iniquities and lawlessness. Hollywood celebrates them in its teen movies, bookstores lift them up in their trashy, ten-dollar novels, and

---

[257] *Hit Parade Magazine*, Feb 1975
[258] Ephesians 6:10-12

society practises them in the countless, mindless acts in which our youth engage during the early years of their lives. Surely we deserve some reward for all this effort we have honed into a blasphemous mockery of fine art? An effigy of Jesus Christ in a bowl of urine? Why stop there? As the posters for British comedian Dennis Pennis proudly proclaim above his gravestone, *"Rest in P*ss."*

This writer was himself a rock keyboard musician during his early twenties and knows well the social rebellion that stems from popular music. Clearly not all modern music is rebellious or demonic, and no one would seriously pretend so. But the connection between moral apostasy – a 'do what thou wilt' attitude - and Crowley's Satanic legacy, as we shall see, was to blaze a sinister trail through rock and roll, pop, rap, funk, punk, club music and the film and theatre industries, undeniably fuelling a most virulent global youth rebellion and commensurate breakdown in law and order throughout society. How do we know Crowley is responsible? Because he has left his signature phrases all over the works in question.

A WAR BETWEEN GOOD AND EVIL?

Once again, just as in times past, the often-flawed Christian Church was to find itself in direct confrontation with a bewilderingly aggressive and seemingly demonically motivated pop culture, progressively turning its back on traditional social morality and pursuing the hot and ready alternatives. That popular music was to concern religious leaders over and above many other facets of modern living seems not to have been coincidental or arbitrary. Legend and Christian church tradition hold that Lucifer was originally the First Angel, who led the worship of YAHWEH with music. If this were indeed the case, the Church reasoned, by what means would the Devil wish to subvert mankind's gift of salvation and redemption through Christ? Music.

ELVIS PRESLEY

Considered a rebel when he comes to fame, Elvis is undeniably viewed as the 'King of Rock and Roll'. Presley claims he has been possessed by a spirit from childhood. At first, he thinks it is his brother directing and guiding him. Later he admits that it isn't his brother. Larry Geller was Presley's hairdresser for many years. In his biography, *If I Can Dream*, Geller is forthright about aspects of Elvis' chronic drug-abuse and strange spirituality:

"In Elvis' mind his life was being directed divinely by the brotherhood of masters and illuminated beings - enlightened entities that

have existed since time immemorial. And he truly felt that he was chosen to be here now as a modern-day saviour - a Christ. Elvis didn't believe that Jesus was the only begotten Son of God. He believed all people had Christ within them and had the same potential."[259]

In the book *Elvis, What Happened?* written by a bodyguard, Elvis is portrayed as a man heavily committed to mind-altering drugs and the dark side of humanity. According to those closest to him, he owned hundreds of books on the occult. His main interest focuses on the writings of Satanist Helena P Blavatsky, whom he quoted at length to his audiences on occasions. In Geller's book, we learn that Elvis formed a back-up vocal trio he named 'The New Age Voice', after Blavatsky's *The Voice of Silence*. This name was later shortened to 'The Voice' to save room on billboards.

Elvis' contra-stance to the teachings of Jesus[260] can be seen in his attitude towards the Luciferian philosophy of self-redemption (*"Say unto thine own heart, I am my own redeemer." (Book of Satan. p.33)*). Wait a minute. Didn't Elvis sing gospel songs?

If I Can Dream
...as long as a man has the strength to dream
He can redeem his soul and fly.

And Jesus said to him, "I am the way, the truth and the life; no man comes to the Father but by me." (John 14:6)

Presley's subsequent depressions, provoking psychoanalysis sessions, drug and food abuses led to the passing of a unique and enduring talent. But 'The King's' final end was to become a tragic hallmark for those stars whose drug deaths would also, along with Presley's, prefigure Crowley's Golden New Age to come.

OTHER '50's STARS
Jerry Lee Lewis: While recording his hit *Great Balls of Fire*, Lewis repeatedly tells his producer he is demon-possessed.[261]

---

[259] Geller, Larry, *If I Can Dream. Elvis' Own Story,* Simon & Schuster, 1988
[260] Farmer, Paula, *Elvis Aaron Presley - His Growth and Development as a Soul Spirit Within the Universe,* Prime Books Inc. 1998
[261] Herman, Gary, *Rock and Roll Babylon,* Plexus Publishing, 2002

Little Richard: *"I was directed and commanded by another power. The power of darkness. The power you've heard so much about. The power people believe doesn't exist. The power of the devil. We must realise that there is a force that is fighting against us in this world... the devil was controlling our minds, directing our lives."* [262]

The top three rock stars of the 1950's, Elvis Presley, Jerry Lee Lewis and Little Richard, all admitted to chronic drug abuse, 'psychiatric disturbances' and demon possession. One can imagine the fertile ground these influences provided for the rampage that subsequently followed. Crowley predicts in *The Book of the Law* that the New Age of Antichrist will be ushered in on a wave of free sex, hallucinogenic drugs and music; that his philosophy of *"Do what thou wilt"* (do whatever you want) shall be *"the whole of the law"*. Crowley declares this in 1904. Was this in fact what eventually came to pass?

'HAIR'

The revolutionary *Hair* musical of Crowlian reactionaries Ragni, Rado and MacDermot hits the world stage in the '60's. Its message, *This is the Age of Aquarius,* becomes the cry of the New Age drug-takers, or 'hippies'. Some of them who are familiar with Christianity see Jesus as the teacher of the Piscean (fish) Age. But now a new teacher is required for the New Age of Aquarius. And from beyond the grave, Crowley is happy, through his teachings, to announce the unhinging of Christianity and the coming of just such a teacher, the Antichrist, whose way must be prepared by his people.

Hair features its anti-heroes in eclectic Greenwich Village, New York City. Claude opens the prologue, seated before an altar and Lucifer's flame. Berger, Sheila, Wolf and Hud are other characters, forming part of 'The Tribe'. The Tribe calls for *Oh, Great God of Power.* They don't get God, but Claude in an evolution monkey suit. The anti-Vietnam *Hair* brings the paradoxical mix of eastern mysticism and rebellion to the fore. Incense, smoking grass, taking psychiatric drugs, orgies and the burning of Vietnam draft cards. One song in particular takes root:

Hare Krishna
Hare Krishna
Krishna, Krishna

---

[262] Schimmel, Joe, *Rock and Roll Sorcerers of the New Age Revolution,* a video presentation, Fight the Good Fight, Simi Valley, CA: 1993.

Hare, Hare, etc..

According to the rites of shamans, the 'power' of endlessly repeating such a verse is to invite possession by spirits or demons. Later in pop, George Harrison gets his followers to chant *My Sweet Lord* over and over, where the chorus sounds all Christian and before you know it, the lyrics change to *Hare Krishna.* Harrison himself admits this is done to deceive Christians.[263]

Crowley also developed a worship rite known as 'OTO'. It employed sodomy, either with a man or woman, as a magic ritual.[264] He taught it as a means of releasing self and attaining a higher consciousness. In the bestselling musical *Hair* we find the following song:

Sodomy
Sodomy, Fellatio
Cunnilingus
Masturbation can be fun
Join the holy orgy
Karma Sutra everyone

Later, *"The Tribe divides into groups to sleep under the light of the moon, and Sheila sings, "Good Morning, Starshine." A mattress is brought out, "The Bed", and the Tribe celebrates it (after all "Never can you sin in bed")"* [265] The 1960's cult of self-deification and moral abandonment.

The *Hair* album has sold in its millions. One of the other tunes sings of *"Me and Lucifer, Lucifer and Me"*. Other tracks include: *Hashish, Going Down, What a Piece of Work is Man* and *The Flesh Failures.* Perhaps the most ironic lines off the entire work are those spoken by a teacher-like figure to his class of children: *"You know, kids, I wish every mom and dad would make a speech to their teenagers and say, "Be free. Be whatever you want. Do whatever you want to do just so long as you don't hurt anybody." And remember, kids. I am your friend."*

---

[263] Schimmel, Joe, op. cit.
[264] Crowley, Aleister, *The Enochian World of Aleister Crowley: Enochian Sex Magick*, New Falcon, 1991
[265] Hair Pages, http://www.stanford.edu/~toots/Hair/hairsynopsis.html

JIMI HENDRIX

Billed as one of the greatest guitarists of all time, Hendrix becomes a hero to millions. Playing guitars with his teeth, smashing up his instruments and setting fire to them on-stage with voodoo rituals, are all part of the 'charm' of this prophet of music. Is Hendrix pushing the one-worldism, free sex, hallucinogenics, eastern mysticism and anarchical philosophies of Aleister Crowley? Right by the book. The album *Axis: Bold As Love* sets it all in motion. Hendrix's tracks include *Voodoo Child, Manic Depression, Castles Made of Sand, All Along the Watchtower, Fire* and *Woke up This Morning and Found Myself Dead*. Which, of course, he eventually does.

Hendrix lives a tortured life riddled with chemicals and finally dies of an overdose. His partner speaks about Hendrix's constant spiritual torments and bouts of screaming and violence against her. Alan Douglas, who administers Hendrix's immense music estate today, tells us:

"Now one of the biggest things about Jimi was what he believed and he believed that he was possessed by some spirit and I got to believe it myself. And that's what we had to deal with all the time. And he was very humble about discussing it with people because he didn't want people to feel like he was being pretentious, and so on. But he really believed it and was wrestling with it constantly."[266]

JIM MORRISON - THE DOORS

According to his own writings, Jim Morrison used psychiatric drug-induced altered states to make contact with the demonic realm. Morrison was having a hard time at UCLA in the '60's and dropped out of film school to live in Venice, California. He writes:

"In that year there was an intense visitation of energy. I left school and went down to the beach to live. I slept on a roof. At night the moon became a woman's face. I met the Spirit of Music.... an appearance of the

---

[266] Schimmel, Joe, op. cit.

devil on a Venice canal. Running, I saw a Satan, or Satyr, moving beside me, a fleshly shadow of my secret mind. Running. Knowing." [267]

Morrison later identifies this Spirit, or Angel of Music, as Satan. He goes on to state that it was through such demonic tutorship that he received many of the ideas for his hit songs, remarking of these drug experiences, *"It was like being at a fantastic rock concert. I just took notes."* [268] Morrison would later state that he was 'led' to write songs with lyrics such as *"Cancel my subscription to the Resurrection. Send my credentials to the House of Detention, I've got some friends inside."* And, *"Music is your special friend. Dance on fire as it intends. Music is your only friend, until the end."*

For an industry so intent on marginalising religion, it's significant how often rock and pop artists discuss religion in their lyrics *and indeed preach their own religious, Luciferian sermons.* Bear this in mind as we proceed.

An enlightening comment is made by Ray Manzarek, the keyboard player of The Doors, who states in a TV interview that the band used its instruments to pound Jim Morrison into a trance on stage during performances. It was said that their drug experiences made possession far easier before the crowds. Manzarek finishes:

"He [Morrison] was not a performer, he was not an entertainer, he was not a showman, he was a shaman. He was possessed, man." [269]

The name 'The Doors' was taken from occult drug mystic Aldous Huxley's *Doors of Perception.* The band gave this full name to a series of band member interviews that can still be purchased on CD. Morrison is another to die a lonely, sordid and early drug death.

THE BEACH BOYS
Over the years Brian Wilson has hired around 40 different psychiatrists and therapists, including the infamous Dr Eugene Landy, to help rid him of his 'voices'. In 1965, Brian had taken LSD for the first time. It was undiluted. Brian later wrote:

---

[267] Ibid.
[268] Hopkins & Sugarman, op. cit.
[269] Schimmel, Joe, op. cit.

"My home life was most tumultuous. Marilyn [his wife] complained that the LSD had changed me.... I didn't see it then, but she was right. The change was gradual, like a slow, allergic reaction. I slept later. I was subject to wider, more unpredictable mood swings, crying one minute, laughing hysterically the next, or no good reason. I ate tremendous amounts of sweets. I refused to be sociable." [270]

'Spirits' caused Wilson such torment that on one occasion, he was bedridden for four years because of the paranoia and mental angst that came upon him. LSD is known to cause symptoms attributed to demon possession and the classic psychiatric definition of 'schizophrenia'. Immense success and musical prestige came to The Beach Boys with a high penalty in suffering. The Beach Boys preached transcendental meditation and eastern mysticism, sometimes taking the Maharishi Mahesh Yogi along with them on tour.

Rolling Stone magazine, 11th August 1988, records: *"Brian Wilson hears voices. They talk to him, they distract him, frighten him, confuse him. Right now, as the genius behind the California surf-rock sound sits in his darkened living room, the Pacific crashing loudly outside his million-dollar Malibu home, the voices are calling. The 46-year-old screws up his face and his eyes roll towards the ceiling...."*

Brian Wilson also experienced the automatic writing/contact phenomenon described by Jim Morrison and could not play the music he recorded. Before embarking on tour, this musical genius had to relearn all his chords and lyrics.

THE ROLLING STONES
The Rolling Stones popularised the taking of heavy drugs and were intermittently in the news with their outrageous exploits. But is there evidence of a more sinister angle to their beliefs? In an interview with

---

[270] CCHR, *Psychiatry – Manipulating Creativity*, op. cit. p.44

Keith Richards, the famous guitarist was asked, *"Do you think of yourselves as servants of Satan?"* Notice how, in his reply, Richards uses his pop-prophet status to preach a sermon of recommendation to his millions of followers:

Richards: *"Kenneth Anger* [Satanist and disciple of Crowley] *told me I was his right-hand man. It all depends whether you've got that good and evil thing together. Left-hand path, right-hand path. How far do you want to go down? Once you've started, there's no turning back. And where it leads is another thing.... It's something everybody ought to explore. There are a lot of possibilities there. A lot of people have played with it and it's inside everybody. (pause) Everybody's Lucifer."*[271]

Sympathy For The Devil
Please allow me to introduce myself
I'm a man of wealth and taste
Been around for a long, long year
Sold many a man's soul and fate
I was around when Jesus Christ
Had His moment of doubt and pain
Made damn sure that Pilate
Washed his hands and sealed His fate
Pleased to meet you, baby
Hope you guess my name....[272]

The Rolling Stones typify Crowlianism. Mick Jagger and Keith Richards have led high-profile public lives before their fans with unrepentant infidelity, drug abuse and an 'anything goes' attitude. The Rolling Stones were prophets to millions of impressionable minds, with an occultic sermon very pronounced in their music. Albums and releases include *Bridges to Babylon, Goat's Head Soup, Their Satanic Majesty's Request, Tattoo You, Through the Past, Darkly* (a Bible misquote), *Voodoo Lounge* (also the name of their London night-club in Leicester Square), *Saint of Me, Out of Control*, etc.... The Stones were undeniably

---

[271] Dalton, David & Mick Farren, *The Rolling Stones: In Their Own Words*, Omnibus Press, 1995
[272] The Rolling Stones, *Sympathy For The Devil,* from the movie, *Gimme Shelter.* This song was performed live at the Altamont Speedway in December 1969. Three people were killed during the concert. Mick Jagger's recorded comment after singing this song and hearing of the deaths in the crowd: *"Something funny always happens when we start that number."*

marketed as the 'bad boys of rock'. The following group however was supposed to be the one your mother preferred:

THE BEATLES/JOHN LENNON

On the front of the Sgt. Pepper Lonely Hearts Club Band album, we have the Fab Four surrounded by a crowd of historical figures. Apart from all the revolutionaries in evidence, from Jung to Marx to, apparently, Adolf Hitler before his face was removed because of protests; top left, the second face in, there is the bald head of Aleister Crowley.

In the *Playboy* interviews, John Lennon sums up the Beatles' philosophy:

"The whole Beatle idea was to do what you want, right? To take your own responsibility and try not to harm other people, right? Do what thou wilst as long as it doesn't hurt anybody."

In the biography, *The Lives of John Lennon*, author Albert Goldman tells how Yoko Ono journeys to South America to make a pact with Satan for a number of things, including John Lennon's career:

"Finally it was time to consummate all these spells by making a living sacrifice and signing a pact with the devil. For Lena was not a white witch, she was the real thing - a practitioner of black magic. There was no knowing what she planned to do to seal the bond with Lucifer. All she would say was that the witch's moon was nigh and she had to make ready the sacrifice."[273]

Goldman goes on to tell how they sacrificed an animal and Ono paid the witch, Lena, $60,000 for her trouble. Goldman explains away this event and others linked with it by stating that John Lennon was grappling with psychiatric disturbances and peer-pressure gremlins.

Upon a more detailed study of his life, John Lennon is found to be extremely antichrist. Often described as a man 'with peace on his lips but war in his heart', Lennon was undeniably the main spiritual driving force behind The Beatles, eclipsing the more moderate and parent-friendly Paul McCartney. Lennon was also their most progressive spokesman. When he makes his infamous comment, *"The Beatles are bigger than Jesus Christ"*,

---

[273] Goldman, Albert, *The Lives of John Lennon*, St Martin's Press, 1984

most just write it off as sensationalism and hype. However, in the same interview with the *San Francisco Chronicle*, Lennon bothers specifically to declare that *"Christianity will vanish."* In his book, *John Lennon: In His Own Write*, Lennon openly blasphemes Jesus Christ and the Holy Spirit: *"I forgive them by the Father, the Sock and Mickey Most."* (Most was a famous record producer in the sixties).

Lennon makes no secret of his open disdain of God, heaven and religion in *Imagine*. As this song is one of his flagship tunes, it is worth examining the sermon that is being taught to his millions of devoted followers. This writer's comments are in brackets:

Imagine
Imagine there's no heaven (*Let's take God out of the picture*)
It's easy if you try (*There's nothing to it*)
No hell below us (*No judgment on wrong-doing*)
Above us only sky
Imagine all the people
Living for today... (*Imagine the whole world embracing the core philosophy of Satanism: "Life is the great indulgence. Death is the great abstinence. Therefore make the most of life here and now."* Book of Satan 4:1)
Imagine there's no countries (*Let's break down national boundaries*)
It isn't hard to do (*It's a snap*)
Nothing to kill or die for (*Let's do away with patriotism*)
And no religion too (*Remove religion and replace it with man's reason (humanism)*)
Imagine all the people
Living life in peace... (*People will live in peace without God*)
Imagine no possessions (*Imagine communism. Nobody owns anything*)
I wonder if you can
No need for greed or hunger
A brotherhood of man (*A Big Brother human government feeding and caring for us all*)
Imagine all the people
Sharing all the world... (*Let's have worldwide communism*)
You may say that I'm a dreamer
But I'm not the only one (*There are lots of people out there who think the same way I do*)

180

I hope some day you'll join us (*Because you aren't with us at the moment*)
And the world will be as one. (*Welcome to the New World Order*)
(John Lennon, *Imagine*, EMI Blackwood Music, Inc.)

While the public was being enchanted with *"All You Need is Love"*, perhaps the Beatles weren't. When the band broke up, they hated one another for years afterwards.

LED ZEPPELIN

Led Zeppelin's guitarist, Jimmy Page, buys Crowley's house above Loch Ness in Scotland, constructed on the site of a church which burned to the ground with its congregation still inside. Page is a fanatic of Crowley's. He stops short of admitting his involvement in the occult however, but states: *"I do not worship the devil but magic does intrigue me."* [274] Astute observers murmur that Page's allegiance to Crowley's Angel of Music has secured a serious career for both himself and his band. Whatever the reason, Led Zeppelin goes on to become the most prolific drug-taking, record-selling rock group of the 1970's, even eclipsing concert attendance records of The Beatles and Rolling Stones.

In his *Book of the Law,* Appendix VII, Crowley describes the skills an initiate is required to master in order to gain the real power of Satan:

a) Let him learn to write backwards with either hand.
b) Let him learn to walk backwards. [This became popular with Michael Jackson]

---

[274] Holmberg, Eric, ibid.

c) *Let the initiate constantly watch, if convenient, cinematograph films <u>and listen to phonograph records reversed</u>, and let him so accustom himself to these that they appear natural and appreciable as a whole.*

d) *Let him practice speaking backwards... thus for "I am He" let him say, "Eh ma I".*[275]

Led Zeppelin's number one hit song of all time is *Stairway to Heaven*. Often this track has been voted the *all-time* favourite rock song in music industry polls and is known by hundreds of millions of fans around the world. What at first listen appears to be a mellow tune in harmony with the topic of heaven turns out to be something altogether very different. The album concerned is *Houses of the Holy*. On the album cover and inside, the titles are all written backwards.

Stairway to Heaven
There's a lady who's sure all that glitters is gold
And she's buying a stairway to heaven.
And when she gets there she knows if the stores are all closed
With a word she can get what she came for.

Is the lady in the song off on the wrong foot right away if she believes all that glitters is gold? It is not apparently possible, according to interviews with ministers, to buy a stairway to heaven, except "by believing in the saving grace of Jesus". In lines 3 and 4, we see Crowley's *'Do what thou wilt'* attitude. With one word, she can get what she wants.

And it's whispered that soon, if we call the tune (*if we're the ones calling the shots*)
Then the piper (traditionally Satan) will lead us to reason (*to the religion of humanism and away from God*)
And a new day will dawn for those who stand long
And the forests will echo with laughter.

The phonograph record can be played backwards to hear the clear Crowlian messages. Disconcertingly, what we discover cannot have been contrived by human endeavour. Much ridicule has been levelled over the years at 'backwards masking', yet the simple fact remains that in one passage alone, the reverse message runs clear for over 40 words. Any

---

[275] Crowley, Aleister, *The Book of the Law*, op. cit.

effort by the musicians or sound engineers to engineer this effect intentionally using backwards masking (especially given the somewhat primitive equipment available in the 1970's) would have totally disrupted the forward sequence and aesthetics of the song. This has not occurred. *Stairway to Heaven* is consistently voted the most popular song in rock and roll. Notice that the clearly heard reverse messages have everything to do with their associated forward lyrics:

FORWARDS: *Your stairway lies on the whispering wind.*
BACKWARDS: **Cos I live with Satan.**
FORWARDS: *The piper's calling you to join him.*
BACKWARDS: **The Lord turned me off.**
FORWARDS: *And it makes me wonder.*
BACKWARDS: **There's no escaping it.**
FORWARDS: *If there's a bustle in your hedgerow don't be alarmed now, it's just a Spring clean for the May Queen. Yes, there are two paths you can go by, but in the long run, there's still time to change the road you're on.*
BACKWARDS: **Here's to my sweet Satan. I want to live it backwards like the Zep, whose power is Satan. He will give you, give you, 666.**

According to Led Zeppelin, there are two spiritual paths their followers can take. They are Keith Richards' 'left-hand path and right-hand path' – evil and good, respectively. Witness Robert Plant's final farewell to the crowd at a concert the band held at the Los Angeles Forum in the 1970's. They have just played *Stairway to Heaven* and told their fans they are all going to hell. Robert Plant calls out: *"LA, goodnight. It's been very funny."*

ROCK AND POP PROPHETS OF THE '80's AND '90's

In the following two decades we have similar trends happening: Madonna praying to some god before a concert on her 'Truth or Dare' movie tour. Apparently it isn't Jesus she's praying to, because a few minutes later she goes on stage and performs acts of gross indecency in front of an audience of eight-year-olds and up.

Prince, among many examples, with his album *1999*, which tells of the rock star recklessly partying all the way up to Judgment Day. If you've seen the videos, you've seen the partying. If the album cover is turned upside down, the special way the artists have drawn the titling gives the following Crowlian effect: Prince's name spells 'EVIL' backwards followed by a fire symbol. The 1999 reads 666 followed by an inverted male penis - the symbol of Crowley's New Aeon for Mankind.

Sting and his band, The Police, with their album 'Ghost in the Machine', referring to spirits in the brain, with its inverted 666 motif on the front cover. Daryl Hall and John Oates, self-confessed followers of Crowley. Metallica and Nirvana with their video images of Crowley and mock crucifixions - the list is endless. Even Duran Duran uses Anton LaVey's satanic symbol on their 1980's album containing the track, *Union of the Snake*. When this writer interviewed one of Duran Duran's management team who chose the symbol for the album, he was told: *"It just came into my head to pick that shape."* On the front cover also: an inverted cross.

Kurt Cobain (centre) in a publicity photo, where he pretends to shoot himself. Taken years before his suicide, this picture would haunt his many fans following the singer's tragic suicide

KURT COBAIN

Nirvana's front-man was a known drug addict who often wrote lyrics about suicide and depression. Highly popular with those who could identify with Cobain's articulated feelings of hopelessness, Cobain's stint at the top with his band was brief and tragic. As a youngster, he had been diagnosed 'hyperactive' by psychiatrists and placed in a chemical straitjacket named Ritalin. One of the most common side-effects of the drug is that it keeps the user awake. In Kurt's case, he was also prescribed sedatives to counteract the effects of his primary 'medication'.

Coming to rely on the stimulation of drugs, Cobain also had physical problems with which he wrestled. A curved spine and a 'burning, nauseous' stomach were constant companions. Cobain often publicly thanked heroin for 'quenching the fire in my gut'. Abdominal pains are a known side-effect of Ritalin.

The pressures of the music business on a mind unable to cope soon took their toll. Cobain's band was signed to Geffen Records and the tours started. Cobain's drug abuse, mixing street drugs with his psychiatric medication, soon became critical. Wishing to help him before it was too late, some of Kurt's close friends, including his wife, Courtney Love, assisted in having the tormented singer taken to a psychiatric drug recovery centre. Within 36 hours, Cobain had bolted and took up refuge in an attic above his garage in a Seattle suburb. Here he placed a shotgun against his head and pulled the trigger. Heroin and 'mother's little helper', Valium, were reportedly found in his body during autopsy.

ANTON SZANDOR LAVEY

Crowley disciple Anton LaVey currently lives in San Francisco. LaVey formed the Worldwide Satanic Church in the famous West Coast city on the sixth day of the sixth month, 1966 and published *The Satanic Bible*.[276] In his writings, LaVey draws from the writings of Crowley and reiterates that man can become a master of music through the practising of Crowley's magic. This magic involves drug abuse and the extension of one's consciousness through contact with shining demonic beings (sometimes 'the Elder Gods' or 'Wise Ones').

Widely regarded today as the High Priest of the Devil himself, Anton LaVey interestingly states that Satanism is not the worship of the devil, per se: *"And he must, as a Satanist, knowing this, realising what his human potential is, eventually, and here is one of the essential points of Satanism, attain his own godhood in accordance with his own potential. Therefore, each man, each woman, is a god or goddess in Satanism."*[277]

True Satanism therefore, as practised, is not worshiping the devil. It is apparently lawlessness, <u>acknowledging no higher power above one, not even Satan</u>. Satanism is man liberated to become his own god, to be whatever he wants to be, <u>and do whatever he wishes to do</u>, with no searing of his conscience. Other Satanists interviewed by this writer were extremely pedantic about ensuring I was clear on this issue.

Is this attitude of open rebellion, along with Crowley's *"Do what thou wilt"*, visible in rock and pop today?

---

[276] LaVey, Anton Szandor, *The Satanic Bible*, Avon Books, 1976
[277] Holmberg, Eric, *The Allure of Rock*, American Portrait Films, P.O. Box 19266 Cleveland, OH 44119, (800)736-4567

THE ROLLING THUNDER

A sampling of lyrics across a wide range of world-famous recording artists will assist in identifying the core Freudian, Crowlian, psychiatric, Luciferian, eugenics and humanistic messages that are preached to millions of our children and youth each day. These are both *religious* (spiritual) and *negative conditioning* messages:

Prince: Rules and regulations, no place in this equation.

Billy Joel remarks, *"Rock and roll is supposed to be rebellious. It's supposed to be about f***ing, and about sneaking around behind your parents, proclaiming your freedom, your independence."* [278]

Digital Underground, *Dowutchalike,* Tommy Boy Records

Hells Bells

I'm rolling thunder, pouring rain
I'm coming on like a hurricane
My lightning's flashing across the sky
You're only young but you're gonna die.
I won't take no prisoners
Won't spare no lives
Nobody's putting up a fight
I've got my bell
I'm gonna take you to hell
I'm gonna get ya
Satan get ya
Hell's Bells...
 (AC/DC, *Hells Bells*)

My Prerogative

It's the way that I want to live
It's my prerogative
I can do just what I feel
It's my prerogative
Nobody can tell me what to do.
 (Bobby Brown, *My Prerogative*, MCA Records)

---

[278] *Rolling Stone Magazine,* 25th January 1990, p.36

Life is Too Short
I live my life just how I please
Satisfy one person I know, that's me...
(Too Short, *Life is Too Short,* Zomba Recording Corp.)

Whatever Makes You Happy
No one should tell you how to live your life
You got to be you, whether you're wrong or right.
Follow your heart and you'll be free
If it's straight with you, it's straight with me.
Being happy is the name of the game
And basically we're all the same.
Different strokes for different folks
Whatever makes you happy.
(Ten City, *Whatever Makes you Happy,* Atlantic Records)

I did it my way.
(Frank Sinatra)

Sitting in the Lap of Luxury
Temptation got the better of me
Temptation said 'Boy, be who you want to be.'
So I started charging by the hour
For my love power.
(Louis Louie, *Sitting in the Lap of Luxury*, CBS Records)

Terrible Lie
Hey God
Why are you doing this to me?
Hey God
Am I not living up to what I'm supposed to be?
Hey God
Why am I seething with this animosity?
Hey God
I think you owe me a great big apology
Terrible LIE!
(Nine Inch Nails, *Terrible Lie,* TVT Records)

Justify My Love
As for the cowardly, the faithless, the polluted
As for the murderers, the fornicators, the sorcerers, idolaters
And all liars, they shall have their part in the lake
Which burns with fire and brimstone.
  (Madonna, *Justify My Love* (The Beast Within Mix) Sire Records)
  The song's above lyrics are a Bible misquote from the Book of Revelation 21:8. Madonna remarks: *"I think they probably got it on, Jesus and Mary Magdalene."*[279]

The Number of the Beast
In the night, the fires are burning bright
The ritual has begun, Satan's work is done
666 the number of the beast
666 the number for you and me.
I'm coming back
I will return
I'll possess your body
I'll make you burn.
  (Iron Maiden, *The Number of the Beast*, Castle Records)

In The Beginning
It has been written
'Those who have the youth have the future'
So come, children of the beast, be strong.
  (Motley Crue, *In the Beginning*, BMG/Beyond)

The Oath
I deny Jesus Christ
The Deceiver
And I abjure the Christian Faith
Holding in contempt all of its works
And I swear to give my mind, my body and soul
Unreservedly
To the furtherance of our Lord Satan's designs.
Do what thou wilt shall be the whole of the law.
  (Mercyful Fayth, *The Oath*)

---

[279] *The Advocate*, 21st May 1991, p.40

JANE'S ADDICTION

One of the most controversial bands of the 1990's is Jane's Addiction. Lead singer Perry Farrell sets out to overturn every moral convention of society, exposing and fondling himself on stage and on occasion performing naked throughout an entire concert. Raised in New York the son of a jeweller and an artist mother who commits suicide when Farrell is four, the young rebel moves to Los Angeles and works as an exotic dancer posing as various rock stars.

Farrell remarks *"I say you don't have anything - you don't have a society, unless that society is completely shameless. If you're shameless, you feel like your sexual impulses, as long as they're within both people's free will, those impulses are fine."*[280]

Farrell titillates his audiences with the 'thrill of shoplifting':

Been Caught Stealing

When I want something and I don't want to pay for it
Then I walk right through the door
Yeah I walk right through the door
Hey all right
If I get by
It's mine.
(Jane's Addiction, *Been Caught Stealing*, Warner Bros.)

The album, *Ritual De Lo Habitual,* features original artwork on the cover by Farrell: three figures with exposed genitalia - a take-off of the Trinity. Saturnalia paraphernalia is also featured.

The song, *Three Days* (of the Resurrection) brings forth Farrell's predictable image of Jesus:

Three Days

...Erotic Jesus
Lays with his Marys
Loves his Marys...
(Jane's Addiction, *Three Days*, Warner Bros.)

---

[280] *Spin Magazine* June 1991, p.80

Written on the album liner is Farrell's personal comment to the world's parents: *"To the mosquitoes: we have more influence over your children than you do."*

MARILYN MANSON

Another out to shock is the latest in grotesque stage shows featuring Marilyn Manson. Although Manson pushes the bounds of indecency further than most, underneath we still have the same brand of religion being pushed. *Rolling Stone* enlightens:

"Imagine Alice Cooper times 10. Picture KISS on an acid and whiskey bender. Marry the gross-out hilarity of G G Allin with the ubiquity of Howard Stern. Combine the 'search and destroy' frenzy of Iggy Pop with the godless zeal of Ozzy Osbourne. Take two cups of the devil and throw in a pinch of P T Barnum, and you still can't fathom all that is... Marilyn Manson.

Spawning a cult following to rival all others, Manson and his rotating band of serial-killer sidemen have created a powerful concoction of Satanic imagery, face-splitting guitars and performance spectacle that has drawn the ire of countless keepers of the public good."[281]

Manson was originally 'discovered' by Nine-Inch Nails[282] frontman, Trent Reznor. The androgenous Manson's first offering was *Antichrist Superstar*, released in 1996, which entered the American charts at No.3. Manson's in-your-face brand of Satanism is widely celebrated among his devoted followers worldwide. The star's web-site proclaims: *"This is the morning of magic and undefiled wisdom. The FLESH prevaileth and a great Church shall be builded, consecrated in its name. No longer shall man's salvation be dependent on his self-denial! 198,677 souls damned since 3.20.99. Now over one million damned."*

---

[281] www.rollingstone.com
[282] This band was so-named for the length of nails believed to have been used to crucify Jesus.

Although Manson likes it known that he doesn't take himself too seriously (that would be uncool), his fans most definitely do. His tours, when not banned altogether, routinely sell out. His Rock is Dead tour however hit rocky weather when the singer was cited as one of the motivations in the Columbine school massacre.

Manson's 2000 album, *Holy Wood (In The Shadow Of The Valley Of Death)*, features a cover showing Manson in a crucifix pose with eyes rolled back and lower jaw missing. The album was deemed offensive by certain retail chains, who responded by selling the album in a cardboard sleeve, using alternate artwork in their advertising campaigns or refusing to stock the record altogether.

MORAL ACCOUNTABILITY AND THE LAW

Notwithstanding the fact that the appeal of rock and roll lies in its iconoclastic rebellion, societies must have judicial law and moral order so they can function. History demonstrates repeatedly that when the family unit is disrupted, when society unhooks itself from the constraints of a collective social moral code, that society has been doomed to implode with tragic results. Is it plain to see that when the concepts of right and wrong are blurred, people see themselves as free to do what is right in their own eyes? Do crime and lawlessness increase as a result? Are lives wrecked? Are the stars themselves happier living the reported 'truths' of their own belief-systems? Or is there not a well-documented destination of misery, heartache and death that lies at the end of the Yellow Brick Road?

As we have seen, the gospel of lawlessness and 'do what thou wilt' is also promoted in psychiatry's fundamental tenets. G Brock Chisholm, one of the 20th century's most influential mental health advocates and former president of the World Federation for Mental Health, chillingly verifies the collective aim of his profession to free man from the chafing constraints of righteousness:

"The reinterpretation and eventually eradication of the concept of right and wrong which has been the basis of child training, the substitution of intelligent and rational thinking for faith in the certainties of the old people, these are the belated objectives of practically all effective psychotherapy.... <u>The fact is, that most psychiatrists and</u>

psychologists and other respectable people have escaped from these moral chains and are able to observe and think freely." [283]

Notice how psychiatrists and psychologists are heaped in with 'other respectable people'. Have 'other respectable people' in our society really escaped from these moral chains? Even the most cursory examination of the views of ordinary citizens will reveal their horror at what is occurring on our streets today.

What effect has psychiatry's unhinging of right and wrong had on our cities and schoolyards? Sixty years ago, such a revolution of violence, illiteracy and misery on our doorstep was unthinkable, even after the horrors of World War 2. But today, the unthinkable is happening, and continues to happen, chiefly due to the pervasive influences of psychiatry, humanism, Satanism, the theories of evolution and 'mental hygiene' in our schools, courts, governments and churches. G Brock Chisholm's agenda for mental health is nothing less than a complete upheaval of society and a restructuring of its mores. Notice how Chisholm willingly shoulders the responsibility for developing the 'glorious, intellectual heritage' bequeathed to the children of the future:

"We have swallowed all manner of poisonous certainties fed us by our parents, our Sunday and day school teachers, our politicians, our priests, our newspapers and others with a vested interest in controlling us. 'Thou shalt become as gods, knowing good and evil', good and evil with which to keep children under control, with which to prevent free thinking, with which to impose local and familial and national loyalties and with which to blind children to their glorious intellectual heritage....

If the race is to be freed from its crippling burden of good and evil, it must be psychiatrists who take the original responsibility." [284]

---

[283] Chisholm, G Brock, "The Re-establishment of Peacetime Society – The William Alanson White Memorial Lectures, Second Series', *Psychiatry: Journal of the Biology and the Pathology of Interpersonal Relations*, February 1946, p.9
[284] Chisholm, G Brock, op. cit. pp.7-9

The Great Childhood Maddening

"Every child in America entering school at the age of five is insane because he comes to school with certain allegiances to our founding fathers, towards our elected officials, towards his parents, towards a belief in a supernatural being, and towards the sovereignty of this nation as a separate entity. It's up to you as teachers to make all these sick children well – *by creating the international child of the future."* - Psychiatrist Chester M Pierce, Harvard University, addressing teachers at a 1973 Childhood International Education Seminar

"I have sworn upon the altar of God eternal hostility against every form of tyranny over the mind of man." - Thomas Jefferson

"If you tolerate this, then your children will be next." - The Manic Street Preachers

The sleepy September day in Greenwood, South Carolina, meandered peacefully as James Wilson loads the small .22 calibre shells into his rifle and works the bolt, driving the first tiny bullet into the breach. Minutes later the 19-year-old walks into the elementary school cafeteria and begins shooting screaming children and a teacher, before working his way through the school, systematically selecting his targets. He kicks open the door to a girls' restroom, where he shoots another teacher, moving next to a third-grade classroom, where he shoots more children. Two children die and seven are wounded in the killing spree.

James' senseless and chillingly unemotional act shocked the world. How could someone do such a thing? Schoolyard shootings, increasingly bizarre and horrifying street murders and drug violence had been increasing since the 1970's in America, and people were at a loss to know why. Wasn't there something other-worldly and, well, frankly demonic about such a scene of carnage, set in the heart of one of the safest zones in society – our schools?

THE CIRCUS SPECTACLE

Violence in society is of course nothing new. Back in Nero's day, the popular sport was setting light to Christians or watching them torn apart by wild animals in the arenas. Hangings, impalings, crucifixions and various executions down through the ages drew large crowds. The French Revolution was extremely popular for those women who used to knit in

193

front of the guillotine, making their garments all the while experiencing the bloody executions of unfortunates right before them. Yet, although violence perpetrated by rulers in the past was ubiquitous, it is interesting to note that private citizens were generally not taking each others' lives the way we are seeing today, even though the weapons to do so were widely available. In America during the '40's and '50's, for example, guns were still commonly owned, even as they are today, yet school shootings and road rage incidents were unknown. The concept of right and wrong prevented explosions of personal violence in the main, and punishment was swift and harsh for those who disobeyed the law.

But today, four decades after 'progressive education' was introduced into classrooms aimed at eroding this same concept of right and wrong, everything has changed. When examining shooting incidents like James Wilson's, we can note some common denominators:

> Often the shooter has given warning signals of impending violence
> The shooter has previously displayed evidence of a blurred understanding of right and wrong
> The shooter often commits suicide after the event
> The shooter has a history of psychiatric drug treatment
> The incidents occur in societies where psychiatric drugs are commonly prescribed
> These psychiatric drugs themselves have an extremely well documented history of altering perceptions, inciting hostility and violence, and dissipating inhibitions

James had been taking psychiatric drugs for years, prescribed to him by Greenwood psychiatrist Willie Moseley. These included Xanax, Valium, Vistaril, Mellaril, Thorazine, Tofranil and Halcion. James Crossen, program director of the Chemical Dependency Recovery Unit at the Medical Center of North Hollywood, California, gives his considered opinion on what could have caused the 1988 shootings to happen: *"That that young man should have been on drugs all his life, since he was fourteen, is ghoulish. The drugs would be a major contributing factor in such a surprising and sudden act of violence – a major contributor."*[285]

---

[285] "Prescription for Murder – Psychiatric Drugs Create Killer", *Freedom*, November/December 1988, pp.16-17

194

Four months after James' rampage, Patrick Purdy, 26, entered a Stockton, California schoolyard and opened fire, killing five children and wounding 29 more, including a teacher, before killing himself. Purdy had an extensive psychiatric drug history.

Two years previously, on 20th November 1986, 14-year-old Rod Matthews had gone on the rampage in Canton, Massachusetts, beating a classmate, Shawn Ouillette, to death with a baseball bat in the woods near his home. The academically gifted Matthews had been taking the psychiatric drug Ritalin since he was nine, and was withdrawing from his medication at the time of the killing.[286] Matthews had told a teacher in the weeks before the killing that he had an urge to kill somebody. The teacher had merely replied that murder was a felony.

Nine months previously, young Timmy Becton, aged 10, had used his 3-year-old niece as a shield while wielding a shotgun at a sheriff's deputy, who had visited the Becton residence with a truant officer. *"I'd sooner shoot you than go to school!"* Timmy reportedly yelled. The month before, he had been taken to see a psychiatrist to help him with his hatred of school. The psychiatrist prescribed Prozac. His parents described that their son had suffered personality changes when the dosage of the drug was increased. They reported violent mood swings, during which Timmy would get 'really angry'.

The first of the school shooting incidents had occurred on 20th May 1988, when Laurie Dann, 30, walked into a school in Winnetka, Illinois, with three handguns and opened fire, killing one and wounding five. Laurie then fled the school and killed a man in a house nearby before committing suicide.

In 1995 in Illinois, Brian Pruitt, 16, fatally stabbed his grandmother in her bedroom and then laid in wait, killing his grandfather when he returned home. Brian had a history of psychiatric drug treatment.

In July 1996, two boys, aged 15 and 16 stabbed a high-school student after they had been taking sedatives, which they later told police made them feel 'invincible'.

---

[286] CCHR, *Psychiatry – Betraying and Drugging our Children*, Los Angeles, 2002, p.17

In 1997 in New Jersey, Sam Manzie, 15, attacked and raped 11-year-old Eddie Werner, who had called on the Manzie home selling items door-to-door for the local PTA. Sam strangled Eddie with an electrical cord after the assault, photographing him with the cord still wrapped around his neck. He then threw away his victim's clothes and possessions in a rubbish bin next to the psychiatric facility where he had been receiving regular treatments, including the drug Paxil. His mother reports that Sam had told her: *"I wasn't killing that little boy, I was killing* [my psychiatrist] *because he didn't listen to me."* [287]

On 25th May 1997, 18-year-old Jeremy Strohmeyer raped and murdered a 7-year-old girl in the ladies' room of a casino one week after commencing the drug Dexedrine.

On 21st May 1988, 14-year-old Kip Kinkel began his brief rule of terror. Kip's problems began when he was diagnosed with dyslexia and placed on Ritalin. His problems persisted. He attended 'anger control' classes and was additionally prescribed Prozac. Kip later went bezerk, entering his Springfield, Oregon high school and opening fire, killing two and injuring 22. He had also shot both his parents to death.

On 20th July 1987, two horrified parents walked into their garage to find their 16-year-old son swinging from the ceiling. After nine years on Ritalin, and undergoing withdrawal from the psychiatric drug, the tormented young man had hanged himself with water-skiing rope.[288]

In October 1993, 15-year-old Gerard McCra shot his parents and sister to death. He had been taking Ritalin since the age of six. While this explosion of violence shocked Massachusetts, the *Boston Globe* was keen to begin its story, not in lamenting the tragedy to the family and the neighbourhood, but citing a quote from a medical spokesman incongruously attempting to cover himself: *"There is no scientific evidence indicating that Ritalin causes, or in any way triggers violence in children who take the commonly prescribed medication for hyperactivity."* [289]

That this ridiculous statement is allowed to be published is all the more unsettling since the manufacturer of Ritalin itself, CIBA

---

[287] "The Hidden Hand of Violence", *Freedom*, Vol.31, Issue 2, Los Angeles, CA

[288] Wiseman, Bruce, op. cit. p.286

[289] Bennet, Philip & Bob Hohler, "Boy, 15, held in killings of father, mother, sister...", *Boston Globe*, 12th October 1993

Pharmaceutical Company, had published the following public warning about its drug *eight years before* in 1985:

DRUG DEPENDENCE: Ritalin should be given cautiously to emotionally unstable patients, such as those with a history of drug dependence or alcoholism, because such patients may increase dosage on their own initiative. Chronically abusive use can lead to marked tolerance and physic dependence with varying degrees of abnormal behaviour. Frank psychotic episodes can occur, especially with parental abuse. Careful supervision is required during drug withdrawal, since severe depression as well as the effects of chronic over-activity can be unmasked.

Gerard McCra was reportedly abused by his parents while on Ritalin. Note that, by the admission of the manufacturers themselves, the purpose of Ritalin is to 'mask' the symptoms of 'over-activity', not cure them.

On 14ᵗʰ September 1989, Joseph Wesbecker marauded through a Louisville, Kentucky printing works, blasting eight former co-workers to death, wounding 12 others before turning the gun on himself. One of his surviving victims shudders: *"I looked up into the face of who was holding the rifle. He was completely gone. There was just nothing there of what makes a person a person. He was gone. And I thought that, soon, I would be even more gone than he."* An autopsy later showed that Joseph had 'therapeutic' levels of the anti-depressant Prozac in his blood at the time of the killings.[290]

Prozac has a long and infamous history of dangerous side-effects. Regulatory agencies around the world consistently receive a string of adverse reaction reports on the drug. Even Valium, a known, highly addictive anti-depressant, only garnered 7,000 adverse reaction reports in the US over 20 years. In just 10 years, Prozac had amassed a stunning 40,000 complaints, including mass murders, suicides, mutilations and more than 2,300 deaths.[291]

On 20ᵗʰ April 1999, Eric Harris, an 18-year-old senior at Columbine High School in Colorado, went on a murderous killing spree. Both Eric and his partner, Dylan Klebold, committed suicide after the event. Blood

---

[290] Daniels, Robert, "Deadly Shell Game", *Freedom* magazine, Vol. 30, issue 1, Los Angeles: 2002, p.16
[291] Ibid.

samples confirmed that Eric had been taking Luvox, a mind-altering drug in the same class as Prozac. Luvox (fluvoxamine) and Prozac (fluoxetine) are known as 'selective serotonin re-uptake inhibitors' (SSRI's), so-named because they block the brain's absorption of the neurotransmitter serotonin, responsible for mood stabilisation. Luvox's manufacturers even warn that Luvox is 'sometimes fatal' to those who take it, and can activate mania and impair judgment and thinking.

Nicholas Regush, producer of medical features for ABC News, stated: *"This is a widely recognised feature of antidepressants, as documented by their very own manufacturers. These drugs are also associated with bouts of irritability, hostility and aggression. Exactly how all this behavioural change is processed in the brain and how long-lasting it might be is poorly understood. Contrary to the big shows of knowledge by psychiatrists, there is a whole lot of guessing going on."* [292]

Eight years before the shootings, Columbine High had been the subject of a 1991 ABC *20/20* documentary for its controversial 'death education' class, in which students discussed such macabre topics as how they wanted to look in their caskets. Both Eric and Dylan had a well-documented obsession with violence, Satanism and weapons, both having been arrested for burglary in 1998 and placed into an 'anger management' program. Both were fans of the infamous pop-star, Marilyn Manson. Eric's web-site alone should have had the alarm bells ringing. Warning statements abounded, such as *"I am the law. If you don't like it, you die!"* and *"You all better... hide in your houses because I am coming for EVERYONE soon, and I WILL be armed to the ... teeth, and I WILL shoot to kill and I WILL... KILL EVERYTHING."*

DEATH IN THE PLAYGROUND
Today, children routinely threaten their teachers with extreme violence - so much so that in America, a special school police force patrols the campus to confiscate weapons and keep an eye on things. When I was at school, threats of that kind, while maybe entertained after a public humiliation, were *never* articulated. Even to breathe a threat to a teacher would have ensured a punishment so swift and solid, our feet wouldn't have hit the ground.

Fifty years ago, children almost never killed. Today it is commonplace. Apart from the above, cases such as those involving James

---

[292] "The Hidden Hand of Violence", *Freedom*, op. cit. p.8

Bulger, the Menendez brothers and Damilola Taylor have horrified the world. Gil Garcetti, District Attorney for Los Angeles County, remarks: *"It's incredible, the ability of the very young to commit the most horrendous crimes was unthinkable 20 years ago."* [293]

Today, robberies are carried out by conscience-deadened youth drug-addicts. Murders, tortures and sadism are practised with Satanic ritual to a degree that was unheard of prior to the advent of the drug culture. Judge Susan Winfield of Washington DC comments: *"Youngsters used to shoot each other in the body. Then in the head. Now, they shoot each other in the face."* [294] But still the 1980 Comprehensive Textbook of Psychiatry persists with its nonsense: *"...taken no more than two or three times a week, cocaine creates no serious problems."* [295]

TEACHER'S COLLEGE

Psychiatry's penetration of the world's schools has long since been accomplished. As early as 1925, more than 1,000 schools in America were changing their educational curricula according to the dictates of the psychiatrists who dominated the highly influential Teacher's College at Columbia University in New York. The new educational system was designed to eliminate what John Dewey, a Teacher's College educational director, referred to as 'stress factors' in the classroom. The 'evils' articulated by the college, which were damaging the pupils, included school failure, academic curricula and disciplinary procedures.

John Dewey

The views of Dewey and his colleagues were congruent with the beliefs of Wundtian psychiatry. Teacher's College was to come to regard children as nothing but animals requiring guidance. Dewey, widely renowned for 'revolutionising' American and Russian education, and later

---

[293] Wilkerson, Isabel, "2 Boys, A Debt, a Gun, a Victim: The Face of Violence", *The New York Times*, 16th May 1994

[294] Lacayo, Richard, "When Kids Go Bad", *Time*, 19th September 1994, p.61

[295] Kaplan, Freedman and Saddock, 3rd Edition, Williams and Wilkins, Baltimore, MD: 1980

world curricula, declared that putting undue pressures on a child to perform was to risk making them mentally ill.[296] In fact, the true agenda espoused by James Earl Russell, Edward Lee Thorndike and John Dewey, who dominated Teacher's College, was no less than exercising complete control over the minds of youth, thereby gaining a more compliant society in the future. Educators, trained in the new principles given to them by Teacher's College, would help all the children 'fit into society':

"The ultimate problem of all education is to co-ordinate the psychological and social factors.... The co-ordination demands... that the child be capable of expressing himself, <u>but in such a way as to realise social ends</u>." [297]

One knows trouble is coming when a luminary such as Thorndike, occupying so powerful a position of influence over the world's teachers, believes that *"...artificial exercises, like drills on phonetics, multiplication tables, and formal writing movements, are used to a wasteful degree. <u>Subjects such as arithmetic, language, and history include content that is intrinsically of little value</u>. Nearly every subject is enlarged unwisely to satisfy the academic ideal of thoroughness."* [298]

Would it be such a stretch to compare this Brave New World with the one envisioned by Weishaupt, Hitler, Galton and other eugenicists? A world wherein a compliant and happy, dullard people, unable even to express themselves or add up, are provided for and exploited by their leaders; a 'human resource' willing to be plundered, educated only so far, so as not to gain the dreaded and dangerous 'personal initiative' that may disrupt the planned global Utopia?

PROTOCOL #5 (EXTRACT) EXPOSED 1905
<u>There is nothing more dangerous than personal initiative</u>. We must so direct the education of the goyim communities that whenever they come upon a matter requiring initiative, they may drop their hands in despairing impotence. From this collision arise grave moral shocks, disenchantments, failures. By all these means we shall so wear down the goyim that they will be compelled to offer us international power of a

---

[296] Thorndike, Edward L & Arthur I Gates, *Elementary Principles of Education*, MacMillan, New York: 1928, p.147
[297] Lionni, Pablo, *The Leipzig Connection*, Delphian Press, Sheridan, Oregon: 1988, p.31-32
[298] Thorndike, Edward L & Arthur I Gates, *Elementary Principles of Education*, op. cit.

nature which by its position will enable us, without any violence, gradually to absorb all the State forces of the world and to form a Super-Government.

YIELD TO OUR 'MOLDING HANDS'

Russell, Thorndike and Dewey remained at Teacher's College for thirty years, presiding over increased funding from the John D Rockefeller-founded and -financed General Education Board. In language reminiscent of the Protocols, which the Rockefellers and other leading eugenicist families of America's Illuminati-influenced Eastern Establishment are widely believed to have endorsed, the Board's *Occasional Letter No. 1* declared:

"In our dreams we have limitless resources and the people yield themselves with perfect docility to our moulding hands. The present education conventions fade from their minds, and, unhampered by tradition, we work our own good will upon a grateful and responsive rural folk. We shall not try to make these people or any of their children into philosophers or men of learning, or men of science. We have not to raise up from among them authors, editors, poets or men of letters. We shall not search for embryo great artists, painters, musicians nor lawyers, doctors, preachers, politicians, statesmen, of whom we have ample supply.

The task we set before ourselves is very simple as well as <u>a very beautiful one</u>; to train these people as we find them to a perfectly ideal life <u>just where they are</u> [i.e. no personal initiative. Keep the masses entertained with bread and circuses]. *So we will organise our children and teach them to do in a perfect way the things their fathers and mothers are doing in an imperfect way, in the homes, in the shops, and on the farm."* [299]

Edward L Thorndike

---

[299] Lionni, Pablo, op. cit.

Social control, eugenics and 'moulding' societies were, as we have seen, the buzz topics in government and philosophy in the 1920's. By 1928, Rockfeller-sponsored Board grants to Teacher's College totalled $2,000,000. By the early 1950's, the infiltration of psychiatric thought and strategy into the US school system and those around the world was staggering. From the horse's mouth itself, *A History of Teacher's College, Columbia University* tells the world in 1953:

"The single most powerful educational force in the world is at 120th Street and Broadway in New York City. Your children's teachers go there for advanced training.... With 100,000 alumni, TC has managed to seat about one-third of the presidents and deans now in office at accredited US teacher training schools. Its graduates make up about 20% of all our public school teachers. Over a fourth of the superintendents of schools in the 168 US cities with at least 50,000 population are TC-trained." [300]

That was fifty years ago.

MENTAL HYGIENE

A British organisation, the National Committee on Mental Hygiene, was founded by Clifford Beers, a former mental patient. Beers received the support of psychiatric leaders William James and Adolf Meyer, a German who had emigrated to the United States. Beers' organisation soon began receiving huge funding from the Rockefeller foundations.

In a 1982 speech before the History of Education Society, the society's president Sol Cohen said, *"Few intellectual and social movements of this century have had so deep and pervasive an influence on the theory and practice of American Education as the mental hygiene movement."* [301] Cohen's views were summed up in the Society's quarterly magazine, under the heading "The Mental Hygiene Movement, The Development of Personality and the School: The Medicalization of American Education".

Britain's John Rawlings Rees, former deputy director of the Tavistock Clinic, the British government's psychological warfare body, was frank about using his own considerable talents to subvert the existing educational system. Imagine the incongruity one of the former chiefs of British psychological warfare stating:

---

[300] Ibid.
[301] Cohen, Sol, *History of Education Quarterly*, Summer 1983, p.124

"We can therefore justifiably stress our particular point of view with regard to the proper development of the human psyche, <u>even though our knowledge be incomplete</u>. We must aim to make it permeate every educational activity in our national life.... We have made a useful attack upon a number of professions. The two easiest of them naturally are the teaching profession and the Church; the two most difficult are law and medicine....

<u>If we are to infiltrate the professional and social activities of other people</u>, I think we must imitate the Totalitarians and organise some kind of fifth column activity! If better ideas on mental health are to progress and spread, <u>we, as the salesmen</u>, must lose our identity.... Let us therefore, very secretly, be fifth columnists [persons secretly aiding the enemy - traitors]." [302]

What were these pervasive influences and doctrines promoted by psychiatry, the Mental Hygiene movement and the British and American governments? Bruce Wiseman enlightens:

"The hygienist's idea on mental illness was that it was the result of improper personality development. If somehow one could reach into the personal lives of humanity and control the growth process of personality, it was reasoned, mental illness would be eliminated.

Regarding children, hygienists believed:

> - *Childhood is the most important period in the development of personality.*
> - *Children are very susceptible to 'personality disorders'.*
> - *The school is the ideal focal point for detecting, preventing and fixing personality disorders.*
> - *The development of personality must take precedence over any other educational objective.*
> - *Shyness, daydreaming, withdrawal, introversion, the 'shut-in personality' are psychiatric danger signals in children.*
> - *Stress is the chief precipitating cause of psychiatric symptoms, and stress warps personality."* [303]

---

[302] Rees, John R, "Strategic Planning for Mental Health", *Mental Health*, Vol.1, No.4, pp.103-106
[303] Wiseman, Bruce, op. cit. p.265-266

Cohen's statement on one of the main strategies of mental hygiene clarifies his view that the child cannot be held responsible for its actions, thus it is up to society (schools) to remove all stress from pupils which may cause them harm: *"Hygienists called upon the teacher to pay less attention to the child's overt behaviour and more attention to understanding the motives, 'more or less conscious', underlying behaviour, <u>over which the child had little control and for which the child could not be held responsible</u>."* [304]

Thomas Salmon, an early director of the National Committee, saw society's urgent need for his services: *"Psychiatry... should be permitted to enter the schools."* [305]

Ralph Truitt, head of the National Committee's Division of Child Guidance Clinics, declared in 1927: *"If we are going to prevent dependency, delinquency, insanity, and general inadequacy, the school should be the focus of our attack."* [306]

VIOLENCE, ILLITERACY AND CONTEMPT

With psychiatry's influences scoring direct hits into schools from the mid-1950's onwards, emphasis was taken off academics and disciplinary procedures and focused on the 'personality disorders' of the pupils. Naughtiness, truancy, abuse and other childhood behaviours were now "not a sin, but a symptom".[307] With the role of parenting transferred from the home to the classroom, successive legislation ensured that psychiatry would become a permanent feature of the educational curriculum, accepted by almost all schools by the mainstream Teacher's College-influenced academics who ran them.

Today we have indeed inherited the legacy of this catastrophic wrong turn with a massive increase in violence, illiteracy and apathy in the world's classrooms. 13% of American 17-year-olds are functionally illiterate, that is, they cannot read above a 10-year-old's level. CCHR reports that the figure may run as high as 40% among minority youth:

"Between 25 and 44 million American adults cannot read the poison warnings on a can of pesticide, a letter from a child's teacher, or the front

---

[304] Cohen, Sol, *History of Education Quarterly*, op. cit.
[305] Lionni, Pablo, op. cit.
[306] Ibid.
[307] Ibid.

page of the daily newspaper. In 1930, 80% of African Americans over the age of 14 could read. By 1990, only 56% could read. 16% of white adults, 44% of blacks and 56% percent of Hispanic citizens are functional or marginal illiterates."[308]

OVER-PRAISING TO REDUCE 'STRESS'
That this psychiatry-induced educational philosophy has permeated the educational halls worldwide today is beyond doubt. The strategy of over-praising children and refusing to punish wrongdoing is alive and kicking. Jenni Murray, writing for Britain's *Daily Mail*, comments:

"Annabel is a case in point. She arrived in our office not very long ago with the air of a woman who has hardly slept for a week, and the tell-tale red eyes of recent tears. One gentle question about what was the matter opened up a floodgate of anxiety. She, like many of her ilk, had signed up for one of the parenting classes so admired by the present government.

Her class tutor had told her it would be all too easy if she followed her advice. 'What advice?' I asked her. 'It's all about being child-centred – praise and positive reinforcement,' she explained.

'You are never allowed to be angry or raise your voice. If the big one's pulling the little one's hair, or hitting him over the head with Thomas the Tank Engine, you have to say, in the sweetest possible tones: "Darling, is it a good idea to do that?"

"If the kid back-chats you, you're supposed to bite your tongue. If they bound into your bed at 4:30am, wanting to play a game, you have to welcome them and be jolly. You've got to be nice all the time and I can't do it!"

Here we note that the suggestion is being made by the course tutor that discipline should be totally retracted in the household. Chaos results. In the same article, Murray recounts her childhood and how it was done 'in the old days':

---

[308] Blumenfeld, Samuel L, "Who Killed Excellence?" *Imprimis*, Vol.14, No.9, September 1985, Killsdale, Michigan, p.3; Kozol, Jonathan, *Illiterate America*, Doubleday, Garden City, New York: 1985, p.4; Frammolino, Ralph, "US Adults Lagging in Literacy, Study Finds", *Los Angeles Times*, 9th September 1993

"Throughout my own childhood and teenage years, unacceptable behaviour was punished by a withdrawal of privileges, and a threat made was invariably carried out.

If I failed an exam, I hadn't tried hard enough. If I was swinging the lead to get another day off school, my mother would get out the thermometer, declare me fit as a fiddle, and pack me off with the warning that you got molly-coddled only if you were a stretcher case. If I didn't get the part I wanted in the school play, she reckoned there was obviously someone more suitable. Mooning over a lost love, I was told there were plenty more fish in the sea.

Dust yourself down, pick yourself up and start all over again – that was the culture. Both parents praised me when I did well, and criticised when I fell short of the mark. There were times when I thought them excessively strict or unfair. It's only as I have grown older and coped with whatever slings, arrows or adulation have come my way that I've appreciated what they did for me – and how much that approach could do for today's children." [309]

Learning the tools and skills with which to cope with life's trials was the legacy of the old, 'tough' educational system of past centuries. Many nations today however have a crisis with the ineffectiveness of their educational systems and lack of disciplinary and punishment procedures. Is it at all questionable that flagrant misbehaviour in the classroom and an increase in criminal activity on school campuses have been the result? In Plato's declaration that *"The direction in which education starts a man will determine his future life"*, we receive another confirmation that education has made the youth what it is today.[310] How then can 'society' be blamed for the decline in social and moral standards that began in our schools and homes? Has the New Way made us happier and more liberated? Let the reader judge.

TELLING KIDS THEY'VE MADE IT WHEN THEY HAVEN'T

Is true self-reliance and an ability to deal with life's problems instilled in a young child through discipline and proper achievement, or by

---

[309] Murray, Jenni, "How we are betraying our children by overpraising and not punishing them", *Daily Mail*, 14th March 2002, p.56

[310] Bartlett, John, *Familiar Quotations*, 16th ed. Little, Brown and Co. Ltd., Boston: 1992, p.75

sheltering a child from the stressful realities of life? How will a child ever know what pinnacles of endeavour humans are capable of, and of what base and degrading states, without studying literature, history and the arts? How can a teenager express and become what cannot be thought of or written? Who now knows what is right or wrong? Is rightness *really* just a matter of an individual's opinion?

A 1993 *US News and World Report* article entitled "A For Effort... Or For Showing Up" illustrates the complete contempt modern educational chiefs have for academia. *"At Harvard in 1992, 91% of undergraduate grades were B- or higher. Stanford is top-heavy with As and Bs too; only about 6% of all grades are Cs. At Princeton, As rose from 33% of all grades to 40% in four years.... For whatever reason (and the feel-good, self-esteem movement is surely one), marks have broken free of performance and become more and more unreal. They are designed to please, not to measure or guide students about strengths and weaknesses."* [311]

Leading educator Alan Larson: *"Children who are told they made it when they didn't absolutely despise adults. They think they are total fools. And when their whole life is like that, they become apathetic about it, because the whole world is crazy. They feel bad about hiding the truth (that they didn't make it) and they withdraw from the area and it produces a complete disassociation of the kid from the subject of education, because it is a lie. And kids know it underneath. Kids know that the only thing that causes self-esteem is confidence and production."* [312]

READY CASH

There is of course no question that there are many children who are experiencing a whole range of problems we will be examining in Part 2. There is nothing fictitious about most of their difficulties, as we shall see. But today, schools and parents are actively encouraged to brand their children 'special needs' or 'learning disordered'. To do so, according to research carried out by *US News and World Report*, guarantees federal grants and supplementary payouts earmarked for the handicapped. [313] In 1990 new federal guidelines allowed an American family to receive $450

---

[311] *US News and World Report*, 18th October 1993

[312] Wiseman, Bruce, op. cit. p.282

[313] "Labelling Away Problem Kids", *US News and World Report*, 13th March 1989, pp.51-61

for each 'ADHD' child. 'ADHD' diagnoses rose from 5% of disabled children to nearly 25% by 1995. Some parents were reported to have coached their children to do poorly at school and act in an aberrant fashion in order to obtain the payout.[314]

So successful has the indoctrination been that, in many countries, by applying the current criteria for 'mental illness' promoted by the neighbourhood psychiatrist and psychologist, teachers can deem well over 50% of their school populations 'mentally ill'.[315] According to Thomas K Fagan, Professor and Coordinator of School Psychology Programs at Memphis State University, in 1920, there were 200 psychologists in American schools. By 1990, this figure had risen to 22,000.[316] Today, American schools spend a combined $1 billion a year on psychologists who work full-time to diagnose students.[317]

And if the campaign is to reduce stress and induce a 'balanced psyche', what are we to make of what is actually being taught? One student relates the following:

"We had an English course in the ninth grade junior high whose title was 'Death Education'. In the manual, 73 out of the 80 stories had to do with death, dying, killing, murder, suicide, and what you wanted on your tombstone. One girl, a ninth grader, blew her brains out after having written a note on her front door that said what she wanted on her tombstone." [318]

Another 'Values Clarification' student, Paulette, has this tale to tell: *"I was 13 when the teacher told our social studies class that we were to have a special film shown to us about 'life'. The film was about a Confederate soldier who was going to be executed. The rope around his neck breaks and he falls into the water and gets away from his captors. He runs down a road towards a woman who is obviously his wife and the whole class cheered, believing that the message was that you can always surmount any odds and that the family was important.*

---

[314] CCHR, *Psychiatry – Betraying and Drugging Children*, op. cit. p.10

[315] Wood, Regna Lee, *Right to Read Report*, April/May 1994

[316] Fagan, Thomas, Memphis State University, USA, private correspondence.

[317] CCHR, *Psychiatry – Betraying and Drugging Children*, op. cit. p.11

[318] CCHR, *Psychiatry – Education's Ruin*, Los Angeles: 2002, p.19

However, just as the man goes to hug his wife, the trap door opens and you see and hear the soldier's body hanging. His getting away was just a fantasy in the last moments before his death. There was shocked silence in the classroom. I had nightmares from this and thereafter didn't trust my teachers. Whenever there was an announcement that another film was to be shown, I'd cut class and I started smoking pot in the park instead." [319]

Tom DeWeese of the American Policy foundation, and an expert on the infamous Outcome Based Education program (OBE), told a Washington press conference in 1995 of a case he had studied: *"A 9-year-old boy told his mother he ranked lumberjacks in the same class as murderers and bigots after a 'Values Clarification' class. These psychology-based programs are harming children.... OBE is not education, it's [state] mind control from womb to tomb."* [320]

In Grand Rapids, Michigan, the local Community Health Service provided staff to teach a course to 20 students, aged 13 to 17, on 'Self-Pleasuring Techniques' and 'Sexual Fantasies' (perhaps to reduce stress?). Parents filed a suit against the authority after their children brought home materials depicting graphic pictures and descriptions of masturbation, group and oral sex.

In 1991, California 13- and 14-year-old pupils were asked to complete a survey in which they were asked how many times they had had vaginal intercourse with girls and anal sex with boys during the past twelve months. The multiple choice ranged from 'never' to 'more than 20 times'. Also requested was whether the pupil was intending to use a condom during the coming year and what their parents would feel about this. [321]

Mental health watchdog CCHR reports similar cases that have been reported and investigated by them:

In a fifth grade 'health class' in Lincoln City, Oregon, homosexuality was presented to 11-year-olds as an 'alternative lifestyle'. Anal intercourse was described. In this same class, a plastic model of female genitalia with a tampon insert was passed around to the boys to encourage their

---

[319] Case on file with CCHR US

[320] DeWeese, Tom, press statement from the American Policy Foundation, 21st June 1995

[321] High School Student Survey, Rand, Santa Monica, California

understanding of tampons. Birth control pills were also passed around and explained. A parent who observed this said: *"At no time was there any mention of abstinence as a desirable alternative for fifth graders* [11-year-olds]. *The morality taught in the classroom that day was complete promiscuity. As a result of this kind of education, we are experiencing pregnancy among 13-year-olds with resulting abortions."*

Beverly Eakman, author of *Cloning of the American Mind, Eradicating Morality Through Education*, summarises her extensive research:

"Most people today suspect that education is not really about literacy, 'basics' or proficiency at anything. What is less well understood is that there exists in this country, and indeed throughout the industrialised world, what can best be described as an 'Illiteracy Cartel' – ostensibly aimed at furthering 'mental health'. This cartel derives its power from those who stand to benefit financially and politically from ignorance and educational malpractice; from the frustration, the crime, the joblessness and social chaos that miseducation produces." [322]

Testimony before the US Department of Education in 1984 revealed the Values Clarification Program, a system launched as a full-on assault against the integrity of the family unit, religion, sexual maturity and traditional values. Freud is no doubt spinning like a lathe in his grave with pride at the destruction of the 'hateful' sexual paradigms of religion. Here are some exercises pupils are regularly required to complete:

- How many of you think there are times when cheating is justified?
- How many of you would approve of a marriage between homosexuals being sanctioned by a priest, minister or rabbi?
- How many of you would approve of contract marriages, in which the marriage could come up for renewal every few years?
- Advise where you stand on the topic of masturbation?
- To whom do you tell your doubts about religion?
- "I would lie if _____."

---

[322] Eakman, Beverly, *The Cloning of the American Mind. Eradicating Morality Through Education*, Hunting House Publishers, 1998; also Eakman, Beverly, *Educating for the New World Order*, National Book Company, January 1991

William Kilpatrick, author of *Why Johnny Can't Tell Right From Wrong*, tells us that in Values Clarification *"...feelings, personal growth, and a totally non-judgemental attitude are emphasised.... No time is spent providing moral guidance or forming character. The virtues are not explained or discussed, no models of good behaviour are provided, no reason is given why a boy or a girl should want to be good in the first place.... They come away with the impression that even the most basic values are matters of dispute."* [323]

The authors of the original 1966 text on Values Clarification stated: *"It is entirely possible that children will choose not to develop values. It is the teacher's responsibility to support this choice also."* [324]

A mother, distraught over her son's drug use and subsequent suicide on 7th September 1981, stated: *"He had used marijuana since junior high school. About a month before he died, He told my husband that he had decided to give up smoking pot. He went into deep depression and took his life by carbon monoxide poisoning. He left a note saying, 'I did it because I couldn't think or nothing.'"*

Only after his death did the parents discover their son had been part of a 'Values Clarification' program with the objective: *"We will attempt to teach the different categories of drugs, their effect and, hopefully, how to make a knowledgeable choice, using your own values system."* [325]

Joey, an 8-year-old African American boy, was part of a 'problem solving' class in his school and was shown a film which depicted a young boy trying to kill himself by tying a rope around his neck. In the film, the boy talks about not being liked at school, being teased and worrying about growing up. Joey's mother did not know about the program as the school curriculum merely stated that it was 'social sciences'. Two days after her son watched this video, she walked into his room and found him hanging by a rope from his bunk bed.[326]

And what about little Sam Back? Was he another victim of society's easy tolerance of drugs? *"His parents had the best possible start in life,*

[323] Kilpatrick, William, *Why Johnny Can't Tell Right From Wrong*, Simon & Schuster, September 1993, www.amazon.com
[324] CCHR, *Psychiatry – Education's Ruin*, op. cit. p.20
[325] Ibid.
[326] Ibid.

and Sam Back deserved the same. Yet before he was two, he had been neglected, abused and murdered. Sam was the victim, not just of inhuman cruelty, but of the drugs which enslaved his mother Emma Back and stepfather Aaron Goodman.... After handing out months of ill-treatment, Goodman, a cocaine and crack addict, punched the child so hard in the stomach that his bowel ruptured. The child's body had 63 injuries, including a bite mark on his leg. His body also contained traces of crack cocaine, which was constantly smoked around him." [327]

Cocaine-addict Sigmund Freud's death knell for traditional biblical morality, sounded decades before, has certainly resulted in his desired removal of religion's *"obsolete, offensive vestments"*. The trouble is, time-honoured values, such as 'Thou shalt not lie...' 'thou shalt not murder...' and 'thou shalt not commit adultery...', traditionally seen as essential for the maintenance of a stable, civilised society, were fed into the shredder along with the cassocks. Let us remind ourselves that decades before, G Brock Chisholm had wished society would hurry up and rid itself of the *"... poisonous certainties fed us by our parents, our Sunday and day school teachers, our politicians, our priests, our newspapers and others with a vested interest in controlling us.... If the race is to be freed from its crippling burden of good and evil, it must be psychiatrists who take the original responsibility."* [328]

But what has been the result of all this freedom from the 'crippling burdens' of good and evil G Brock wanted our children to enjoy?

"A young woman is phoning for help from her apartment.... Just before the tape goes dead – police believe the phone was ripped from the wall – she can be heard screaming, 'Don't harm my baby!'... Over the next several minutes she was beaten bloody with a mop handle and raped. The attacker was a neighbour who had apparently become infatuated with her. The woman, who survived, is 22. The accused rapist, Andre Green, is 13." [329]

---

[327] *Daily Mail*, 14th March 2002, pp.1, 8

[328] Chisholm, G Brock, op. cit. pp.7-9

[329] CCHR, *Psychiatry – Education's Ruin*, op. cit. p.28

And They Call This Science?

"Through psychiatry's stigmatising labels, easy-seizure commitment laws, and often brutal, depersonalising 'treatments', thousands needlessly fall into a coercive system which denies the most basic of human rights." – Jan Eastgate, International President, Citizen's Commission on Human Rights

The image of the mental health professional - calm, knowledgeable, trustworthy, in touch with the latest science - is the same picture portrayed to the public through films, literature, the courts and newspapers. But let's examine the 'science' of psychiatry and get to the bottom of its favourite diagnostic procedures and terms to see if we can conclude upon what firm ground, if any, this profession has sunk its scientific pilings.

New classifications of 'mental illness' have been steadily added since the mid-1800's. Like recipes for a ghastly new cookbook, psychiatry has dreamt up mental disorders by the dozen to pathologise every quirk of human nature and, as we shall see, has also taken *regular physical disease manifestations* and performed precisely the same sleight of hand.

THE MYTH OF 'MENTAL ILLNESS'

Psychiatry's strange dilemma is that their 'mental' diseases are at the same time physical to the brain, which has never been proven, and yet totally within the realm of the brain, which psychiatry views as separate from the body. Having carved out for itself an exclusive right to champion anything in the territory above the eyebrows, psychiatry defends its physical turf with cold-as-dawn, dogged determination. So entrenched has the popular view of psychiatry become in our society today, most believe that anyone who is mentally troubled, depressed, hyperactive or exhibits eccentric behaviour of any kind is in fact *sick* in the head. The public has been adroitly conditioned to imagine, when we are looking at someone who has been psychiatrically diagnosed, that there are physical imperfections in that person's brain; chemicals awry in the head, brains misshapen or chromosomes plotting the downfall of their wretched human host.

Professor Emeritus of Psychiatry, American Dr Thomas Szasz shocked the world in 1960 with the publication of the first edition of his landmark work, *The Myth of Mental Illness*. Szasz, one of the leading whistleblowers of psychiatry, cannot be reasonably ignored or ridiculed by his profession, since he became one of its most meteoric peers:

"We call problems in living 'mental illness'. Individuals who consult psychiatrists or are compelled to submit to them by force or fraud are 'mental patients', their complaints or the complaints of others are 'mental symptoms', and the conditions imputed to them that allegedly 'cause' and 'explain' their conduct are 'mental disease'.... We call psychiatric inquiries, whether invited by consenting clients or imposed on them against their will, 'diagnoses', and psychiatric interventions, 'treatments'.... And since we even have a National Institute of Mental Health [in the USA] it is easy to see why the right-thinking person considers it unthinkable that there might be no such thing as mental health or mental illness. If that were so, we would be victims of our own folly." [330]

Szasz states that the word 'disease' can only be used in connection with an observable anatomical lesion or other physiological defect. Use of the word 'disease' beyond that, in Dr Szasz's opinion, is not only misleading, but fraud.[331] Indeed, sickness in regular medicine means exactly that - a clearly identifiable and observable physical derangement of the body, such as infection, injury, a cancer, blocked arteries or high temperature. Yet these types of physical observations are always noticeably absent with the psychiatrist's 'mental disorders'. The US Congress Office of Technology Assessment Report of 1992 reiterates the point: *"Research has yet to identify specific biological causes for any of these [mental] disorders. Mental disorders are classified on the basis of symptoms because there are as yet no biological markers or laboratory tests for them."*

Loren Mosher was a former National Institute of Mental Health researcher and a 30-year member of the APA. He resigned in 1998, telling the American Psychiatric Association president he believed *"...biologically based brain diseases are convenient for families and practitioners alike.... It is 'no fault insurance' against responsibility. We are just helplessly caught up in a swirl of brain pathology for which no one, except DNA, is responsible.... The fact that there is no evidence confirming brain disease attribution is, at this point, irrelevant."* [332]

---

[330] Szasz, Thomas, *The Myth of Mental Illness*, Harper and Row, New York: 1974
[331] Ibid.
[332] Mosher, Loren R, in his letter of resignation to APA president, 4th December 1998

Dr Elliot Valenstein, in his *Blaming the Brain*, also declares: *"Contrary to what is claimed, no biochemical, anatomical or functional signs have been found that reliably distinguish the brains of mental patients.... Theories are held on to not only because there is nothing else to take their place, but also because they are useful in promoting drug treatment.... All of the impressive knowledge of neuropharmacology has not really brought us closer to understanding the origin of mental disorders.... People with mental disorders may be encouraged when they are told that the prescribed drugs will do for them what insulin does for a diabetic, but the analogy is certainly not justified."* [333]

Quirky behaviour in Aunt Ethel, who has lost her keys again, becomes one of the many 'dementias'. A child, who has been drinking 10-12 sodas a day, each containing the equivalent of at least eight teaspoons of sucrose, laced with phosphoric acid, a known neurotransmitter disrupter, and consumed out of aluminium cans, is described as 'hyperactive' and is then put on a cheap form of cocaine, known as Ritalin. Incredibly, at no time will most psychiatrists even entertain the notion of a physical causation to the behaviours they are examining. Szasz and his colleagues in the psychiatric ranks, who have vociferously spoken out against the profession in which they were so highly trained, reserve their most stinging criticism, scorn and derision however for psychiatry's famous 'bible' – the DSM.

THE DIAGNOSTIC AND STATISTICAL MANUAL (DSM)

In the 1840's, there was but one general classification of mental illness, that of idiocy/insanity. By 1880, around 40 years after the formation of the American Psychiatric Association, there were seven categories of mental disorders: mania, melancholia, monomania (irrationality when discussing subjects), pareses (syphilitic brain condition later found to poisoning brought on by mercury-based medications offered to syphilitics), dementia, dipsomania (alcoholism) and epilepsy. Bruce Wiseman sums up the important deviance from the road of true science psychiatry inevitably took:

"...The budding profession of psychiatry initiated the practice of declaring illnesses they assumed were there instead of naming what they actually observed. They believed the 'patient' must be sick because he behaved abnormally. By declaring his conduct as symptoms, they concluded they must be caused by an illness. Not surprisingly, psychiatry

---

[333] Valenstein, Elliot S, *Blaming the Brain*, op. cit. pp.4, 6, 125, 224

has spent the past century unsuccessfully trying to prove this position. No 'brain lesions' have been found. No mutant nerve connections have been discovered. No substantiated genetic proof has come forth, even with modern technology." [334]

In 1933, the first official compendium of mental illnesses was published. Named the *Standard Classified Nomenclature of Disease*, it was subsequently revised twice to include further disease listings. Almost twenty years later in 1952, the *Diagnostic and Statistical Manual for Mental Disorders* (DSM) appeared and became the official psychiatric bible for its disease classifications. The first DSM had expanded 'mental disorders' from an original one – insanity – to a staggering 112. These included brain disorders, psychotic disorders, a plethora of 'neuroses', personality disorders, sexual deviations among which it named homosexuality, transvestism, paedophilia, fetishism, rape assault and sexual sadism. What most members of the public however do not recognise is that, in spite of all the seeming science, professorships and training that psychiatry has come up with in defence of its profession, there has never been one shred of proof presented in a scientific context indicating that these conditions are physical 'diseases of the mind'.

DSM II
1968 saw the revising of the original DSM into DSM II. The original 112 disorders had risen to 163. New categories included 6 new drug dependence ailments, 8 new sexual deviance conditions, 6 new schizophrenic disorders, 5 more neuroses and a whopping 13 new categories of alcoholic disorders. Also sneaking in were 3 new personality disorders. DSM II also saw a new classification that was to have huge repercussions in future educative policy - a new diagnosis for 'hyperkinetic' youngsters. Having decided at last to dispense with the quaint notion of providing anything approaching empirical proof, DSM II also reveals that these disorders are being established by a committee which, disconcertingly, *votes* on whether or not these disorders exist. In other words, if psychiatry votes a mental illness in, it apparently exists. There is no attempt at science, as we shall see. The intellectual mediocrity, yet arrogance behind this disease-fiction process is, according to critics, simply staggering. That psychiatry cannot even make its mind up about schizophrenia, one of its bulwark mental disorders, is also very noteworthy. The manual itself admits: *"Even if it had tried* [which

---

[334] Wiseman, Bruce, *Psychiatry – The Ultimate Betrayal*, op. cit. p.349-350

presumably it hadn't], *the Committee could not establish agreement about what this disorder is; it could only agree on what to call it."*

DSM III

In 1980, a third revision to the DSM was unveiled, with the number of disorders haring up to 224. Homosexuality had been struck off the Sexual Deviation category, in deference to busy and furious lobbying by the homosexual community. Even though over half the DSM committee opposed this amendment, political expediency won the day. A vote was cast across the APA membership and Homosexuality duly went from being Sexual Deviancy to a scientifically-declared form of 'sexual preference.'

On this matter, psychiatrist Walter Afield told CCHR: *"I was just talking last weekend to somebody who was on the commission to do the DSM IV that was coming out, and I said, 'Well now, tell me, homosexuality used to be considered a disease and then it was not a disease. What's it going to be in DSM IV?' And he said, 'Oh, we've totally cured it now. It doesn't exist.'"* [335]

It is evident that much thought had gone into targeting children in DSM III. In the 'Infancy, Childhood and Adolescence' section, 32 further mental disorders were added, including Attention Deficit Disorder, Conduct Disorder, Developmental Reading Disorder, Developmental Arithmetic Disorder, Developmental Articulation Disorder, Separation Anxiety Disorder, Overanxious Disorder. Any of the foregoing 'mental illnesses', of course, may arise out of lax discipline in the classroom, kids missing their parents, bad teaching... or maybe kids just being kids. (See Part 2) The point rapidly becoming understood among teachers and psychologists/psychiatrists alike was that youth 'patients' so diagnosed were often eligible for insurance reimbursement and/or federal/government funding. The DSM codes for each disease are vital in order to claim for insurance payouts. [336]

Quite disturbingly, this medicalising of common childhood behavioural traits was extended to other social vices in DSM III. New chemical substance abuse 'mental disorders' included Hallucinogen Organic Mental Disorders, Cannabis [Marijuana] Organic Mental Disorders, Tobacco Organic Mental Disorder and Caffeine Organic Mental Disorder. In the introduction of DSM III, can we any longer be

---

[335] CCHR interview with Walter Afield, 11th January 1994
[336] Eakman, Beverly K, *Cloning of the American Mind*, op. cit. p.95

flabbergasted to discover the crashingly frank admission that *"...there is no satisfactory definition that specifies precise boundaries for the concept 'mental disorder'"*?

DSM-III-R

When DSM III-R (revised) came out in 1987, the world now had 253 mental illnesses with which to contend. Psychiatrist Matthew Dumont was upset:

"They say... 'While this manual provides a classification of mental disorder... no definition adequately specifies boundaries for the concept....' They then provide a 125-word definition of 'mental disorder' which is supposed to resolve all the issues surrounding the sticky problem of where deviance ends and dysfunction begins. It doesn't.

They go on to say: '...there is no assumption that each mental disorder is a discrete entity with sharp boundaries between it and other mental disorders or between it and no mental disorder.' This is a remarkable statement in a volume whose 500-odd pages are devoted to the criteria for distinguishing one condition of psychopathology from another with a degree of precision indicated by a hundredth of a decimal point [the DSM disease coding system]."[337]

PATHOLOGISING CRIMINAL BEHAVIOUR

The DSM-III-R committee also attempted to include an 'illness' named Paraphilic Rapism (also known as Paraphilic Coercive Disorder). This was to include persons fantasising or attempting sexual assault/rape, persons experiencing intense sexual arousal or a desire associated with it for at least six months. This move provoked sharp anger from women's groups across the US that rape was being de-criminalised in favour of a soft psychiatric diagnosis in court. In 1986, Maryland activist Roberta Roper went on the warpath when her daughter was raped by two men who subsequently received light sentences by the court. Benevolent psychiatric evidence was heard excusing the men's behaviour on grounds that they were unable to control themselves. Roper later remarked: *"I don't think the public has a whole lot of confidence in psychiatric evaluations. I don't see who benefits except the psychiatrists."*[338]

---

[337] Caplan, Paula J, *They Say You're Crazy*, Addison-Wesley Publishing Company, New York: 1995, p.222

[338] "Lawyers Fear New Psychiatric Labels", *San Francisco Examiner*, 15th August 1986

Assistant Attorney General Lois Harrington gives her opinion on the case: *"The only time we ever see psychiatrists in the courtroom is when they're telling us about a defendant's mitigating circumstances so sentences will be more lenient.... This* [Rapism] *is going to be absolutely devastating to victims."* [339]

DOMESTIC ABUSE

Given psychiatry's antipathy towards anything that smacks of bridling the sexual urge, and also given that its main goal is the usual frontline assault on the family and Chisholm's *'poisonous certainties fed to us by our parents'*, Masochistic Personality Disorder arrived right on cue in DSM-III-R, along with Premenstrual Syndrome (PMS). Again women's organisations were outraged, as they saw this as a deliberate attempt to blame a wife's 'masochistic urges' when domestic violence erupted in a household. An effort was made to placate the women, according to Dr Lenore Walker, the chair of the women's caucus of the Council of Representatives for the American Psychological Association. Shortly after the furore exploded, the APA came up with another mental illness – Sadism. Such an effort, Dr Walker complained, *"...shows the disrespect psychiatrists have for scientific research.... There was no talk of* [a 'Sadism' category] *before the flap over Masochism."* [340]

The APA however did not drop the diagnosis of Masochism completely, but changed the name to Self-Defeating Personality Disorder. Then, after a fresh bout of trouble from woman groups, it listed the 'illness' under a new classification: Disorders 'Needing Further Study'.

In describing why the APA didn't dump the Masochism classification altogether, DSM-III-R advisor, psychologist Paula Caplan explains: *"The APA Board had had chances to defeat the proposals several times before but had nevertheless charged right ahead. As one senior APA official told me privately, Board members who leaned toward discarding all three categories* [Rapism, Masochism and PMS] *were accused by their colleagues of 'giving in to the women.'"* Caplan tells of the *"truly astonishing extent to which scientific methods and evidence are disregarded as the handbook is being developed and revised."* [341]

---

[339] Ibid.
[340] "Politics, Women and Mental Disorders", *Los Angeles Herald Examiner*, 15th August 1986
[341] Caplan, Paula, op. cit. p.108

Another psychologist attending DSM-III-R hearings was quoted by *Time* magazine as stating: *"The low level of intellectual effort was shocking. Diagnoses were developed by majority vote on the level we would use to choose a restaurant. You feel like Italian, I feel like Chinese, so let's go to a cafeteria. Then it's typed into a computer. It may reflect on our naïveté, but it was our belief that there would be an attempt to look at things scientifically."* [342]

DSM-IV

DSM-IV was released in 1994. Mental disorders increased from 253 to 374. More childhood ailments were born, including the enormous Learning Disorder and a Reading Disorder illness, whose diagnosis sounds suspiciously like the results of poor teaching. Elsewhere in DSM-IV, the women apparently won. Self-Defeating Personality Disorder had slunk out of the revised manual, leaving behind it the highly profitable PMS, now no longer listed under the section 'needing further study'.

Psychiatrist Al Parides concludes that such watery diagnoses made upon consent or demand render the DSM *"a masterpiece of political manoeuvring."* Normal problems of life become mental disorders, to the great profit of psychiatry and their now-keen pharmaceutical manufacturer supporters.

Psychiatrist Walter Afield confides: *"I think what's happened is we have a tendency to identify more illness or define illness which never used to be defined as illness."* Dr Afield remembers a recent conference where *"...Russian psychiatrists were talking about [how] in America you talk about treating marital maladjustment reactions and in Russia we just call that bad luck."* [343]

DISEASE-MONGERING

The *British Medical Journal* featured an article entitled *Selling Sickness: the Pharmaceutical Industry and Disease-Mongering*. The report, which readers are strongly advised to read for themselves, reveals the calculated manner in which unnecessary fear of disease is instilled into the public mind, in order then to market equally unnecessary drugs and related pharmaceutical services. In the introduction to their study, the *BMJ* authors state:

---

[342] Ibid. p.90
[343] CCHR Interview with Dr Walter Afield, 11ᵗʰ January 1994

"There's a lot of money to be made from telling healthy people they're sick. Some forms of medicalising ordinary life may now be better described as disease-mongering: widening the boundaries of treatable illness in order to expand markets for those who sell and deliver treatments. Pharmaceutical companies are actively involved in sponsoring the definition of diseases and promoting them to both prescribers and consumers. The social construction of illness is being replaced by the corporate construction of disease....

Although some sponsored professionals or consumers may act independently and all concerned may have honourable motives, in many cases the formula is the same: groups and/or campaigns are orchestrated, funded, and facilitated by corporate interests, often via their public relations and marketing infrastructure. A key strategy of the alliances is to target the news media with stories designed to create fears about the condition or disease and draw attention to the latest treatment. Company-sponsored advisory boards supply the 'independent experts' for these stories, consumer groups provide the 'victims' and public relations companies provide media outlets with the positive spin about the latest 'breakthrough' medications." [344]

Through information taken from leaked documents and other sources, the authors accuse GlaxoSmithKline, Merck, Pfizer and Roche of engaging in this practice to one degree or another. The authors summarise their report as follows:

> ➤ *Some forms of 'medicalisation' may now be better described as 'disease-mongering' - extending the boundaries of treatable illness to expand markets for new products.*
> ➤ *Alliances of pharmaceutical manufacturers, doctors, and patients groups use the media to frame conditions as being widespread and severe.*
> ➤ *Disease-mongering can include turning ordinary ailments into medical problems, seeing mild symptoms as serious, treating personal problems as medical, seeing risks as diseases, and framing prevalence estimates to maximise potential markets.*

---

[344] Moynihan, Ray, Heath, Iona & David Henry, "Selling Sickness: the pharmaceutical industry and disease-mongering", *British Medical Journal Online*, BMJ, 13th April 2002

> Corporate funded information about disease should be replaced by independent information." [345]

The pharmaceutical/psychiatric view is that if you have a 'cure', you have a vested interest in marketing the 'disease'. If you think you are well, you simply haven't had enough tests yet. Psychiatrist and author David Kaiser believes the DSM classifications are nothing but *"...a pseudoscientific enterprise that grew out of modern psychiatry's desire to emulate modern medical science."* [346]

Margaret Hagen, author of *Whores of the Court*, is more unkind: *"Given their farcical 'empirical' procedures for arriving at new disorders with their associated symptoms lists, where does the American Psychiatric Association get off claiming a scientific, research-based foundation for its diagnostic manual? This is nothing more than science by decree. They say it is science, so it is."* [347]

Mark Syverud, editor of the *Daily Messenger*, reflects the temperature of scorn and anger felt by many informed citizens around the world at the fraud that is the Diagnostic and Statistical Manual of Mental Disorders:

"Beware. A new book shows that an epidemic of mental illness is sweeping the nation.... Does your 10-year-old dislike doing her math homework? Better get her to the nearest couch because she's got No. 315.4, Developmental Arithmetic Disorder. Maybe you're a teenager who argues with his parents. Better get some medication pronto because you've got No. 313.8, Oppositional Defiant Disorder.

And if your wife won't tell you that she snuck out to the mall last Saturday, then she's definitely got 313.2, Selective Mutism....

Trust me, I am not making these things up (that would be Fictitious Disorder Syndrome). The number of mental diseases identified in the manual has risen from 100 to 300 in the last 15 years. That translates to a virtual epidemic of madness sweeping the country. Only a decade ago, psychiatrists said one in 10 Americans had a mental illness. Now, according to the manual, half the population is mentally ill.

---

[345] Ibid.
[346] Kaiser, David, "Against Biological Psychiatry", December 1996
www.antipsychiatry.org/kaiser.htm
[347] Hagen, Margaret, *Whores of the Court*, HarperCollins, 1987

How the other half stays sane remains a mystery.

The manual will have to be updated annually because mental health professionals and defence lawyers keep discovering new illnesses. Just since the beginning of the year, the experts have unearthed these new disorders:

Lottery Stress Disorder [perhaps appropriately referred to as 'LSD']: *A London psychiatrist discovered the outbreak among lottery losers who experienced 'definition of mood and feelings of hopelessness' when their numbers didn't come in.*

Chronic Tax Anxiety Syndrome (CTAS): A Washington psychotherapist specializes in treating couples who suffer from excessive worry, sleeplessness and marital squabbling every April.

Premenstrual Syndrome (PMS): It's not new, but now it has won recognition as a bona fide mental illness from the American Psychiatric Association.

I know there are some cynics who will scoff at these new diagnoses. Maybe you think it is all psychobabble, just a gimmick to make money for the therapists. You wouldn't be caught dead on a psychiatrist's couch. You people are in serious denial. As a matter of fact, your unwillingness to seek professional help is itself a symptom of a serious mental problem. It's right here in the book: 15.81, Non-Compliance with Treatment Disorder." [348]

It's an indication of psychiatry's descent into mindless, unscientific technicality that it cannot, in the main, even see the ridicule often levelled against it and its practitioners. Is there a diagnosis named Lack of Sense of Humour Disorder? A good laugh at the clowns has always been the best medicine.

PUTTING PSYCHIATRY ON THE COUCH
DOES PSYCHOANALYSIS WORK?

Bruce Wiseman believes we are dealing with nothing less than fraud of gigantic and destructive proportions when it comes to evaluating

---

[348] Syverud, Mark, "Don't Stop the Insanity, My Therapist Needs the Money", *Daily Messenger*, 13th August 1995

whether psychiatry has ever been capable of performing the cures to which it lays claim:

"A study reported in American Psychologist in 1978... covered a 1939 project which had the goal of reducing delinquency in underprivileged children. More than 600 children between the ages of five and thirteen were randomly divided into two groups. Half received individual psychiatric counselling for five years while the other half received no therapy. The therapists reported that about two thirds of the boys receiving treatment 'substantially benefited' from it. More than 35 years later, almost 80% of the original 600 were located and follow-up studies were done. The results? 'Almost without exception,' the study said, 'therapy appeared to have had a negative, or at least a non-positive effect on the youngsters in later life.' The treated boys were <u>more</u> likely to have committed more than one serious crime. And when evaluated for alcoholism, mental illness, stress-related diseases, and job satisfaction, the treated group was worse off than the control group."[349]

Joan McCord, the author of the follow-up to the study Wiseman quotes above, has her own conclusions: *"The objective evidence presents a disturbing picture. The program seems not only to have failed to prevent its clients from committing crimes – thus corroborating studies of other projects – but also to have produced negative side-effects."*[350]

Two researchers reviewing data on how therapists relate to their patients actually published their negative conclusions in a psychology handbook: *"The odds are two out of three that* [the therapist] *is spending his energy, commitment and care for mankind wastefully; he is either ineffectual or harmful. Two out of three of his colleagues, he can be quite certain, are ineffectual or harmful."*[351]

At least Nicholas Cummings, former president of the American Psychological Association, was constrained to admit that *"It may be that the mental health movement has promised the American people a freedom from anxiety that is neither possible nor realistic, resulting in an*

---

[349] Wiseman, Bruce, op. cit. p.5

[350] McCord, Joan, "A Thirty-Year Follow-Up of Treatment Effects", *American Psychologist*, March 1978

[351] Truax, C B & K M Mitchell, "Research on Certain Therapist Interpersonal Skills in Relation to Process and Outcome", quoted in Bergen A E & S L Garfield (editors), *Handbook of Psychotherapy and Behavior Change*, John Wiley & Sons, New York: 1971, p.340

expectation that we have a right to feel good. We may never know to what extent we ourselves have contributed to the steep rise in alcohol consumption and the almost universal reliance on the tranquilizer." [352]

H J Eysenck studied several thousand cases of mentally disturbed servicemen and women in hospitals. Eysenck found that 44% were helped after psychoanalysis. Yet several hundred servicemen and women had received no therapy at all. Their improvement rate was 72%. One psychology textbook sums up Eysenck's findings: *"These data led some scientists to compare psychoanalysis with 'witch-doctoring' and to suggest that psychoanalysis might actually* retard *the patient's progress."* [353] Eysenck's analysis showed that untreated neurotics enjoyed a 'spontaneous' remission rate of 45% within a year of the commencement of their problems and 70% remission within two years. After five years, fully 90% were either greatly improved to the point where they could function well in society or completely cured. [354]

Author Thomas Kiernan, in his psychotherapy guide entitled *Shrinks, Etc.*, is stentorian about the bottom line: *"The results of over forty studies on neurosis reported in psychotherapeutic literature during the past twenty years (covering over 14,000 cases and dealing with both psychoanalytic and eclectic therapies) indicate that the aggregate percentage of positive effect in such therapies is just a hair's breadth above 50%."* [355] Kiernan also notes that most non-psychiatric physicians are all too aware of the failure of modern mental health medicine to effect a cure almost all of the time. Kiernan states that this explains why most doctors are loathed to refer patients to 'mental health specialists', but rather prefer to allow time and nature to take its course with the healing.

Bernie Zilbergeld, in his *Shrinking America*, declares: *"It was not until the last ten or fifteen years that therapists, and not all of them, have been willing to consider the possibility that change can be for the worse, that therapy can fail not only by not producing change but also by producing the wrong kind of change.... The findings... do indeed indicate that counselling makes some people worse, but this has been hard to see*

---

[352] Cummings, N A, "Turning Bread Into Stones", *American Psychologist*, 1979, 34, pp.1119-20
[353] McConnell, James V, *Understanding Human Behavior: An Introduction to Psychology*, Holt, Reinhart & Winston, New York: p.587
[354] Ibid.
[355] Kiernan, Thomas, *Shrinks, Etc.*, Dial Press, New York: 1974, p.55

and admit because of the positive thinking of those who do the counselling." [356]

Bruce Wiseman also covers other significant examples of psychiatry's failure when compared to nature and time taking its course: *"An extraordinary story from World War 2 also validates the notion that psychiatric intervention may be useless or unnecessary in a large percentage of cases. A French mental hospital lay in the path of the oncoming German army. All patients were returned home to relatives except 153 who were considered too ill to leave. The Germans arrived faster than the French anticipated and the patients were left to fend for themselves. After the war a commission was formed to determine the fate of these people. Of those traced, 37% of these abandoned, untreated and 'hopeless' patients were found to have adjusted to the community."* [357]

The DSM-III-R states that schizophrenia – the everyday man's idea of the lunatic – is apparently incurable, usually requiring medication for life. Yet, of 118 schizophrenics discharged from Vermont State Hospital who were followed up years later, for the most part long after treatment, 68% of these deemed 'incurable' had lost all symptoms and returned to a functioning role in the community. [358] Yet DSM-III-R is quite forthright: *"A return to full pre-morbid functioning in this disorder is not common."* [359] What would have happened if those 118 had remained in hospital, drugged up and restrained? Is it likely they would ever have been rehabilitated? Or would psychiatry have not once again fulfilled its role by claiming to have 'controlled' its patients' 'mental illness' and kept them out of their families' hair for the remainder of their lives?

---

[356] Zilbergeld, Bernie, *The Shrinking of America*, Little, Brown & Co, Boston, Mass: 1983, p.26

[357] Menninger, Karl, "The Course of Illness", *Menninger Clinic Bulletin*, Vol. 25, No.5, September 1961, quoted in Wiseman, Bruce, *Psychiatry – The Ultimate Betrayal*, op. cit. p.37

[358] Boffey, P M, "Schizophrenia: Insights Fail to Halt Rising Toll", *New York Times*, 16th March 1986, pp.1, 32

[359] "Schizophrenia", *DSM-III-R*, American Psychiatric Association, Washington DC: 1987, p.191

By Their Fruits You Shall Know Them
(Psychiatry: the social and criminal implications)

Given the all-encompassing expertise on mental health apparently possessed by psychiatry, it would follow that psychiatrists and psychologists should be among the sanest, wisest and most stable of all the population, especially in light of the fact that they are responsible for our 'mental health' and constantly advise the public on what is best for us. It would follow that they would be paragons of mental stability, have great marriages, and set an enduring example to society which would prove that the tenets of psychiatry can stand the tests of pressure and time.

The truth is very different.

PSYCHIATRIST SUICIDES

In America, arguably the nation with the most 'medically developed' approach to mental health, psychiatrists commit suicide twice as often as doctors in general.[360] This figure is <u>five times</u> the rate of the general population. During their residencies, psychiatrists are committing suicide almost <u>nine times</u> as often as the general population to whom they give mental health advice. Psychiatrist deaths are by far the leading suicides in any medical profession, and this suicide rate is quite stable.[361] *The Journal of Clinical Psychiatry* found that *"...the occurrence of suicides by psychiatrists is constant year-to-year, indicating a relatively stable oversupply of depressed psychiatrists from which the suicides are produced."*[362]

Other studies were to confirm this alarming trend: *"A joint study carried out by the American Medical Association and the American Psychiatric Association in 1987 confirmed that psychiatrists have the highest suicide rate of any medical profession. Researchers interviewing the surviving families found that by far the most common reason given for the death – in 94% of the cases – was 'to escape from mental pain',*

---

[360] Zilbergeld, Bernie, *The Shrinking of America*, Little, Brown and Co, Boston, Mass: 1983, quoted on p.11

[361] Campbell, Harvey D, "The Prevalence and Ramifications of Psychopathology in Psychiatric Residents: An Overview", *American Journal of Psychiatry*, 139:11, November 1982, p.1406. Psychiatric resident suicide rates are 106 per 100,000.

[362] Rich C L & F N Pitts Jr., "Suicide by Psychiatrists: A Study of Medical Specialists Among 18,730 Consecutive Physician Deaths During a Five-Year Period", 1967-1972, *The Journal of Clinical Psychiatry*, 41, 8th August 1980, p.261

which, of course, is the very thing psychiatrists claim they can alleviate. Additionally, 'more than half (56 percent) of those in the suicide group had prescribed a psychoactive drug for themselves.' Forty-two percent had been seeing a mental health professional at the time of their death."[363]

A Swiss study compares the military conscription records of those who later went on to become psychiatrists with those who later became doctors, internists or other medical specialists. Significantly more of the eventual psychiatrists *had themselves been declared unfit for military service due to psychiatric disorders.*[364]

ALCOHOLISM
When the physician membership of Alcoholics Anonymous in the United States was studied, it was found that 17% were psychiatrists, even though psychiatrists in America make up only 8% of the medical profession.[365] A similar study in 1983, this time reviewing female psychiatrists, discovered that 22.1% of the alcoholic female doctors were psychiatrists, even though they make up only 9.5% of women doctors. Whether male or female, psychiatrists appear to be twice as likely to become alcoholics than doctors from other branches of the medical profession.[366]

GETTING HIGH ON THEIR OWN SUPPLY
Today's problem of drugs, of course, extends throughout society. Most however don't even consider the concept of drug-taking by physicians and psychiatrists. Phil Hammond MD states that substance abuse is often a 'safety valve' for the incredible stresses that build up among healthcare workers. Examining the problem in the UK, the famous British broadcaster reports: *"Drinking and drug abuse are clearly coping mechanisms picked up in medical school, but it is impossible to predict which of the many heavy student drinkers will go on to develop a problem. The British Medical Association estimated that up to 13,000 practising UK doctors are addicted to drugs or alcohol. If each makes 2,000 clinical decisions a year, at a conservative estimate, that is 26 million decisions affecting patient care* [including prescribing potentially

---

[363] Wiseman, Bruce, op. cit. p.45;

[364] Maeder, Thomas, "Wounded Healers", *Atlantic Monthly*, January 1989, p.38

[365] Ibid.

[366] Bissell, LeClair and Jane K Skorina, "One Hundred Alcoholic Women in Medicine", *Journal of the American Medical Association*, 5th June 1987, p.2940

lethal drugs] *made by doctors who can't function without alcohol or other drugs."*[367]

A 1986 report in the *New England Journal of Medicine* provides a bleak insight into psychiatry getting high on its own supply. Nearly half the psychiatrists surveyed reported that they were <u>currently</u> taking self-prescribed psychotropic (mind-altering) drugs. The report also stated that *"psychiatrists had much higher rates for all types of* [psychotropic drug] *use at any time (83%)... than did other groups of physicians."*[368]

One clinical psychoanalyst's view of his profession? *"I question your calling it a myth that therapists are crazy because the <u>fact</u> is that most of them <u>are</u>. If you need any proof, let me tell you that every patient who comes into this office who has had a previous experience with another therapist has some kind of horror story to tell, about some major failing on the therapist's part, including, quite often, sexual abuse, verbal abuse, things that cross the boundary of mere bad technique and come pretty damn close to the criminal."*[369]

THE 'IRRESPONSIBLE' MILLIONS

How qualified, in the light of the above studies, are psychiatrists to analyse and 'cure' society's apparent rampant problems of mental illness? Consider that mental health promoter Tipper Gore, the wife of the erstwhile Vice President, is doggedly telling everyone that 28% of the American population is mentally ill because of problems outside of their control.[370] This translates to over 70 million Americans not deemed responsible for their actions, an unsettling belief held by the wife of a one-time presidential hopeful aiming to lead the most powerful nation on Earth. Mrs Gore goes on to state that over a quarter of her country's population cannot help themselves and therefore are in need of the ministrations of the psychiatric profession, almost half of whose physicians are themselves apparently dependent on self-prescribed psychoactive medication.

---

[367] Hammond, Phil, *Trust Me (I'm a Doctor)*, Metro Books, 1999
[368] McAuliffe, William E, et al, "Psychoactive Drug Use Among Practicing Physicians and Medical Students", *New England Journal of Medicine*, Vol. 315, No. 13, 25th September 1986, pp. 805, 808
[369] Maeder, Thomas, op. cit.
[370] Wiseman, Bruce, op. cit. p.44

"What do you do when you don't know what to do?" muses British psychiatrist R D Laing in 1985. *"No wonder there are more suicides among psychiatrists than in any other profession."* [371]

SEXUAL TURMOIL

A survey in *Medical Economics* illustrates that the problems of psychiatrists don't end with alcoholism, suicide or drug abuse. Psychiatrists also lead other branches of medicine in marriage difficulties – including sexual problems. In a personal interview, Dr Al Parides, Professor of Psychiatry at UCLA in Los Angeles, declared that psychiatric values had been *"very influenced, especially by the Freudian influence in regard to sex and morality generally.... If you look at the personal lives of all Freud's followers – his initial disciples – these people certainly have an unbelievable amount of particular problems in the sexual area... The amount of deviancy as far as their sexual behaviour and so forth is enormous. If you are saying that psychiatry promotes a certain form of morality that is a deviant morality in regard to many areas including sexual behaviour - yes, I would agree."* [372]

Today's psychiatrists, according to studies, have the shortest marriages of seven branches of medicine studied and are most likely to have extra-marital affairs, as are their spouses.[373] But extra-marital affairs *with whom... and where...?*

"Barbara Noel felt herself floating towards consciousness. It was Friday, 21st September 1984, and she was in her psychiatrist's office in Chicago, waking from a dose of sodium amytal, a barbiturate he had been giving her in order to help her explore her subconscious. This morning though, instead of awakening dreamily by herself, she says she felt a weight on top of her. A man was breathing heavily onto her shoulder. Still sedated, Noel moaned and stirred. The breathing stopped, and the body on top of her carefully lifted away. Pretending to sleep, Noel opened her eyes a crack. She could make out a person standing at a sink with his back to her. He was bald, with a tanned back and stark

---

[371] Laing, Ronald D, *Wisdom, Madness and Folly,* McGraw-Hill, New York: 1985, p.126

[372] Interview between Bruce Wiseman and Al Parides in 17th December 1993

[373] Kirchner, Merian, "What Makes Other Marriages Lousy", *Medical Economics,* 1st October 1979, pp.42-3

white buttocks. Noel's heart stopped. The man, she says, was Dr Jules Masserman, her psychiatrist of 18 years."[374]

Subsequent action against Dr Jules Masserman solicited a fervent denial by the latter of the charges. Psychiatry all over the world winced as they followed the descending fortunes of Masserman, the 1979 president of the American Psychiatric Association. The case was finally settled when Masserman agreed to pay malpractice settlements to Noel and three other women. He also signed an agreement never to practise psychiatric therapy again in the United States.[375]

WHEN IS A RAPE NOT A RAPE?

Psychiatry is naturally aware of the widespread sexual misconduct of its practitioners, but understandably fights shy of admitting rape. The term used to describe sexual intimacy between a psychiatrist and patient is the morally neutral 'psychiatrist-patient sexual contact'.[376] Bruce Wiseman comments:

"Like other 'non-judgmental' and 'values neutral' phrasing that psychiatry seems to enjoy, 'psychiatrist-patient contact' says nothing of the damage this activity inflicts or even whether it is good or bad.... Should we be surprised to find such a closet full of sexual abuse in this profession?

Perhaps not.... [Psychiatrists] *have long preached the foolishness and stressfulness of morality. Their primary philosophy is that they are mere bodies ruled by biochemistry and, therefore, like all other humans, who are rife with irresistible impulses and diminished capacities, there are times when they cannot help themselves. The majority of the profession are atheists and agnostics, thus have no religious standards to answer to.*"[377]

As we have seen, key leaders and 'founding fathers' of psychiatry have consistently preached sexual promiscuity and carnal relations with their

---

[374] "Barbara Noel's explosive accusation – that her psychiatrist sedated and sexually assaulted her during therapy – throws profession into turmoil – Waking to a Nightmare", *People Weekly*, 7th December 1992, Vol.38, No.23, p.87
[375] Ibid.
[376] Gartrell, Nancy et al., "Psychiatrist-Patient Sexual Contact: Results of a National Survey, I: Prevalence", *American Journal of Psychiatry*, September 1986, 143:9
[377] Wiseman, Bruce, op. cit. p.306

231

patients, in brazen defiance of the Hippocratic Oath. Doctors who take the Oath swear that: *"Whatever houses I may visit, I will come for the benefit of the sick, remaining free of all intentional injustice, of all mischief and in particular of sexual relations with both male and female persons, be they free or slaves."*

Yet many patients, as will soon become evident, walked into their therapist's office free, but became slaves and thus victims to the carnal and *criminal* depravations of the errant philosophies of psychiatry. And the example was set right at the top. In 1990, *US News and World Report* told the world: *"many practitioners, among them some of Freud's disciples – even married former patients or conducted lengthy affairs with them in full public view."* [378]

In March 1988 an Australian behavioural science student named James Spencer sexually assaulted and penetrated a seven-year-old girl. He filmed the act on video. When brought to court, Spencer claimed that he had been conducting 'psychological research'. Dr Neville Yeomans, a Sydney psychiatrist, defended Spencer's actions by stating that child rape was perfectly permissible in certain psychiatric situations, and filming the experiment was proof that Spencer only had the interests of his science in mind. Besides, Dr Yeomans reasonably pointed out, the child appeared to be enjoying it. The judge didn't agree. Spencer was jailed for five years. [379]

Child psychiatrist Dr Wuld Aschoff, former head of Germany's Albert-Schweitzer clinic, was charged in 1999 with photographing and videoing naked children and playing with their genitals. In police interviews, Aschoff claimed his therapy *"helped his patients to get a more intense feeling for their body"*. Two days before his criminal trial, the German psychiatrist committed suicide. [380]

James Tyhurst, a Canadian psychiatrist, was charged with sexual assaults on four of his female patients, who told the court Tyhurst had insisted they enter into slave/master relationships as part of the therapy. Tyhurst was a professor emeritus at the University of British Columbia. He

---

[378] Goode, Erica, E, 'The Ultimate Betrayal", *US News and World* Report, Vol. 108, No. 10, 12th March 1990, p.63
[379] Delora, J & C Warren, "Understanding Sexual Interaction", Houghton Mifflin, Boston: 1977
[380] Schneider, Kerstin, "Walls of Silence", *Stern*, 2nd March 2000

denied whipping, beating and having sexual intercourse with the four women. He was sent to prison for four years.[381]

In April 1988, Louis J Poetter pleaded guilt to 19 counts of sodomising young boys. As founder and director of the Anneewakee psychiatric centre for adolescents at Douglasville, Georgia, Poetter had encouraged sex between staff and children as 'good for the boys'. The settlement to resolve the eight lawsuits was a massive $35 million, believed to be the biggest in Georgia's history. Louis Potter went to prison for eight years.

A few cases from the Citizen's Commission on Human Rights (CCHR) investigations reveal that the abuse is constant and taking place at all levels of the psychiatric ladder:

In 1989, Dr Paul A Walters, psychiatrist in charge of student health at Stanford University, Massachusetts, and former head of Harvard University's Health Services' mental health Division, was forced to resign after allegations that he had 'frequent sex' with a female patient. The patient, who had been the victim of sexual abuse as a child, was awarded more than $200,000 in an out-of-court settlement. She said Walters had used her to perform oral sex on him 'sometimes as often as two out of three psychiatric analysis sessions per week'.

In 1990, Robert Ferguson, a psychologist, pleaded guilty to state child sex-abuse charges and federal charges of transporting child pornography.

In 1975, A New York Jury convicted psychiatrist Renatus Hartogs of malpractice, awarding $350,000 in damages to Julie Roy, a secretary at Esquire magazine whom Hartogs had seduced while she was his patient.

Early in 1992, John Hamilton, deputy medical director of the APA, stepped down from office and had his license suspended for only a year, after having sexual relations with a patient who, in turn, filed a complaint. Ironically Hamilton wrote and edited the APA peer review manual.

In 1991, Orange County, California, psychiatrist James Harrington White was charged with and convicted of the forced sodomy of a male patient. White was also found to have drugged young men, then

---

[381] "Sex Doctor Jailed for Four Years", *The Valley Sun*, 25th June 1991

videotaped himself having sex with them. The psychiatrist was also alleged to have sodomised his adopted son for years, drugged him, forced him to dress as a female, and to have given him hormones to make him look feminine. To guarantee the boy's co-operation and silence, the court heard how the doctor is said to have administered sodium pentothal and electroshock with hypnosis. Even when the young man finally left home and married, his psychiatrist 'father' continued the sexual abuse, ultimately castrating the young man when he discovered the man's wife was pregnant. James Harrington White was sent to prison for seven years. [382]

In the US, Lisa Roth underwent 'therapy' at Jefferson County Mental Health Center for depression and alcoholism. Her 'treatment' involved sleeping with her female therapist. The therapist, Lynda Robinson, also invited Roth to sleep with her husband. During a 1994 civil suit by Roth seeking damages for this unorthodox 'treatment', Robinson's defence attorney stated that the therapist couldn't remember anything about the psychotherapy she had given Roth or any bedroom incidents because her silicone breast implants had leaked, causing toxicity in her brain and, conveniently, memory loss.[383]

COWED INTO SILENCE
Many ask why the abused patients themselves don't go to the medical authorities or the police. Kenneth Pope and Jacqueline Bouhoutsos are two psychologists who have studied therapist/patient sexual interaction extensively. They have constructed a hypothetical model, based on the experiences and accounts of victims, of common circumstances that lead to psychiatric rape and the silencing of the victim:

"Karen is a 14-year-old victim of incest. Dr Louis, a hypnotherapist, is treating her for the incest trauma. He makes her lie on the couch and attempts to put her in a deep trance. She is so nervous that she is unable to concentrate on what he is saying. She does not trust him, does not want to be seeing him, and lies on the couch, her face covered by her hands, crying.

He says that it looks like she needs reassurance, and he lies down next to her. He tells her she has nothing to be afraid of, that he will protect her and

---

[382] Letter to the Office of the District Attorney, Orange County, California, regarding James Harrington White, 18th January 1991. Cases quoted from Wiseman, Bruce, op. cit. pp.309-310

[383] Lindsay, Sue, "Trial pits live-in patient against therapist", *Rocky Mountain News*, 4th December 1994

comfort her. He presses himself against her and, before she can scream, puts his hand over her mouth. He holds her so that she can neither cry nor move. He rapes her.

When he is finished, he tells her it never happened, that she is crazy and imagined the whole thing. He tells her that if she tries to tell anyone, that no one will believe her. Everyone will believe that she is psychotic and needs to be put away in a hospital. If she tries to tell anyone, they will know that she was just making up stories about the incest, so they will either return her to her father or put her in jail. No matter where they put her, he will still be in charge of her treatment and they will always believe a famous hypnotherapist rather than a hysterical little girl who is always making up fantastic stories that show what a dirty mind she has.

He may even tell the authorities that she tried to seduce him and told him that she had made up the stories about the incest because she had been unable to seduce her father. He told her that if she tried to tell anyone what she had imagined had happened, that he would prescribe drugs that would make her a vegetable and might even operate on her brain. If he felt like it, he might arrange for her to die. As she got dressed to leave, he slapped her to stop her from crying. He told her not to be late for their next appointment." [384]

WHERE ARE THE THOUGHT POLICE?

That charges of psychiatric rape should be glossed over by the American Psychiatric Association, or attempts made to trivialise the charges, is not so surprising, given the explosion in class action lawsuits and a commensurate rise in malpractice insurance that would inevitably result. Once again, the APA, and hence world psychiatry find themselves in the dock with an image problem. Why aren't psychiatric chiefs clamping down on the rank and file? Researcher Kenneth Pope offers one explanation. His 1988 American study discovered that a higher incidence of sexual abuse existed among prominent doctors in psychiatry – tenured professors and chairmen of ethics committees - than among the rank and file. [385]

But some do speak out, and the extent of the problem has proven a monumental embarrassment and further tarnished the already tattered reputation of psychiatry. Psychiatrist Nanette Gartrell, a member of the APA Committee on Women, reports that increasing numbers of class

---

[384] Pope, Kenneth S & Jacqueline C Bouhoutsos, *Sexual Intimacy Between Therapists and Patients*, Praeger Publishers, New York: 1986
[385] Goode, Erica E, op. cit.

action and malpractice suits are being filed as the wall of silence comes down:

"It became clear that this was a problem which potentially was affecting large numbers of women patients throughout the country and undoubtedly larger numbers than we were even hearing about."[386]

Psychiatry was still dismally failing to police itself in this area six years later. APA president Lawrence Hartmann told the Association in 1992: *"For posterity's sake, I would like to record that perhaps never in the history of the American Psychiatric Association has an APA president been called upon to spend so much of his time considering psychiatrist-patient sexual contact as this year."*[387]

CCHR reports: *"A Los Angeles survey showed that 10% of male psychiatrists engaged in sexual contact with their patients.*[388] *In a nationwide survey reported in a 1986 article published in the American Journal of Psychiatry, 7.1% of the male psychiatrists and 3.1% of the female – over 6% of the respondents overall – acknowledged having what is euphemistically called 'sexual contact' with their patients.*[389] *Yet 65 percent of psychiatrists questioned said they had treated patients who were sexually involved with previous therapists. Only 8 percent reported the misconduct, which might serve further to illustrate how much responsibility is assumed by the profession's members in policing themselves.*[390]

Be that as it may, this casts a suspicious light on that 10 percent figure. In fact, in a 1990 US News & World Report *article, experts put the sexual shenanigans at more like 25 percent, or one out of every four*

---

[386] Gartrell, Nanette, op. cit.; "Sexual Contact With Patients" tape transcriptions, American Psychiatric Association, May 1986

[387] Hartmann, Lawrence, "Presidential Address: Reflections on Humane Values and Biopsychosocial Integration", *American Journal of Psychiatry*, September 1992, 149:9

[388] Kardener, Sheldon H, et al, "A Survey of Physicians' Attitudes and Practices Regarding Erotic and Non-Erotic Contact With Patients", *American Journal of Psychiatry*, October 1973, p.1080

[389] Gartrell, N, et al, "Psychiatrist-Patient Sexual Contact: Results of a National Survey, I: Prevalance", *American Journal of Psychiatry*, Vol.143, No.9, September 1986, p.1126

[390] "Sex and Psychotherapy", *Newsweek*, 13th April 1992, p.53

psychiatrists.[391]*And a 1973 California study claims the figure is an astronomical 51 percent."*[392][393]

HANDS IN THE TILL
But what are we to make of a 'doctors' who believe they can get away with raping or sexually assaulting their patients, *and then billing their time to their victims' insurance companies as 'therapy' services*?

Dr Paul A Walters, a Riverside, California psychiatrist, was charged with 16 counts of 'inappropriate sexual activity', grand theft, fraud and prescribing drugs for no legitimate medical purposes. Lowinger billed medical insurance giant Medi-Cal for 'therapy' consisting almost entirely of having sex with his patients. The case was settled in August 1994 when a payment of $7.1 million was made to the plaintiff, ex-patient, Francine Rahn.

A New Zealand group of psychotherapists, headed up by psychiatrist Bill Rowntree and psychiatric nurse Bert Potter, was investigated by authorities for sexually abusing children in its care as 'therapy'. This service to the community was charged out at inflated rates. Potter presided over one incident involving a three-year-old girl performing oral sex on men, who was later given the drug Ecstasy as part of her treatment. Potter was also charged with having sex with an adolescent in his care to remove an 'emotional block' to her personality. Potter, in spite of being sent to prison for six years for his crimes, remained unrepentant: *"Sexual activity initiated by the child and kept at their level is not harmful."*[394] Freud would have been proud.

FINGERS IN THE TILL
Even psychiatrists who do not sexually assault their patients have discovered the tremendous cash benefits of 'creative accounting'. One scheme being bilked for all it was worth was the federal Civilian Health and Medical Program in the United States (CHAMPUS). CHAMPUS has been a veritable cash cow for psychiatry. Outraged US Congresswoman Pat Schroeder headed up an investigation into psychiatric fraud that was to

---

[391] Goode, Erica, E, "The Ultimate Betrayal", *US News & World Report*, 12th March 1990
[392] Kardener, Sheldon H, et al, op. cit. pp.1077-81
[393] Wiseman, Bruce, op. cit. pp.48-49
[394] CCHR, *Psychiatry – Betraying and Drugging our Children*, Los Angeles: 2002, p.26

have far-reaching implications for the industry. Addressing the House Select Committee on Children, Youth and Families, she thundered:

"We are here this morning to shed light on, and we hope help to put a stop to, one of the most disgraceful and scandalous episodes in the history of health care in America. I am referring to the unethical and disturbing practices in mental health care that are taking place from coast to coast." [395]

David Mancuso, Assistant Inspector General for Investigations for the Department of Defense (DOD), was the administrative watchdog for CHAMPUS. During the hearings, Mancuso outlined several scams psychiatrists were employing to receive maximum payouts under the health scheme:

"Investigations have disclosed a scheme known as 'contract max'. We have found the 'contract max' fraud in psychiatric care as it concerns hospital stays. Patients have actually been kept in the hospital for extended periods because the maximum stay allowed by their insurance had not been reached." [396]

Louis Parisi appeared at the hearings to give testimony. As Director of the Fraud Division of the Department of Insurance for the State of New Jersey, Parisi rolled off a whole litany of schemes he had investigated within private psychiatric institutes. These included:

> ➤ Forcefully confining patients, often against their will, in private psychiatric hospitals until their insurance coverage had expired. Once expired, the patients were dumped out on the streets and pronounced 'cured'.
> ➤ Billing insurance companies for services not performed.
> ➤ Billing insurance companies for services provided by unlicensed, unqualified personnel, made to look like they had been carried out by doctors.
> ➤ Billing insurance companies for higher rates than patients without medical coverage.

---

[395] Minutes from the Hearing-House Select Committee on Children, Youth and Families Regarding Fraudulent Practices in the Mental Health Industry, 28th April 1992
[396] Ibid.

- Billing insurance companies for an endless battery of tests without sound medical reasons to inflate the bill.
- Billing insurance companies for an endless supply of potentially harmful, mind-altering drugs which were prescribed to patients without sound medical reasons to inflate the bill.
- Organising bonuses for staff within the hospital, where those who kept the highest number of patients in the hospital for the longest period of time (until their benefits ran out) were paid the highest commission on top of their basic salaries.

Mancuso's appraisal was withering: *"A situation has developed in this country in the field of medical care where some hospitals and substance abuse centres can achieve a reputation for professionalism and a high level of patient care and that reputation is only a façade. The reputation for professional medical care has been replaced with a reputation for a sure-win moneymaker for the principals involved in the stock ownership and upper management levels of these billion-dollar businesses."* [397]

Parisi cited many abuses, including how patients were often released on the very day their benefits expired. *"We even discovered situations where the local municipal police were called to a hospital to remove a patient from the facility. The insurance benefits had terminated but the patient had not been successfully treated and did not want to return to a life of substance abuse uncured."* [398]

Texas State Senator Mike Moncrief presented his evidence as Chairman for the Texas Senate Interim Committee on Health and Human Services. Moncrief had received a pamphlet in the mail from an anonymous source. The material was entitled 'Books as Hooks'. The handout, commissioned by a national psychiatric health group, described how pamphlets such as these were highly effective, inexpensive marketing tools for increasing psychiatric patient intake. One substance abuse centre director especially was quoted: *"We've been using these books for three years.... Families love these books and they do help us fill the hospital."* [399]

---

[397] Ibid.
[398] Ibid.
[399] Moncrief, Mike, Texas State Senator: Testimony – US House of Representatives; Select Committee on Children, Youth and Families, Texas State Interim Committee on Health and Human Services, 28th April 1992

AIRPORT BLUES

At the time these investigations were being conducted in the United States, the Canadian government was doing its own research into excessive bills charged by US psychiatric hospitals to Canadian insurance companies. Canadian nationals were apparently being lured south of the border for their psychiatric treatment with complementary airfares, limousines and luxury accommodation in treatment programs in California, Florida and Texas.

Bruce Wiseman also investigated the scam uncovered by Moncrief: *"It was a goldmine while it lasted. The aggressive marketing resulted in claims from US hospitals for Ontario patients alone increasing from $5.4 million in 1988 to $51.3 million just two years later. In 1990, approximately 2,500 Ontario residents were brought to the US for treatment. One man was referred to as the 'half a million dollar man'. He reportedly received more than 20 months of psychiatric treatment in five different Houston hospitals and returned to Canada a cocaine addict."* [400]

Moncrief reported that after the Canadian government moved to crack down on the US fraud, imposing strict limits to the levels of insurance reimbursement to US hospitals, reports were received of dozens of Canadian patients being taken to Houston airport by psychiatric hospitals in the region and dumped with no return tickets.

Moncrief's huge accumulation of psychiatric fraud evidence cited other instances:

> ➤ In San Antonio, Texas, 1-800 (free) numbers were publicised as 'suicide hotlines', which in turn referred the caller to a 1-900 (toll) number, *"where they make $2.00 a minute off of your call while you're deciding whether to take your own life."*
> ➤ Dozens of ex-patients provided testimony on how they were miraculously cured and suddenly discharged on the day their insurance benefits ran out.
> ➤ Others related how they voluntarily checked into clinics for eating disorders and other troubling ailments and then were incarcerated against their will.
> ➤ A bill was submitted for a patient for 36 prescription drugs in one day, including 8,400mg of the anti-depressant Lithobid,

---

[400] Wiseman, Bruce, op. cit. p.328

almost five times the maximum dose listed in the Physician's Desk Reference, and lethal had it been given to the patient.

➢ A mother who was persuaded to check into a Texas psychiatric hospital for a few days to be with her daughter, who, a psychiatrist had determined, may have been sexually molested by a family member. Both were covered by the federal CHAMPUS reimbursement scheme. The mother and daughter however were kept apart and only allowed to see each other at mealtimes. When the mother came to check out, testimony later given to the local Chief of Police stated that she had been overpowered by several hospital staff and given an injection. Both mother and daughter were later released after they contacted the local police department, who came to investigate.[401]

MONEY FROM CHILDREN

But by far the most lucrative boost to psychiatry's social and financial fortunes has come from their ability to evolve the education system from one that teaches children the knowledge and skills they need to a system that minutely analyses the child population for evidences of eccentric or abnormal behaviour that may indicate the existence of a 'mental illness' requiring psychiatry's services. So much has been made of these 'childhood problems' in the media that the public has become resigned to accepting that a significant percentage of our kids 'must have something wrong with them'. And so, we defer to the experts. It is an indication of how much blind faith we place in these doyens of the mind sciences, that we allow our children and elderly folk to be medicated with highly addictive, behaviour-altering medications, all the while ignoring the ethical conflicts in the backs of our minds. Yet, after all we have learned so far, can we any longer fool ourselves, even for a fleeting instant, that these treatments are 'all for the best'?

---

[401] Moncrief, Mike, Testimony provided to the Committee by the Chief of Police of Shenendoah, Texas, op. cit. p.10

As it Was.... As it is Today

"Loaded down by the weight of guilt and fear... the unfortunate human race, deprived by these incubi of its only defences and its only reasons for striving, its reasoning power and its natural capacity to enjoy the satisfaction of its natural urges, struggles along under its ghastly, self-imposed burden." [402] - G Brock Chisholm

And so, here we have psychiatry and the modern mental health system. How can we survive them? Let us be clear that it was leading American mental health advocate G Brock Chisholm who so shaped post-war Earth's psychosocial attitudes towards itself, who flatly saw the concept of guilt over committing wrongdoing as the main reason for mankind's mental slavery. The morally beleaguered 20th century human, Chisholm reasoned, should be liberated to do whatever he wants to do.

It isn't hard to see how this naughty, self-liberating opinion took root in the aftermath of World War 2, and we have examined the fruits of such philosophies, which have undermined our school systems, permeated our justice, law enforcement, literature, art and our media entertainment, and introduced everyday drug usage into the care and safety of our precious youngsters and elderly.

Bruce Wiseman: *"The TV set that once showed awed viewers live coverage of man's first steps on the moon now flashes nude flesh, bloodied bodies, and perverse messages to grown-ups and children alike. In discussing the quality of television programming, the word "wholesome" has vanished from our vocabularies. In fact, those who use it are ridiculed....*

It would appear that over the years – like some dinosaur in a tar pit – we have stepped from the solid ground of inherited cultural wisdom to become mired in a new religion of plummeting mores and standards. And now we struggle, so anxious about our survival that we have forgotten exactly how we got there....

---

[402] Chisholm, G Brock, "The Re-Establishment of Peacetime Society" – The William Alanson White Memorial Lectures, Second Series, Psychiatry: Journal of the Biology and the Pathology of Interpersonal Relations, February 1946, p.9

What has [psychiatry] done to our justice system, our schools, our homes? And how many lives have been changed for the worse by people heeding the advice of healers who – though they may mean well – by statistics, are themselves less capable of dealing with life than the average man in the street? Perhaps the public's gut suspicions about psychiatry are not so far off, after all." [403]

In trying to be all things to all people, psychiatry has ended up meaning nothing to anyone. It has cost nations billions and delivered little to benefit. On the downside, the impact of its philosophies on our societies has been disastrous and in certain cases perhaps irreversible. In order to avert bringing the dreaded 'mental illness' onto our children, we are today restrained from punishing their wrongdoing. Today, our youth is in bloody revolt. In trying to protect the rights of our murderers, rapists and perverts, psychiatrists have told the courts to 'understand their anguish', and have failed in society's most basic commitment to punish criminal activity and protect the victims. Today, our streets are war-zones. Those decent citizens who try to protect themselves and their families from robbery and violence because the police are unable to, are themselves sued by their attackers, labelled in the media and courts as 'vigilantes', and often locked up for their self-defence.

SHABBY AND UGLY
World War 2 veteran and world-famous author George MacDonald Fraser scoffs at the notion that those who push psychiatry's liberal ethos and political correctness have in any way benefited society:

"The very core of their philosophy is a refusal to accept truth, to look it squarely in the face, unpalatable as it may be. Political correctness is about denial, usually in the weasel circumlocutory jargon which distorts and evades and seldom stands up to honest analysis.... Why do I, and millions of my contemporaries think the way we do? ...To one of my generation, who remembers pre-war, wartime and post-war and who has travelled widely, the United Kingdom begins to look more like a Third World Country – shabby, littered, ugly, running down, without purpose or direction, misruled by a typical Third World Government, corrupt, incompetent and undemocratic.

My generation has seen the decay of ordinary morality, standards of decency, sportsmanship, politeness, respect for the law, the law itself,

---

[403] Wiseman, Bruce, op. cit. pp.22, 26, 53

family values, politics and education and religion, the very character of the British.... I am sorry for the present generation, with their permissive society, their anything-goes philosophy, and their laid-back, 'in-yer-face attichood'. They regard themselves as a completely liberated society, when the fact is that they are less free than any generation before them since the Middle Ages. We could say what we liked, they can't. We were not subject to the aggressive pressure of special-interest minority groups, they are. We had no worries about race or sexual orientation, they have. We could, and did, differ from fashionable opinion with impunity and would have laughed political correctness to scorn, had our society been weak and stupid enough to let it exist; they daren't.

We had few problems with bullies because society knew how to deal with bullying, and was not afraid to punish it in ways which would send today's progressives into hysterics. We did not know the stifling tyranny of a liberal establishment determined to impose its views, and more and more beginning to resemble Orwell's Ministry of Truth....

Today I read of huge cash payments to griping incompetents who can't do their jobs, and to policemen because they were upset by doing what policemen used to do as a matter of course, or firemen being counselled and compensated after a disaster which would once have been regarded as an unpleasant day's work, and people being 'traumatised' by hardship or harrowing experiences which their grandparents would have taken in their stride....

I look at the old country as it was in my youth, and as it is today, and frankly, to use a fine Scots word, I'm scunnered." [404]

IT'S MORE THAN WHAT YOU THINK

In 1989, the American Psychiatric Association's Public Affairs Network produced a 'Campaign Kit' to its members in order to give the negative image of psychiatry a much-needed boost. Much can be learned of the minds behind psychiatry by studying the contents of this kit. The new campaign, the kit tells us, is *"on behalf of the millions of Americans who suffer mental illness"*. But the bottom-line purpose of the campaign? *"[To] work together to fix psychiatry and psychiatrists in the public's*

---

[404] Fraser, George MacDonald, "Battle Cry for the Silent Majority", *Daily Mail*, 15th April 2002

mind as a positive healing force at work constantly across the country. [405]

Implementing the policy that if you believe you have 'a cure', you have a vested interest in promoting the disease, the APA began to bombard the American and, thus, world peoples, with "Mental Illness Awareness Week – It's More Than What You Think". Here we see the classic tactic of psychiatry attempting to create its own usefulness and market. Are millions of Americans mentally ill? No, they are not. But if you keep telling Americans they are, over and over and over again, they will eventually believe you.

As part of "Mental Illness Awareness Week", the APA carpet-bombed the public with a dazzling smorgasbord of new ailments, such as school phobias, anxiety, drug withdrawal symptoms, smoking- and alcohol-related problems, hyperactivity, dream anxiety and supposed 'mental' problems. The campaign PR kit also instructs the APA member on how to improve the 'bad rep' psychiatry has with non-psychiatric doctors, thereby increasing income: *"An increase of psychiatry's profile among non-psychiatric physicians can do nothing but good. And, for those who are bottom-line oriented, the efforts you spend on building this profile have the potential to yield dividends through increased referrals."* [406]

As the campaign's sales pitch hit across America, the APA was unbelievably advising its members to take advantage of even schoolyard tragedies, such as shootings or suicides, to push the notion that children were particularly vulnerable to 'mental illness':

"Tell someone that millions of teens need some sort of help with a mental illness and they'll yawn and scratch absently. But lead a bewildered community, gathered after a teen cluster suicide, to an understanding that the problems their kids face are 'real', and they will listen. You will seldom have such dramatic opportunities to reach your audience, but there will be other opportunities to hit them – literally – where they live, if you keep a sharp lookout." [407]

---

[405] American Psychiatric Association Campaign Kit, 1989. Opening letter by Harvey Ruben MD.
[406] Ibid. Section on "About the Public", p.11
[407] Ibid. p.2

Isn't it interesting that at precisely the time when the APA was encouraging its members to 'hit them literally where they live', psychiatric drugs, electroshock and psychotherapy were already empirically responsible for schoolyard killings, teen atrocities, psychiatric drug-induced insanity, depression, marriage break-ups, suicides, infidelity and rape across America. Using its now all-too-familiar sales pitch, the APA, without a vestige of trauma-inducing shame, builds its fictional market right before our eyes, its leaflets brazenly making up figures to scare the public into support of its practices:

"No one is immune to mental disease. In fact, you probably know someone who suffers from a diagnosable and treatable disorder. The US National Institute of Mental Health recently learned [from whom?] *that one in five Americans has some sort of mental illness in any given six months* [illnesses, perhaps, like 'Lottery Stress Disorder' and 'Chronic Tax Anxiety Syndrome']. *That means between 30 million and 45 million people – possibly your friends, family members and co-workers – suffer from symptoms that can be effectively treated.... You may have heard someone comment, 'Harry just isn't the same these days.' Perhaps you said it yourself about an average person* [i.e. the public is being encouraged to turn each other in]. *Harry is overly sensitive or irritable or he's drinking too much.... All these behaviour changes suggest a possible mental disorder which, with appropriate diagnosis and treatment, can be cured or controlled."* [408]

Cured and controlled? Appropriate diagnosis and treatment? Could the fact that psychiatrists are the first to sell themselves on their own tommyrot be the reason they have the highest self-prescribed drug consumption of any branches of the medical profession, and by far the highest suicide and patient rape rates too? Who would trust such people with the mental welfare of even one classroom, let alone a nation? Who among us is so blind we cannot see the obvious and disastrous effects these criminally defective and offensive tactics have had on our world?

The APA campaign PR kit goes on to educate its psychiatrist members on how to become 'a media source', i.e., the professional journalists often call to get a 'psychiatric' opinion on a story. *"What are the advantages or payoffs for your hard work? Your reputation with reporters, editors and*

---

[408] Ibid. "Let's Talk About Mental Illness", Column #1

producers can often shape or limit a story."[409] Not to mention all those referrals and increased consultancy fees.

The campaign closes with its usual proclamation on the dire state of American mental health. This same proclamation is routinely read out in the US Senate and House of Representatives whenever issues of increased psychiatric funding from the public purse crop up. This writer's comments are inserted in square brackets:

Whereas mental illness is a problem of grave concern and consequence in American society, widely but unnecessarily feared and misunderstood; [Here the fraudulent premise is established that there actually is a 'grave' problem with 'mental illness', i.e. diseases of the brain.]

Whereas 31 to 41 million Americans annually suffer from clearly diagnosable mental disorders involving significant disability with respect to employment, attendance at school, or independent living; [Who but psychiatry could come up with these absurd, unsubstantiated figures? Who but psychiatry has given itself the 'expertise' to diagnose such 'mental disease'? We have just learned, from the APA itself, that it cannot competently even explain what a mental disorder is, let alone what causes it, or how one differs from another! How then can these 'disorders' be *clearly diagnosable?* Who but psychiatry has infiltrated the schools, police stations, the courts and the workplace to tell the public what is right or wrong behaviour? What gives psychiatry the expertise to make such proclamations when its own membership exhibits a level of perversion, moral bankruptcy and criminal activity, involving fraud, rape, torture and sexual deviancy on a scale that beggars belief?]

Whereas more than 10 million Americans are disabled for long periods of time by schizophrenia, manic depressive disorder, and major depression; [How many of these conditions does psychiatry actually know how to evaluate? It has officially admitted it does not know what causes schizophrenia or even what it is! How many of these conditions are merely being treated with drugs, electroshock treatments and psychosurgery to make the patient forget what he was worried about in the first place? How many psychiatrists are trained to know the real <u>physical</u> causes of manifestations such as these? (See Part 2)

---

[409] APA Campaign Kit, 1989, "About the Media:, p.3

Whereas between 30 to 50 percent of the homeless suffer serious, chronic forms of mental illness; [This writer lived and worked in Santa Monica, California for many years, the American West Coast's leading community for displaced or homeless persons. Many of these citizens were interviewed at great length and found to have been prescribed psychiatric drug 'straitjackets' and then summarily turned loose on the streets under the infamous deinstitutionalisation programs of past decades. Twenty-five veterans interviewed told this writer, and proudly displayed the appropriate military patches, that they had been soldiers in Vietnam who, upon returning to America, had become depressed at not being able to readjust to civilian society, traumatised by what they had experienced, and resentful of the American public's attitude towards them as 'baby killers'. They had 'sought help' for depression and had inadvertently become psychiatric drug addicts and victims of electroshock].

Whereas alcohol, drug, and mental disorders affect almost 19 percent of American adults in any six-month period; [These figures are completely arbitrary and unverifiable. Which profession but psychiatry, in collusion with the CIA, was the first to prescribe hallucinogenics such as LSD to the public and leading Hollywood figures, like Cary Grant, *for recreational purposes only?* Which profession stands the most to lose if drugs cease to be a problem in society – and a problem verifiably exacerbated by psychiatry itself in the first place?]

Whereas mental illness in at least twelve million children interferes with vital developmental and maturational processes; [The audacity of this statement is breathtaking. Children who are distracted, 'speak too much', 'fidget in class', 'answer out of turn' and 'play too noisily' are branded 'ADD' or 'ADHD' and then prescribed Ritalin, an amphetamine almost identical to cocaine. What is Ritalin likely to do to a child's developmental and maturational process, if not inculcate in that child a predisposition to drug addiction? (See Part 2)

Whereas mental disorder-related deaths are estimated to be thirty-three thousand, with suicide accounting for at least twenty-nine thousand, although the real number is thought to be at least here times higher; [What has been the real cause of these suicides? How many of these 'mental' patients were prescribed drugs such as Ritalin, Prozac, Halcion, Dexedrine and Xanax which themselves can create severe emotional torment when taken and withdrawn from? (See Part 2) How many of these suicides come from depressed members of the public inundated in sexual and pornographic imagery, horror films, splatte

248

videos and soap operas featuring faces contorted in constant rage, anger and hatred? In an interview with *Science News*, psychologist Joan McCord, who authored the follow-up to a study reported in *American Psychologist* on the utter failure of psychiatric counselling and treatment to reduce delinquency in children, tells us: *"I've got some hunches. It's possible that people become too dependent on counsellors, and therefore they do not acquire the skills of those who do not have therapy. They come to see themselves as 'needing help'."* [410]]

Whereas research in recent decades has led to a wide array of new and more effective modalities of treatment (both somatic and psychosocial) for some of the most incapacitating forms of mental illness; [Welcome to UCLA psychopharmacologist Ronald Siegel's brave new drug world. This book has researched and reported on these 'more effective modalities of treatment', which include drugging up our children and old folk with mind-bending psychotropic drugs, experimenting on prison populations with drugs, psychosurgery and electroshock, teaching our kids to have sex at progressively earlier ages, the rape and sexual abuse by psychiatrists of their vulnerable and trusting patients, and the conviction dismissals of criminals who have been told their calculated wickedness is a 'symptom' of a 'sickness' and they need *"psychiatry's more effective modalities of treatment"*. How many more times do we want to ride this roundabout of perversion? What has been the result for our justice and law enforcement systems?]

Whereas appropriate treatment of mental illness has been demonstrated to be cost effective in terms of restored productivity, reduced utilisation of other health services, and lessened social dependence....; [Gasp! *Cost effective in terms of restored productivity?* Psychiatry has successfully defrauded taxpayers all over the world to the tune of billions of dollars a year for its treatments and infrastructure. And what benefits has society received in return? How many millions of American, British, Australian and other nations' kids will go to school today, to be taught bogus reading methods, the 'joys' of sexual perversion, politically correct history and social 'sciences', all the while drugged up by their teachers and 'health counsellors' because of a fraudulent 'mental illness' diagnosis? Has psychiatry's interference *lessened social dependence,* or has it not fostered one of the most crippled and drug- and therapy-DEPENDENT societies the world has ever seen? The reader must be the judge. What kind of society have we become that even when the

---

[410] "Thirty-Year Follow-Up. Counselling Fails", *Science News*, 28th November 1977

obvious stares us in the face, studiously and with embarrassed apathy we just turn and look the other way?]

Interestingly, the above declaration does not even mention the American Psychiatric Association. By its phrasing and context it deceitfully appears to come from the hearts of America's legislators and seems to represent the concerns of all Americans. The truth however is that this lying 'proclamation', couched in the familiar political rhetoric of the US Senate, is nothing more than a sales pitch at the nation, the end result of taxpayer-funded, expensive and persistent PR and lobbying efforts by the American Psychiatric Association to pony up more business for its psychiatrists.

WHAT IS THE REAL OFFENCE?

In trying to compel our children in schools to become 'model, docile, compliant world citizens' for the future New World Order, our liberal teachers are encouraged to host lessons on how children can enjoy homosexuality and perversion, glorify death, ridicule the Ten Commandments and conformity, spurn mental and physical discipline for fear of feeling 'inferior', and despise academic achievement. Today, the kids we nurture and love are illiterate and atheist; they are often drug-addicted, pregnant and afflicted with a sexually transmitted disease; foul-mouthed, violent, lazy, drunk, fat and crude, with more metal in their heads than British Steel. Emotionally today, they are sexually confused, morally adrift, bewitched by the occult, unable to write, read, articulate proper language vocally, or describe a self-formed, independent opinion on paper.

Congratulations, John Dewey and the host of your acolytes across the world who have made this a reality. You have presided over the implosion of our national societies, sown the seeds of anarchy which have reached a terrible maturity on our streets and in our schoolyards; you have destroyed the innocence of our precious little ones, polluted and laid waste our religious institutions, perverted our justice system and corrupted whole generations with drug addiction and moral unaccountability. No attack on a nation has ever been so carefully and meticulously executed and with such devastating effects. In short, have these not been acts of treason?

In times gone by, a group which attacked a country with the view to damaging its infrastructure and destroying its society was deemed the enemy, and if they were part of the nation they were attacking, they were branded fifth columnists and traitors. No effort was spared to root out these conspirators and bring them to justice. And they received their traitor's lot.

When we cast our eyes back over the information covered in Part 1 of this book and conclude how psychiatry's insidious tentacles have spread through the 1800's, the First World War, the Second World War, the corruption of our culture with drugs, the traumatising effects of its barbaric electroshock and psychosurgery 'lobotomy' techniques; how our best loved Hollywood and music stars have suffered at the hands of psychiatric 'experts'; how our youth has been driven from the classics and politeness to illiteracy, school shootings, drug addiction and contempt for their peers. How our elderly are often drugged up and incarcerated against their will, sometimes in collusion with their families, who don't want to be bothered with them any more. How our religious institutions, the institution of family, and the social deference we used to show each other have been ridiculed, attacked, decimated and consigned to the scrap heap. When we consider these weighty matters, what other conclusion can we form than one which recognises that our nations have been deliberately attacked and changed for the worse, and our attackers still gloat over their victories in our midst? And the fact that we allow it to be so – what does this say about *us*? Does our apathy and silence not make us *less* than men? Churchill's lament from 1920 comes back to haunt us:

"From the days of 'Spartacus Weishaupt, to those of Karl Marx, Trotsky, Rosa Luxemburg and Béla Kun, this worldwide conspiracy for the overthrow of civilisation has been the mainspring of every subversive movement during the nineteenth century, and now at last has gripped the Russian people by the hair of their heads and become the undisputed master of that enormous empire."[411]

Has Weishaupt's revolution become the undisputed master of our own civilisation today? Can it be thwarted if decent citizens rouse themselves to action in time? What CAN be done?

And what of the 'mentally ill'? Yes, we have people in the world who are disturbed and can be described as 'insane', 'emotionally deranged' and 'hyperactive'. And yes, we need to involve ourselves in assisting them, as well as society, in moving towards healing and health. Every human being on this planet has a right to live their life far away from oppression,

---

[411] *Sunday Illustrated Herald,* London, 8th February 1920

251

violence and crime. Every man, woman and child has a right to emotional freedom and a moral happiness, and it was of course the duty of our political, social, religious and judicial infrastructures to ensure that was to be the case. Our institutions have conspicuously failed the citizen.

I believe in self-reliance. I believe in personal initiative. For the past 17 years I have taught Life Management, the study of helping others to develop the skills and tools each of us needs to survive and thrive on 21st century Earth. I believe the time has come for the public to reclaim and examine these tools, which have been taken from us, and familiarise ourselves with them with a joyful heart. Let us relearn the integrity our ancestors jealously guarded; self-reliance, personal initiative, duty, bravery, honesty, and personal accountability for our actions. If our nations are to be saved from the yawning chasm of lawlessness and anarchy opening at our feet, and also from the coming global super-state we are told will save us from ourselves, we must set ourselves to the task with steely determination and without delay. For if we do not reclaim our nations and, yes, our sanity, and fast, then I fear we must expect to be led, like lambs to the slaughter, into a dark, foreboding future. One, I fear, from which there can be no return.

Thomas Szasz, one of psychiatry's luminaries, who blew the whistle on corrupt and criminal practices within his industry

Bruce Wiseman, of the Citizen's Commission on Human Rights (CCHR), whose *Psychiatry – The Ultimate Betrayal* helped thousands to learn the truth about their 'mental disorders'

Beverly Eakman, one of America's foremost educational researchers, linked psychiatry with the globalisation agenda of restructuring society through sabotaging education

Jan Eastgate, international president of mental watchdog, CCHR – a tireless advocate for those who have been abused by the mental health system

Jovan Raskovic inflamed the Serbian people with a peculiar brand of religious Freudianism. The popular Serbian revolutionary confessed just before his death in 1992 to having incited the war which subsequently engulfed the Balkans

Slobodan Milosovic, a former psychiatric patient of Karadzic's, later went on to lead extremist Serbs in their murderous, campaign of 'ethnic cleansing', ridding their country of 'undesirables' in the most brutal and inhuman acts witnessed in Europe since World War 2

Radovan Karadzic, psychiatrist and former patient of Raskovic's, survived the war, and, at the time of writing, still remains at large. Karadzic was another, like Raskovic, who was recognised by a resolution signed by the Council of Europe as one of the chief architects of genocide during the Balkan crisis

Dr Hendrik Verwoerd, a psychologist completed his mental health training Berlin, Leipzig and Hamburg in the 1920's, then a hotbed of racist and eugenics philosophies. Verwoerd late became South Africa's first prime minister, under whom tens of thousar of black South Africans were kept ir abandoned mining compounds and murderously abused by psychiatrist

- Part 2 -
Physical Illnesses
that Affect the Mind

Let Your Food be Your Medicine...

Please note that the following information is for educational purposes only and must not be construed as medical advice. A qualified health practitioner should always be sought in the matter of any illness. On no account should any patient discontinue their medication without professional medical supervision

Doctors and psychiatrists are not trained in nutrition, so the idea that food can affect mental performance is not readily appreciated, but invariably overlooked in favour of the psychiatrist or doctor prescribing his favoured drug or treatment. Yet are we not what we eat and absorb? And if this is the case (and it is!), then why wouldn't doctors and psychiatrists be trained in nutrition, this most basic of body sciences?

The fact that doctors and psychiatrists are trained in institutions funded by the chemical and drug industry is widely known, yet most do not appreciate the extent to which this skewing of interests affects the way medicine in practised. Many studies have been done on the effects of nutrition and diet on mental and physical performance, and we are going to study a number of these in a moment. But how many of us actually read these studies? Very few. *"But the newspapers tell us everything we need to know on the medical front!"* folks insist, indignant at any hint of a conspiracy. *"What about those medical correspondents who write tirelessly, telling us the latest breakthroughs and problems in the medical industry?"*

Newspapers fund themselves on circulation and, you guessed it, advertising. How many drug companies advertise their concoctions in newspapers for everything from asthma relief, through to antacids, toenail fungus treatments and products to combat hair-loss? Is this advertising revenue important to newspapers? Do you think newspapers want to compromise this income by writing about non-patented nutritional ideas which might conflict with their advertisers' products?

In *Health Wars*, we examined heartburn. The leading over-the-counter, non-prescription medicines for heartburn are antacids. Go to a supermarket and you will see shelves full of them. Yet the answer to heartburn and reflux, in almost all cases, is a switch to the *Food for Thought* dietary regimen (see end section and book of same name) and a consistent intake of water (four pints a day plus). Are newspapers going to

255

annoy and anger their pharmaceutical clients by telling the public this? It isn't likely, is it?

And the same is true in the realm of 'mental illness'. The same pap is marched out before us in the media, with such terms as 'mentally disturbed', 'chemical imbalances in the brain' and 'schizophrenia'. The same baleful psychiatric spokespeople intone sombrely on the state of the nation's mental health and trot out their pet theories on why children are killing parents, parents children, and children killing other children. We've read all about the problems in Part 1. And now welcome to some great solutions in Part 2.

MENTAL OR PHYSICAL?

The discussion on whether physical illnesses can manifest themselves as 'illnesses of the mind' has been ongoing. Richard Hall and Michael Popkin wrote in the *American Journal of Psychiatry* back in 1967:

"The most common medically induced psychiatric symptoms are apathy, anxiety, visual hallucinations, mood and personality changes, dementia, depression, delusional thinking, sleep disorders (frequent or early morning awakening), poor concentration, changed speech patterns, tachycardia [rapid heartbeat], nocturia [excessive urination at night], tremulousness and confusion.

In particular, the presence of visual hallucinations, illusions, or distortions indicate a medical etiology [cause] until proven otherwise. Our experience suggests this to be the most reliable discriminator. We were able to define a specific medical cause in 97 out of 100 patients with pronounced visual hallucinations." [412]

This is an astonishing admission. According to these researchers, 97 out of 100 patients they studied exhibiting the classic hallucinations of one of the major mental disorders, 'schizophrenia', are actually suffering from traditional medical problems, which can be solved, as we shall see, with measures peculiar to the physical body's requirements. Other studies support this incredible conclusion.

Erwin Koryani reported in 1979 that 43% of 2,090 patients suffering alleged psychiatric illnesses were suffering from one or more major, undiagnosed *physical* illnesses, including malaria, syphilis, hepatitis,

---

[412] Hall, Richard & Michael Popkin, *American Journal of Psychiatry*, p.vi 2, 1967

anaemia, epilepsy, heart disease, asthma, cancer, hypoglycaemia and metabolic, nutritional deficiency diseases. These illnesses were often the sole cause of their mental symptoms:

"Conditions believed to be primarily psychiatric or 'psychosomatic' in nature, but in fact concealing a physical illness, may don the apparel of a depression, anxiety state, apathy... aggression, a variety of sexual problems, delusions, hallucinations, confused states, or changes in the customary features of the personality. No single psychiatric symptom exists that cannot at times be caused or aggravated by various physical illnesses." [413]

In 1980, a major study presented to the American Psychiatric Association convention confirmed these findings and many other data reported by separate studies when, out of 100 patients it studied exhibiting mental illness symptoms:

- 76% were reported to be psychotic at the time of admission
- 46% were found to have an undiagnosed physical illness which contributed or aggravated their mental illness symptoms
- 28 out of the 46 patients above showed a dramatic recovery and a clearing of their mental symptoms when their diagnosed physical conditions were properly treated
- 18 more patients showed a significant improvement in their mental performance after medical treatment for their physical ailments
- 80% of the group had previously undetected, physical illness conditions which required treatment.

The Citizen's Commission on Human Rights reports the case of Jeanette Wright of Bear Creek, Wisconsin:

"For thirty-five years [Jeanette] was labelled by psychiatrists as variously schizophrenic, manic depressive, and acutely psychotic. She was treated with large quantities of psychiatric drugs as well as electroshocks. After enduring this nightmare for most of her life, she was

---

[413] Koryani, Erwin K, "Morbidity and Rate of Undiagnosed Physical Illnesses in a Psychiatric Clinic Population", *Archives of General Psychology*, Vol.36, April 1979, p.414

finally correctly diagnosed by a physician as having hypothyroidism. She was cured in 11 days."[414]

Dr H L Newbold taught psychiatry at Northwestern Medical University School, USA, until he discovered the link between nutritional disorders and mental illness. His 1975 publication, *Mega-Nutrients for Your Nerves*, describes hundreds of case histories, including his own, where a change of diet and nutritional supplementation removed symptoms of depression and anxiety.[415]

George Watson, a former professor of philosophy of science at the University of Southern California, also noted the mental health/nutrition connection. His book *Nutrition and Your Mind: The Psychochemical Response* again studied hundreds of cases which responded favourably to a physical diagnosis and treatment. Watson states:

"The rate of improvement we have found among those suffering from virtually every kind of mental illness is very high – about 80% - and we have seen dramatic case histories of complete clinical remissions in what heretofore have been considered almost intractable illness."[416]

This is the best news we can wish to hear. Let us review some of the common 'mental disorders' and see what the scientific literature has to say. Notes on nutritional and lifestyle changes are placed at the end of each section. In summary, we shall examine a dietary regimen that takes us back to nutritional basics and gives us the optimum opportunity to avoid all the problems.

---

[414] Wiseman, Bruce, op. cit. p.365

[415] Newbold, H L, *Mega-Nutrients for Your Nerves*, Peter H Wyden Publishers, New York: 1975

[416] Watson, George, *Nutrition and Your Mind: The Psychochemical Response*, 1972, no longer in print.

Attention Deficit Disorder
Also: ATTENTION DEFICIT HYPERACTIVITY DISORDER

In 1987, ADHD was voted into existence with a show of hands by the APA during the compilation of its DSM-III-R. Within one year, 500,000 children in America alone had been diagnosed with an affliction, created by a show of hands, which had no apparent corresponding physical brain disorder. Many children were subsequently prescribed drugs to control their behaviour. By 1997, 4.4 million had been labelled ADHD. In 1975, US federal law had provided funding and psychology-based education for 'learning disabilities'. By 1989, 1.9 million had been diagnosed as having Learning Disorder (including attention deficit). At the end of 1996, 2.6 million American children had been branded 'special needs'.[417] Did funding play a factor in this mass diagnosis? Today, ADHD is said to account for a third to half of all child mental health referrals.[418]

SYMPTOMS: Little Billy has a problem. He doesn't finish his homework. He is rowdy in class. He can't sit still at mealtimes and fidgets constantly. When his parents buy him a new toy, he smashes it or wears it out. He is a beast with the furniture, tumbling around the room and getting into things with boundless energy.

But Billy's temper tantrums have caused problems at school as well as home. He is unpopular with his peers, defiant of authority, sometimes exhibits a speech impediment and lies to get out of trouble. Billy's parents have been warned by the principal to 'get something done' or Billy won't be allowed to return to school to disrupt others. *"Billy needs help,"* the head intones sombrely. He gives them a telephone number to call. Drugs such as Ritalin are routinely prescribed.

In millions of households across the world, parents have noticed aberrant behaviour in their children. These traits, as we have seen, have been prescribed medical epithets or disease classifications by psychiatry. But are these 'mental diseases', or do they have more straightforward explanations? Is it likely millions of children have suddenly become 'mental ill'?

---

[417] CCHR, *Psychiatry – Betraying and Drugging Children*, op. cit, p.9
[418] Baughman, Jr, Fred A, ibid.

259

COMMENTARY: Retired California neurologist Fred A Baughman Jr sent a letter in January 2000 to US Surgeon General David Satcher in response to Satcher's Report on mental illness. *"Having gone to medical school,"* Baughman wrote, *"and studied pathology — disease, then diagnosis — you and I and all physicians know that the presence of any bona fide disease, like diabetes, cancer or epilepsy, is confirmed by an objective finding — a physical or chemical abnormality. No demonstrable physical or chemical abnormality: no disease!"*

"You also know, I am sure," Baughman continued, *"that there is no physical or chemical abnormality to be found in life, or at autopsy, in 'depression, bipolar disorder and other mental illnesses.' Why then are you telling the American people that 'mental illnesses' are 'physical' ...?'"*

Baughman concluded his six-page letter to Satcher by declaring that *"your role in this deception and victimization is clear. Whether you are a physician so unscientific that you cannot read their* [the American Psychiatric Association's] *contrived, 'neurobiologic' literature and see the fraud, or whether you see it and choose to be an accomplice — you should resign."*

Journalist Kelly O'Meara interviewed Dr Baughman for *Insight* magazine and posed the questions most parents would choose to get to the bottom of the ADD/ADHD fraud. Here is an excerpt of that interview:

Insight (Kelly O'Meara): His direct, no-nonsense style has made Baughman a pariah among the psychiatric and mental-health communities and a hero to families of children across America who believe they have been 'victimized' by the attention-deficit/hyperactivity disorder (ADHD) label. *"The 'disease'"*, Baughman tells Insight, *"is a total 100 percent fraud,"* and he has made it his personal 'crusade' to bring an end to the ADHD diagnosis.

Insight: You've spent 35 years in private practice as an adult and child neurologist, diagnosing real diseases. What spurred your interest in the ADHD diagnosis?

Fred A Baughman Jr: Through the 1970's and 1980's the ADHD 'epidemic' began to impact all of us, and the numbers of children being referred to me were increasing dramatically. I'd examine these kids to determine whether they did or did not have real diseases. After giving them thorough examinations, doing such tests as I deemed were necessary, I couldn't find anything wrong with them.

I was becoming more and more aware that something was afoot from the tone with which the diagnoses were being made in schools and by psychiatrists who were part of the school team. And never mind that I could find no scientific basis for the diagnosis. But here were paediatricians and school psychiatrists practicing mental health in ways that did not make sense. Principals and teachers would threaten that if I didn't diagnose ADHD they'd find someone who would. As a neurologist, I'm in the business of diagnosing real diseases, so this attitude on the part of people who should know better was very disturbing.

Insight: You are among a small number of physicians publicly to challenge the psychiatric community about this diagnosis. Why do you think so many doctors are diagnosing ADHD when they, too, must know there is no scientific data to support it?

Fred A Baughman Jr: Most physicians, like the public, have bought into the whole psychiatric line. The populace at large has been so brainwashed by this 'tyranny of the experts' that they cannot bring themselves to believe things are other than what the psychiatric industry and the pharmaceutical companies tell them. The population has been told again and again that these 'diseases' exist, despite the fact that there is no scientific proof to back up their claims.

People have been lied to so often that they can't disabuse themselves of the notion that these so-called diseases are chemical abnormalities of the brain. Psychiatry has never proved that ADHD, let alone depression, anxiety or obsessive-compulsive disorder [OCD], even exists. Yet this hasn't stopped doctors from diagnosing them. It was simply decided during the early days of psychopharmacology — of psychiatric drugs — that these were nice theories and they were fed to the public as fact.

Insight: With the diagnosis comes the 'fix', the prescription pills that reportedly help control these diseases.

Fred A Baughman Jr: Yes, that's right, and like the unscientific diagnosis, no one really knows how these drugs work on the brain. It's all just theory at this point.

But then this same psychiatric community says even depression is a disease resulting from a chemical imbalance. They also say that OCD is a disease with a known chemical abnormality of the brain. In neither case is there proof to support either claim. Through the years, though, they've... fudged their line a bit, saying instead: *"Well, it's a psychiatric disorder."*

Insight: You've testified before Congress on this issue, and several of your papers on these matters have been published in medical journals. Recently you travelled to France to address a committee of the Parliamentary Assembly of the Council of France as a counterweight to ADHD advocates. What kind of response did you get?

Fred A Baughman Jr: I was charged with presenting the argument against the diagnosis and treatment of ADHD. I never expected it to go so well.

Three European psychiatrists presented the case for the ADHD diagnosis using the same old slide-show presentation, presumably showing brain atrophy in the patients diagnosed with ADHD.

I pointed out to them, as I've done numerous times here in the States, that all the patients in the slides whose brains showed atrophy also had been on stimulant therapy, so there was no way to know that the atrophy was not, in fact, caused by the drugs rather than the alleged brain disorder ADHD. A member of the council committee summarised what had transpired during the day and basically said they didn't believe what the psychiatrists had presented about ADHD — that they were sceptical about the appropriateness of the drugs recommended for the diagnosis.

One of the psychiatrists was so intimidated by my argument that he threatened to leave the meeting. It was just amazing to see this guy get so frazzled. The council was terrific, and I couldn't have imagined so favourable a response. It was so unlike a typical US response. I think the Europeans are trying to resist this whole ADHD business.

Insight: You set up a website, www.adhdfraud.org, to help get information out to parents who have been impacted by the ADHD diagnosis. What kind of response are you getting from parents?

Fred A Baughman Jr: I hear from many families who have been victimised by this diagnosis. By the time they find me their eyes usually have been opened and they realise the fraud of the diagnosis. But they also realize how serious the diagnosis is for the child and the problems it can create for families.

On the other side of the coin, of course, are the perpetrators at the National Institute of Mental Health [NIMH] and the academic psychiatrists who put out the ADHD propaganda. These people also know who I am and try not to respond to the letters and papers I write. They don't want to see me at medical conferences and seminars because they know that I have the facts, take no prisoners and am willing to show that they are perpetrating a fraud. If they can keep the public in the dark about the facts of this alleged 'disease', then science is beside the point.

I'd love to debate the Surgeon General or anyone in the hierarchy of academic psychiatry, but I don't think any would agree. The Surgeon General wouldn't even respond to the letter I wrote to him about his Report on Mental Illness, so I don't see him stepping up to the plate anytime soon.

Insight: You've testified in court for nearly two dozen families who were fighting the ADHD diagnosis. What should parents do when their child has been diagnosed?

Fred A Baughman Jr: People are being told in no uncertain terms that this 'disease' exists and should be treated with drugs, so it's extremely difficult to get the truth out. The essential first step of the perpetrators is to label the child with ADHD. I've seen how these things turn out for those who try to go up against the system, and it is very sad. Before parents find themselves in a legal, adversarial relationship with the school system and county officials, they should get their child out of that school and either home-school them or put them into a parochial or private school. I tell parents with children caught up in this fraud that, for now, going against the system is a no-win situation.

Insight: What will it take to turn the establishment around on this issue?

Fred A. Baughman Jr: I'm trying to expose the medical fraud and to get just and appropriate medical treatment for children when it is needed and, where it isn't required, I'm trying to get appropriate education, parenting, disciplining and training so these children can achieve self-control. They are all certainly capable of it. We've got to do something because we're talking about 6 to 8 million children who have been diagnosed with ADHD. This just can't wait.[419]

POTENTIAL CAUSES OF HYPERACTIVITY OR ADD

There can be many, varied reasons for children behaving abnormally. The fact that aberrant behaviour has been observed increasing in our youth since the sixties is no accident. Dr Carl Pfeiffer is a world-renowned mental health authority and principal of the Princeton Bio Center in New Jersey, which provides organic, nutritional medicine to its mentally troubled patients. Pfeiffer states that substantial evidence links the decline in our children's behaviour to declines in social morality, school teaching

---

[419] O'Meara, Kelly, *Insight*, 18th February 2002

standards, lax discipline at home and at school, boredom in class and a range of toxicological and nutritional problems with diet.[420]

Teachers, such as Angela Devlin, a 25-year educator of special-needs children, have researched the connection between a child's failure during education and subsequent criminal or delinquent behaviour later in life. Devlin's book, *Criminal Classes – Offenders at School*, reports research demonstrating that a high percentage of young offenders were dyslexic and hyperactive at school and were punished for their failures. Turning Point, an alcohol and drug rehabilitation centre, was the focus of a study by Drs Morton and Hardman, who found that 98% also had dyslexia and/or ADD. A follow-up of 64 adolescents, who had been diagnosed as hyperactive as children, discovered that 25% were still prone to anti-social or delinquent behaviour ten years later.

Can ADD/ADHD be neurological in nature, or is it the result of social shortcomings, such as bad parenting, lax discipline, poor teaching, lack of self-esteem and boredom at not being stretched academically? Can it be caused chemically by food allergies, blood sugar problems, chemical intolerances or nutritional deficiency? Each of these causes individually has been shown to bring on the symptoms of hyperactivity or attention deficit. In today's society, as we learned in Part 1, many of these potential causes are commonly found in dysfunctional households. Certainly, with the progressive dismantling of a workable educational system, anarchy reigns in more than a few classrooms.

Teachers in turn are not allowed to punish wrongdoing for fear of being punished themselves for generating a mental disorder. Kids, being kids, are bound to take advantage. By the way, kids being kids is NOT a new phenomenon! As far back as 425BC, Socrates was lamenting: *"Children nowadays are tyrants. They contradict their parents, gobble their food, and tyrannise their teachers."*

Teachers are also not being trained to teach reading in the successful, phonics manner (see section on Dyslexia), so children, who fail to read and spell correctly because of how they were taught, fail to develop self-esteem and confidence. They begin to lose interest.

---

[420] Pfeiffer, Carl & Patrick Holford, *Mental Illness – The Nutrition Connection*, ION Press, London: 1996

OTHER THEORIES

Some researchers think that 'foetal stress' during pregnancy may be a factor. Other research has shown that the family history of an ADHD child exhibits many disorders associated with altered biochemistry, as well as immune and metabolic causations. Both these theories may also be explained by social factors, such as the quality or otherwise of education, diet and lifestyle.

Genetics has seized the day and claimed a hereditary factor for ADD/ADHD. Yet again this may be explained by factors traditional to the family. Dr Fred Baughman is unequivocal:

"I wrote to the Food & Drug Administration (FDA), the Drug Enforcement Administration (DEA), to Ciba-Geigy (manufacturer of Ritalin), to Children and Adults With Attention Deficit Disorder (CHADD) and <u>four times</u> to leading ADHD researchers at the NIMH, requesting that they direct me to one or a few articles in the peer-reviewed, scientific literature that constitutes <u>proof</u> of a chemical or physical abnormality in ADHD, thus making it a 'disease'.

Paul Leber MD of the FDA wrote in response: '...as yet no distinctive pathophysiology for the disorder has been delineated.' Gene Haislip of the DEA responded: 'We are also unaware that ADHD has been validated as a biologic/organic syndrome or disease.'

I have yet to receive anything which would constitute proof of an abnormality – one that can be tested for patient-by-patient – one proving that we are not drugging up entirely normal children. Even the APA admits in its DSM-IV that there are '...no laboratory tests that have been established for 'Attention Deficit/Hyperactivity Disorder.'" [421]

Common symptoms of kids exhibiting behavioural disturbances can include an abnormal thirst, as well as eczema, skin rashes and asthma. These are often associated with prostaglandin imbalance - chemical modulators that affect the brain, inflammatory reactions and water balance. This in turn led some researchers to wonder whether the body sometimes has problems converting essential fats into prostaglandins and neurotransmitter hormones.

---

[421] CCHR, *Psychiatry: Betraying and Drugging Children*, op. cit. pp.10-11

Researchers Bunday and Colquhoun tested the theory to see whether supplementing with essential fatty acids would make any difference. They tested evening primrose oil, a rich source of gamma-linolenic acid (Ω3), on children who had been diagnosed ADD/ADHD. The following, provided by the Hyperactive Children's Support Group, is typical of such anecdotal reports:

"Stephen, aged 6, had a history of hyperactivity, with severely disturbed sleep and disruptive behaviour at home and at school. Threatened with expulsion from the school because of his impossible behaviour, his parents were given two weeks to improve matters. They contacted the Hyperactive Children's Support Group, and evening primrose oil was suggested. A dose of 1.5g was rubbed into the skin morning and evening. The school was unaware of this, but after five days the teacher telephoned the mother to say that never in 30 years of teaching had she seen such a dramatic change in a child's behaviour. After three weeks, the evening primrose oil was stopped, and one week later the school complained. The oil was then introduced to good effect."[422]

Scientists at Purdue University in the US have found that children exhibiting hyperactivity have altered fatty acid metabolism and lowered levels of these essential nutrients in their blood, compared to controls. One fatty acid, DHA, has shown to be low in children marked with low mental performance. Fish oils are rich in DHA. Other evidence however demonstrates that genuine hyperactivity and attention deficit may not be caused by poor nutrition alone. Two other elements play large in causation – that of chemical toxins and food allergies.

HOMING IN ON THE PROBLEM – DIET
Essential fats can only be converted into prostaglandins by two enzymes, which themselves are dependent upon the presence of vitamins B3 (niacin), B6, biotin, zinc and magnesium. Dr Abram Hoffer explored the possibility of a link between B3 and B6 deficiencies and ADD. Hoffer gave 3g of Vitamin C and over 1.5g of B3 (niacinamide) to 33 children. Only one failed to respond favourably. Children with low levels of the essential neurotransmitter hormone serotonin have been helped with B3 and B6 supplementation. Zinc and magnesium deficiencies are well known to cause immune system problems, coupled with excessive fidgeting, anxiety, loss of co-ordination and learning difficulties in the presence of a

---

[422] Provided by the Hyperactive Children's Support Group, www. hacsg.org.uk

normal intelligence. The magnesium, zinc, copper, iron and calcium levels of plasma, erythrocytes, urine and hair in 50 children aged 4 to 13 years with hyperactivity were examined by atomic absorption spectrometry. The average concentration of all trace elements was lower when compared with the control group.[423]

HOMING IN ON THE PROBLEM – CHEMICAL TOXINS

Certain chemicals, now extremely common in our environment, can act as 'anti-nutrients' – that is, they bleed away or bind essential nutrients in the body. Lead produces symptoms of aggression, poor impulse control and attention span. Sugar, as we will see, produces a kaleidoscope of problems with poisoning and hyperactivity. Excess copper and aluminium cause hyperactivity and have been found in excess amounts in children with behavioural disorders. *"Copper and lead deplete zinc levels and may contribute to deficiency,"* Dr Pfeiffer remarks.[424] Phosphorus and phosphoric acid are known mental impairment agents. So is Monsanto's infamous artificial sweetener, aspartame (Nutrasweet, Equal and Canderel).[425] Perhaps one of the most dangerous pastimes a child can indulge in is the consumption of soda beverages. These contain high levels of phosphoric acid and up to 8-10 teaspoon equivalents of refined sugar in one aluminium can. Children drinking 6-8 sodas a day may be ingesting over 70-80 teaspoons of sugar just from the soda drinks alone. In addition, there are the excess sugars found in their processed foods and candies to consider.

HOMING IN ON THE PROBLEM – ALLERGIES

Perhaps the leading cause of ADD/ADHD worthy of investigation however is in the realm of food toxins and allergies. Dr Neil Ward is a scientist who has been at the forefront of additive research. A press release from his university in Guildford, UK, reports:

Children's disruptive behaviour can be linked to food choice. Hyperactivity, attention deficit disorder... and antisocial or aggressive behaviour in children can be traced back to what they eat. According to Dr Neil Ward from the University of Surrey's Chemistry department, some children can react to the additives, preservatives and colourants in food products, causing certain behavioural problems. *"Parents should identify the*

---

[423] Kozielec, T, et al, "Deficiency of Certain Trace Elements in Children with Hyperactivity", *Psychiatr. Pol.* 28, pp.345-353, 1994
[424] Pfeiffer, Carl & Patrick Holford, *Mental Illness – The Nutrition Connection*, op. cit. p.153
[425] Day, Phillip, *Health Wars*, op. cit. Index on 'aspartame'.

products which cause the reaction and eliminate it from the child's diet," he said.

Dr Ward monitored groups of children in schools. He aimed to find out whether behavioural disturbance linked to chemicals appeared in isolated groups or if all children were at risk. He found that certain colourants could lead to an adverse reaction within 30 minutes of consumption. He identified toxic metals like lead and aluminium and food colourants as the main culprits. Reactions to these chemicals included behavioural or body reactions like rash or physical impairments.

The soda additive tartrazine is a known problem. Dr Ward discovered that adding tartrazine to drinks increased the precipitation of zinc in the urine. Ward speculated that tartrazine was binding to zinc, rendering it unavailable to the body, which then excreted it. Ward found behavioural changes *in every child who consumed the drink containing tartrazine.* Four out of ten children in the study had severe reactions, three developing eczema or asthma within 45 minutes of ingestion. Ward concludes in the above press release:

"Children in primary schools are under a lot of peer pressure to consume certain products, and they tend to favour products containing a lot of sugar. The problem is that these products often also contain some 'nasty' chemicals. Consumers often don't understand the information on food labels. They were a bit more conscious of labels when concerns about e-numbers were first raised, but since organic food hit the shelves, people seem to think everything is safe now. It is very important that not only children but in many cases their parents should be encouraged to learn more about the foods they choose to consume, how they are stored, prepared and cooked in terms of providing optimum nutritional value to their diet."[426]

OTHER SOMATIC INDICATORS
Physiological indicators to watch for in a child labelled ADD/ADHD are those symptoms usually associated with allergy: excessive mucus, ear infections, skin rashes, facial swelling, tonsillitis, discolouration around the eyes, bloating and digestive problems, bad breath, bedwetting, eczema and asthma.

---

[426] Press release, 12th April 2002, University of Surrey at Guildford. Enquiries: Liezel Tipper, Press Officer, Tel: +44 (0)1483 689314 or E-mail: press-office@surrey.ac.uk

Gluten allergies to wheat, barley, rye and oat products are very common and lead to bloating and an auto-immune reaction known as Coeliac (Celiac) disease. Studies show that 1 in 33 of us may be susceptible. Others indicate that the incidence of gluten/gliaden intolerance may be as high as 1 in 10.[427] The unmanageable, sticky gluten protein can disrupt the lining of the intestinal wall, destroying villi which absorb nutrients, and allowing the permeation of food particles and toxins through the intestinal wall and into the bloodstream. The effects range from self-poisoning conditions, such as Chronic Fatigue Syndrome and 'Leaky Gut Syndrome' through to the symptoms listed in the previous paragraph.

In 1975, Dr Ben Feingold reported successful treatment of ADD by removing chemical additives, dyes from the diet, as well as foods containing salicylates, found coffee, tea, as well as some fruits, nuts and berries. Sensitivity, even to some natural foods, is believed to be the result of auto-immune reactions to known chemical antagonists found in processed problem foods, such as junk foods, pizzas, sweets, candy, sodas and their 'diet' equivalents. Dr Schoenthaler found an empirical connection between sugar/junk food intake and anti-social and criminal behaviour. Other problem foods connected with ADD/ADHD may be eggs, chocolate, rape oil (canola) and unfermented soy food derivatives (soya 'milk' and meat substitute foods).

NUTRITIONAL VERSUS DRUG APPROACH
The optimal approach to helping a child, or indeed any adult, with hyperactivity problems involves a strategy which tackles all the above factors. It isn't so hard to see that children wander aimlessly through a nutrient-deficient and chemical minefield with the diets they consume today. Many parents also, cramming white bread, biscuits, doughnuts, hot dogs and pizza down the throats of their co-operative brood, still believe the old adage that if the kids are 'full', they have eaten well.

One of the first measures recommended by specialists like Dr Pfeiffer and nutrition expert Patrick Holford, founder of London's Institute of Optimum Nutrition (ION), is to have a problem child undergo an allergy testing procedure. These tests are relatively inexpensive and often available at nutrition clinics. Pinpointing problem foods and chemicals in the early stages precludes the need for a trial and error approach with diet. If allergy testing is not possible, then removal of potentially harmful

---

[427] www.mercola.com. Search on 'gluten' and 'celiac'

269

foodstuffs from the diet for a period of time (60 days) will highlight whether these food(s) are the 'trigger' for such allergy problems.

COMPARISONS BETWEEN DRUGS AND NUTRITION
Child medication for ADD/ADHD is a hotly contested and debated subject. As I travel around the world, hundreds of anxious parents ask for my views on the subject. Turning to the scientific literature, the controversial LSD promoter Dr Humphrey Osmond conducted a study comparing Dr Bernard Rimland's studies on the effect of the nutrient approach to ADD on 191 children. Osmond reported the total number taking each ADD drug, the number helped, the number worsened and the 'relative efficacy ratio' – the number helped divided by the number worsened. Osmond's index would therefore report '2' if twice the number of patients were helped rather than worsened by the drug. The results of his studies are illuminating. They demonstrate that over EIGHTEEN TIMES the number of patients are helped by nutrition than worsened by it. Interestingly, the accumulation of data appears to indicate that drugs overall do very little. Mellaril was the best drug overall. The main culprits for worsening conditions were, according to Osmond, Ritalin and Dexedrine:

Vitamins vs. Drugs – Which Work Best?				
Medication	Total	Helped	Worse	Ratio
Dexedrine	172	44	80	0.55
Ritalin	66	22	27	0.81
Mysoline	10	4	4	1.00
Valium	106	31	31	1.00
Dilantin	204	57	43	1.33
Benadril	151	34	25	1.36
Stelazine	120	40	28	1.43
Deanol	73	17	10	1.70
Mellaril	277	101	55	1.84
All drugs	1591	440	425	1.00
Nutrition	191	127	7	**18.14**

RITALIN (methylphenidate)
Profile: An amphetamine similar to cocaine. Manufactured by CIBA Pharmaceutical Company. Primary treatment used in ADHD. Today used

by millions of children in America alone.[428] Side-effects published by the *International Journal of the Addictions* list over 105 adverse reactions to Ritalin, including anxiety, hair loss, convulsions, nausea, insomnia, headaches, stomach pains, weight loss, slowing of growth, and compulsive nervous behaviours.[429] A 1975 study in the *Canadian Medical Association Journal* reported that *"Findings suggest that children who take* [Ritalin] *even in moderate doses for several years may in some cases fail to grow at expected rates."*[430]

CIBA issued the following Ritalin advisory in 1985:

DRUG DEPENDENCE: Ritalin should be given cautiously to emotionally unstable patients, such as those with a history of drug dependence or alcoholism, because such patients may increase dosage on their own initiative. Chronically abusive use can lead to marked tolerance and physic dependence with varying degrees of abnormal behaviour. Frank psychotic episodes can occur, especially with parental abuse. Careful supervision is required during drug withdrawal, since severe depression as well as the effects of chronic over-activity can be unmasked.

Note that, by the admission of the manufacturers themselves, the purpose of Ritalin is to 'mask' the symptoms of 'over-activity', not cure them. And what is the definition of parental abuse in today's world? Apart from the obvious, can it also be when children and teenagers disagree with their parents? Suicide and suicidal tendencies have dogged withdrawal from Ritalin from its outset. Even DSM-III-R states that *"suicide is the major complication"* of withdrawing from Ritalin and similar drugs. The tragic legacy these drugs have to our children is discussed in Part 1 – 'The Great Childhood Maddening'.

ENHANCES PERFORMANCE?
If Ritalin really worked to improve school performance, there should be abundant proof of this in the scientific literature. There isn't. The number of well-designed studies in which Ritalin has been shown to

---

[428] Breggin, Peter, "The Scapegoating of American Children", *Wall Street Journal*, 7th November 1989, p.1

[429] Physicians Desk Reference (PDR)

[430] Weiss, Gabrielle, et al, "Effect of Long-Term Treatment of Hyperactive Children with Methylphenidate", *The Canadian Medical Association Journal*, Vol.112, No.2, 25th January 1975, p.164

enhance long-term learning is a telling 'zero'.[431] The litany of condemnation and negative reporting however is legion. A sampling of these is given below:

"...all the conclusions converged: 'stimulant drugs have little, if any impact on... long-term academic outcome." (*The Learning Mystique*, 1987)

"...we again find no support for the assumption that 'learning' – in any general sense – improves as a consequence of drug treatment." (*American Journal of Orthopsychiatry*, 1976)

"The belief that long-term drug intervention will continue to be of value or produce better outcome in hyperactive children has not been substantiated by this or other studies." (*Journal of Abnormal Child Psychology*, 1981)

"The ideal dose for the suppression of conduct problems may actually impair cognitive effects which, theoretically, could negate any beneficial effect on academic achievement or even exacerbate the child's learning problems." (*Journal of Learning Disabilities*, 1983)

"The present results suggest that continued use of Ritalin and possibly other drugs to control hyperactivity may result in compliant but academically incompetent students.... The control of hyperactivity by medication, while effective, may be too costly to the child, in that it may retard his academic and social growth, a human cost that schools and society can ill afford." (*Journal of Applied Behaviour Analysis*, 1975)

Educator Larson has his own opinions after years of observing children on long-term Ritalin prescription: *"...as near as I can tell, and this is completely unscientific, but by our work with them, they have got brain damage. The tragedy is deepened by the fact that the labelling of children with ADD is not because of a problem the kids have; it is because of a problem teachers who cannot tolerate active children have."*[432]

---

[431] Kohn, Alfie, "Suffer The Restless Children", *Atlantic Monthly*, November 1989, p.98

[432] Televised interview with Dr Alan Larson for educational close-ups, Part 2, Oregon, January 1990

To neurologist Fred Baughman, the greatest tragedy is that, after being diagnosed, children believe they have something wrong with them that only a drug can fix. More poignantly, the child sees that his parents and schoolteachers believe this also.[433]

PROZAC (fluoxetine)

Profile: Manufactured by Eli Lilly. Designed as a 'mood brightener', released in 1987 and instantly became part of Hollywood chic. Prozac is now routinely prescribed to 'problem' children. Side-effects can include abnormal dreams, bronchitis, agitation, chills, diarrhoea, dizziness, loss of appetite, paranoid reaction and insomnia (*Physician's Desk Reference*). The side-effects list for Prozac in the PDR runs to over 100 adverse reactions.

Sales of Prozac reached $125 million in 1988 and $350 million the following year. The drug attracted massive publicity, both in support and condemnation. In 1993, Peter Kramer, a columnist for the *Psychiatric Times*, wrote his bestseller *Listening to Prozac,* in support of the drug. In spite of 160 lawsuits brought against the manufacturer for alleged suicidal or violent reactions to their product, Eli Lilly's sales of Prozac in 1993 reached a staggering $1.2 billion.[434]

The medical journal *Cancer Research* published research which demonstrated that Prozac and other anti-depressants *"bind to growth-regulatory... receptors"*, propagating malignant cancer growth in rats.[435] Interestingly, it appears that the famous American 'Delaney Amendment', designed to outlaw consumption of drugs which provoke cancer at *any* dosage, was not invoked in the case of Prozac.

ADD/ADHD – THE NUTRITIONAL APPROACH

There are a number of well-designed studies showing the efficacy of nutritional supplementation for learning and hyperactive disabilities. There is also abundant evidence for the addictive and psychological damage these drugs prescribed to children can do, with little appreciable upside, save that of *altering the child's behaviour,* or, in the case of

---

[433] Baughman, Fred, quoted by Richard E Vatz, "Attention Deficit Delirium", *The Wall Street Journal,* 27th July 1994

[434] Freudenheim, Milt, "The Drug Makers Are Listening to Prozac", *The New York Times,* 9th January 1994

[435] Brandes, Lorne J, et al, "Stimulation of Malignant Growth in Rodents by Anti-Depressant Drugs at Clinically Relevant Doses", *Cancer Research,* Vol.52, 1st July 1992, p.3796

Prozac, drugging the patient so they cannot remember what they were worried about in the first place. Yet the American Academy of Pediatrics overwhelming endorses the use of these drugs as first resort for ADD/ADHD conditions.[436] There is not one mention of nutrition in the American Academy of Pediatrics position paper on ADHD.[437] In 1995, the AAP did produce a video on nutrition however. It was funded by the Sugar Association and the Meat Board.[438]

The title of a fact sheet promoted by the American Dietetic Association, focussing on ADHD, is "Questions Most Frequently Asked About Hyperactivity". The fact sheet asks two questions: *"Is there a dietary relationship to hyperactivity?"* and *"Should I restrict certain foods from my child's diet?"* These were answered with the same word – *"No."* [439] The source quoted for the fact sheet is The Sugar Association (again), which also produced its own consumer guidelines, including the awesome statement: *"Sugar has a mildly quieting effect on some children."*[440] [441]

Researcher Egger showed that 79% of hyperactive children improved when artificial colourings, flavourings and sugar were eliminated from their diet. In fact 48 different foods were found to be allergy-positive, producing medical symptoms among the children tested. For example, 64% reacted to cow's milk, 59% to chocolate, 49% to wheat and gluten-bearing products, 45% to oranges, 39% to eggs, 32% to peanuts and 16% to sugar.[442] Researcher Schoenthaler's immense work in this area indicated that 47% of his juvenile delinquent subjects noticeably improved their problem behaviour (theft, insubordination, hyperactivity, suicide

---

[436] "Medication For Children With An Attention Deficit Disorder (RE 7103)", American Academy of Pediatrics, Committee on Children With Disabilities, Committee on Drugs; *Pediatrics*, 80(5), November 1987
[437] Ibid.
[438] O'Connor, Amy, "In The News", *Vegetarian Times*, October 1995, p.20
[439] *Journal of the American Dietetic Association*, September 1994, p.975
[440] "Questions Most Frequently Asked About Hyperactivity," Produced by the Sugar Association, Inc., Washington, D.C.
[441] "Consumer Fact Sheet: Diet and Behaviour," The Sugar Association Inc., Washington, DC.
[442] Egger, J, et al., "Controlled Trial of Oligoantigenic Treatment in the Hyperkinetic Syndrome," *Lancet*, 1985, p.540

attempts, etc.) when artificial colourings, flavourings and sugar were eliminated from their diet.[443]

Carl Pfeiffer and Patrick Holford recommend the following dietary changes for those diagnosed with ADD/ADHD. Please note that a qualified health practitioner should supervise each individual case to ensure protocols and safety measures are observed. *Patients MUST NEVER discontinue any psychiatric medications unsupervised*:

> **Eliminate chemical additives and sugar.**
> **Test and eliminate allergens (often wheat, diary and eggs).**
> **Supplement essential fatty acids (both Ω 3 & 6).**
> **Supplement B-complex (inc. B1, B3, B5, B6), calcium, magnesium, zinc and other key nutrients.**
> **Test for and detoxify toxic elements.[444]**

A perusal of other relevant literature recommends the following for children suffering from hyperactivity or behavioural problems associated with ADD/ADHD:

> **Discontinue junk foods, especially sodas and other chemically-laden, high-street food attractions.**
> **Avoid sugar, refined flour and polished (white) rice.**
> **Avoid pork, aspartame, saccharin, synthetic/fake fats, sweets/candy and fluoridated water.**
> **Eat organic, whole, living foods, a high percentage raw. (see *Food for Thought* dietary regimen)**
> **Eat good quality fish, rich in oils.**

---

[443] Schoenthaler, Stephen, "Institutional Nutritional Policies and Criminal Behavior," *Nutrition Today*, 20(3), 1985, p.16; see also: Stephen Schoenthaler, "Diet and Crime: An Empirical Examination of the Value of Nutrition in the Control and Treatment of Incarcerated Juvenile Offenders," *International Journal of Biosocial Research*, 4(1), 1983, pp.25-39. Stephen Schoenthaler, "Types of Offenses Which can be Reduced in an Institutional Setting Using Nutritional Intervention: A Preliminary Empirical Evaluation," *International Journal of Biosocial Research*, 4(2), 1983, pp.74-84. Stephen Schoenthaler, "The Los Angeles Probation Department Diet Behavior Program: An Empirical Evaluation of Six Institutions," *International Journal of Biosocial Research*, 5(2), 1983, pp.88-98
[444] Pfeiffer, Carl & Patrick Holford, *Mental Illness – The Nutrition Connection*, op. cit. p.150

- Ensure that 70% of the diet comprises high-water-content, high fibre, living, whole organic foods.
- Avoid foods that may contribute to allergies. These are typically, as Pfeiffer notes, wheat, dairy, sugar, eggs, oranges and chocolate.
- Drink 3-4 pints of clean, non-chlorinated, non-fluoridated water a day.
- The basic supplement program (see 'A Guide to Nutritional Supplements')
- ENSURE ADEQUATE EXERCISE to burn off excess energy.
- Examine and evaluate high lead levels in the child's environment, together with any other chemical factors which may be relevant.
- Watch for somatic, allergic reactions in the child, including bloating or irregular bowel movements, excessive mucus, ear infections, skin rashes, facial swelling, tonsillitis, discolouration around the eyes, bloating and digestive problems, bad breath, bedwetting, eczema and asthma.
- Apply a firm but loving discipline on the child.

NOTES

Ensure that the child is co-operative with dietary changes. Obviously, in more than a few cases, this is not easy. Ensure consistency in applying dietary amendments. Discontinuing psychiatric drugs may be considered by a qualified health practitioner familiar with an orthomolecular approach to these conditions. Discontinuing psychiatric medication must never be undertaken without professional supervision.

School - Programmed Retardation
(Learning Disorder, discipline problems and dyslexia)

"This is no longer an educational system. Its character has been completely transformed and it now clearly reveals itself to be what for many decades it has been in the process of becoming: namely, an agency working for the barbarisation of youth."
George Reisman, professor of economics
Pepperdine University, Malibu, CA
'The Intellectual Activist'

Many children experience problems at school. From drugs, bullying and truancy through to challenges in learning and retaining new information. Some fall behind their classmates in reading and maths and cannot adjust to the learning environment. Others have problems with naughtiness or merely fitting in and socialising with other children.

We have examined physical problems that invariably lead to a sick and unhappy child. Food allergies and blood sugar imbalances, as well as toxins in the diet and environment, impair cognitive ability. The lack of consistent and effective nutrition is also one of the chief causes of childhood developmental and behavioural problems.

But many parents remain unaware of the tremendous toll psychiatric influences have wrought on the way our children are taught and raised at school. The baleful influences of Dewey, Russell and Thorndike, radiating out of the all-powerful Teacher's College at Columbia University, have indeed infected our societies with a rot that is proving very challenging to extirpate.

PERSONAL INITIATIVE
Prior to the 1920's, direct emphasis was placed on achieving academic brilliance. At the heart of this were the three 'R's – reading, 'riting and 'rithmatic. But children went to school to learn, not only academic subjects, but also the social skills they would need to survive and prosper in the adult world that beckoned within a few short years. They learned courage on the sports fields, and politeness and respect for their elders in the classrooms. They learned about law and the mistakes man had made in history and economics. The child was thus fashioned, becoming learned in the knowledge that if he did not learn the lessons of history, he would be doomed to repeat them.

Perhaps more importantly, children under the old system discovered, or were taught how to hone 'personal initiative'. They learned the skills they needed to solve problems, rely on themselves, lead others, triumph against superior odds. They were taught how to conceive an idea, plan its operational phase and then carry it through to a successful conclusion. Children were given projects to do which would last the whole summer. Their work was critically examined when turned in. Lots of red ink was used. Schools taught that failure was not an option. Excellence was the goal. Lack of discipline or bad behaviour were not tolerated. Oikishness and yobbery were given short shrift. Bullying met with a swift and summary justice. British broadcaster Jeremy Paxman, in his very readable polemic, *The English*, gives us a feel for how it was at one of these leading schools 'back then':

"Once away from home, a good thrashing was accepted as an essential part of the process of turning out a gentleman. The champion flogger was the Reverend Dr John Keate, appointed headmaster of Eton in 1809, who beat an average of ten boys each day (excluding his day of rest on Sundays). On 30th June 1832 came his greatest achievement, the thrashing of over eighty of his pupils. At the end of this marathon, the boys stood and cheered him. It says something about the spirit of these places that he was later able to tell some of the school's old boys of his regret that he hadn't flogged them more often." [445]

Neither was it profitable for a boy to whinge to his parents about the disciplinarian, spartan regime of his school. After all, that was what his parents were paying for. This was the price, Paxman reminds us, of turning him into one of the Breed.

THE WHOLE ENCHILADA
While there were of course teachers and headmasters who 'went over the top' with their disciplinarian ways in those days, few will deny that reasonable discipline plays a pivotal road in shaping a child through adolescence. I was schooled at Charterhouse in the UK between 1973 and 1977 along with my elder brother, James. My younger brother, Ian, was sent to Sutton Valence, a private school in Kent. Charterhouse's avowed aim was to take a snivelling thirteen-year-old (me) and machine him into an adult. For this to work, I had to have a complete understanding of the outside world and how its complicated parts interrelated one with

---

[445] Paxman, Jeremy, *The English*, Penguin, London: 1998, p.179

another. I had to be able to express ideas, argue my principles, learn to discharge stress, keep myself fed and maintain a high degree of physical fitness. I had to exhibit unflinching courage in the face of adversity. I had to learn how to suffer with stoic determination that my failures would not be repeated.

The breadth of the curriculum was awesome. My subjects included English, English Literature, Physics, Biochemistry, Biology, Economics, Latin, German, German Literature, French, French Literature, Mathematics, Advanced Mathematics, Geography, History and Ancient History. These were merely the preliminary subjects I had to take for 'O' Level grades. A 'D' in any exam was a disgrace and would rightly have earned a thrashing in Keate's day. 'C's would have had the Housemaster's lip curling in a withering contempt. 'B's were second best and simply unacceptable. The 'A' was the only game in town. The teachers in the main had colossal brains. You failed them at your peril.

I flogged myself to exhaustion and distinction, earning 11 'A's and 2 'B's. I later earned 'A' levels too before leaving the majestic old institution. During my studies, I represented the school in cricket, rugby and soccer. I became an accomplished sportsman. I learned how to speak in public and argue with the best of my teachers in the scheduled library debates. I learned how to be proud of, and love my country. I was taught how to blast the ace out of a playing card at thirty paces with a rifle, earning my marksman's certificate in the process.

The point is, I had worked hard for my accomplishments and they were my own. I had not been humoured, patronised or over-praised. It had not been easy. It was sink or swim and you learned the pecking order and your place in it. I once had *A Concise History of 18th Century Europe* slammed over my head by my Housemaster for failing to pay attention to what he was saying about the Industrial Revolution. There was nothing concise about that book. The headache stayed with me for days. No thoughts of litigation ever entered my throbbing brain. Yet, sore head or not, my achievements at school had bred an indefatigable confidence, discipline, respect and a self-reliance that has stayed with me to this day. My mission at school was thus accomplished. I was now an independently functioning, educated adult that knew the difference between right and wrong. I could now go out and serve others.

Britain built the most formidable empire the world has ever seen on the bedrock laid down by this no-nonsense system of education. The stoicism and courage infused by its methods have been evident in its laws, its literature, its art and in a thousand desperate actions, from Rourke's Drift to El Alamein, from the Spitfire skies of Kent to the churned up poppy fields of Flanders. Even those who hated Britain took the best parts she had to offer and made them their own. Still today, many see it as their emigration destination of choice. Yes, there were flaws and abuses and victims and heartaches in the British system, but nothing foreign there to the plight of the human condition. For decades, the sun had never set on the British Empire. But the final twilight eventually came when the candle of her national and creative initiative was dampened and then extinguished at the wellspring of her educational font. To destroy an empire, you must first destroy her children's ability to imagine it, to want it. To inherit it.

LIGHTING THE FUSE

It was psychiatry which provided the canker that rotted the school system, not just in Britain, but overseas as well. America was particularly hardest hit. Ralph Truitt, head of the National Committee for Mental Hygiene, declared in 1927: *"If we are going to prevent dependency, delinquency, insanity, and general inadequacy, the school should be the focus of our attack."*[446]

Psychiatrists, mental hygienists and reformers believed stress was the main cause of a child's mental woes. They targeted the three main areas they saw as the instigators of this stress: school failure, a curriculum centred on academics, and disciplinary procedures. Eliminate the emphasis on achievement and academics, and you would rid the child of the stress of school failure.

But, in targeting academics, the Teacher's College doyens were destroying personal initiative and, as crucially, the context in which a child finds himself in the world. For instance, in avoiding proper history, the child is not taught that his acts affect not just himself, but others too, and sometimes long after the doer of the deed has gone. Bruce Wiseman gives us other examples:

"With no awareness of, say, the Great Fire of London in 1666, and other such disasters, the building contractor of today thinks modern fire codes are 'stupid'. So he cuts corners to avoid what he thinks are pointless regulations. Catastrophe results. Shoddy workmanship. Racial hatred.

---

[446] Lionni, Pablo, op. cit.

Economic chaos. All can and do result from a society that has no understanding of all that has gone before.... And so we spend our own last breaths – and our children's – to learn the same lessons again.

Science is another academic subject. It covers the field of electronics, biology, medicine, chemistry, physics and a host of others. Without an elementary grounding in the sciences, we are creating people who are becoming more and more dependent on technological advances, while becoming less and less aware of the basic information upon which these advances are based. We end up with a population that does not understand the mechanics of disease, building structures, electricity, bodily functions, nutrition, plant growth – the list is endless. Yet these are things that touch all our lives and our knowledge or ignorance of them can mean the difference, literally, between life and death." [447]

Here we see the Protocols of Zion coming into their own; a dullard, ill-educated people spending 12 years in an educational system being taught a fraction of what their forebears learned. They are not even, as we shall discover, taught to read properly. Gradually the technological knowledge of society aggregates into the hands of the few, which is of course the whole point of social control. The people may not like the controllers. They may smash up a few city blocks in the annual May Day, anti-New-World-Order riots to express their frustration at 'being controlled' by the 'multi-nationals'. But in the end, 'bread and circuses' always win out for the dullards. These days, no-one grows their own food anymore. We have to rely on Ford and Toyota for our cars, on Monsanto, WalMart and Safeways for our food, on Ted Turner and Rupert Murdoch for our news and entertainment, and on our medical peers to heal us when we're sick. The newspapers may patronisingly express our concerns in the most indignant and satisfying vitriol. But things stay just the same. And the whole game of control moves to Sega Level 4.

THE ARTS

And when mankind's most valuable emotional expressions – the arts – become a laughable parody of their former brilliance, what indeed becomes of us? Art gives us visual and auditory perceptions of the very heights to which mankind may aspire. A society weaned on comic books, MTV, Andy Warhol, gangsta rap and Jerry Springer loses the wonderful breadth of language and expression of art in every available field to evaluate and give meaning to the kaleidoscopic strata of achievements,

---

[447] Wiseman, Bruce, op. cit. p.273-274

places, technologies, customs, ideas and all that is godly, human, of this earth and beyond. If knowledge promotes understanding and tolerance, what does ignorance promote? Maybe the kind of behaviour we increasingly see on our streets and in our schools?

WHERE HAS ALL THE TALENT GONE?

All of which leads up to the question of educational standards. During the course of my research into this subject, I have spoken to a great number of teachers over the years. I would estimate that a full 80% of them *themselves have learning disabilities or lack of social control skills based on how __they__ were taught.* Today in Britain, we suffer from a shortage of 'old-school' teachers - even those from abroad are now balking at entering 21st century schoolyard Britain and America. Talent has been migrating out of the school systems across the world for years. What little remains finds itself bewildered, under siege, underpaid – which of course, once again, is the whole idea. Little wonder that homeschooling has become so popular in America – a system that has developed off the back of the frustration and anger many parents feel towards the declining standards and corruption of moral ideals in the classroom. Parents have decided to act. And they have used their personal initiative.

DYSLEXIA AND READING PROBLEMS

Eight percent of America's children are said to suffer from a reading and spelling disorder, known as dyslexia, an alleged defect in the language centre of the brain which prevents literacy.[448] Other nations are reporting similar figures. What is not being reported however is how dyslexia has only struck in the past seventy years when, prior to this, illiteracy was solidly on the wane. In 1930, the illiteracy rates in America were as follows:

- 1.5% among native-born whites
- 9.9 % among foreign-born blacks
- 9.2% among urban blacks
- 16.3% among blacks in general

The only reason many were illiterate was that they simply had not gone to school. Today, the illiteracy rate among blacks in the US is around 40%. For whites, the figure varies from 7-30%, the exact figure being

---

[448] "A Closer Look – Special Education", *Right to Read Report*, January 1994

unknown.[449] In 1990, 700,000 US high school graduates could not even read their own diplomas.[450] Of the 190 million Americans (of all races) over 16 with an average school attendance of 12.4 years, almost 25% cannot read grade school lessons. Around 28 of 29 students would not be able to earn college credits in any other nation but America. This is a nation that has spent billions supposedly to ensure reading success among its 'socially disadvantaged populations' via its Special Educations programs.[451]

PHONICS

Destroy a child's ability to read and write, and you effectively mutilate the chain of educational links that lead to the development of that child's intellect. The tried and tested method for teaching a child to read is the phonics system. This involves giving children the tools they need to decode the mysteries of the written word by breaking down words phonetically. This system is actually an extension of the 'baby talk' parents use instinctively to communicate with their little ones. Leading American educator Beverly K Eakman, quoting from an Associated Press article, explains the connection:

"Every infant needs to master the phonetic elements of speech.... parents' baby talk universally exaggerates the vowel sounds in a high-pitched, drawn-out, sing-song manner that allows babies to absorb key building blocks of language – especially the 'ee', 'ah' and 'oo' sounds. Tiny infants younger than six months of age, say researchers, are learning their very first words and 'learn to categorise vowel sounds that are meaningful in their native languages while ignoring the subtle variations'. Apparently... 'biology has structured us [parents] *to know what to do. When the biology of people produces this effect across three cultures* [America, Sweden and Russia]... *that tells you something.'*

What it tells us is that the sounds of language are important, and that in an alphabetic structure, it is a crime not to teach children how to relate these sounds to certain letters and letter combinations, thereby enabling them to break the 'code' of written language. But by high school today, spelling instruction generally means placing a bunch of unrelated

---

[449] Blumenfeld, Samuel L, *The New Illiterates – And How You Can Keep Your Child From Becoming One*, Paradigm, Boise, ID: 1988
[450] Schatzer, Vaughn, *The Truth Behind the Declaration of Independence*, a video commentary, PROACTIVE, 1627 W Main Street #213, Bozeman, MT 59715 USA
[451] Eakman, Beverly, K, op. cit. p.380

words on the chalkboard and telling children to learn them for a test next week. No approach is given concerning how to proceed in a logical way to spell them. In other words, there is no transfer value from one list of words to the next." [452]

THE 'WHOLE-WORD' METHOD

Psychiatry's contribution to illiteracy has been the introduction of the 'whole-word' system of reading tuition. Otherwise known as 'Look-Say' or 'Sight-Word', this program was introduced by Wundt graduate and psychologist James Cattell, a Teacher's College faculty member. Here, the child is taught, not phonetics, *but to memorise each individual word as a picture.* When the system was first introduced, many teachers were uncomfortable deserting what had traditionally worked, and so mixed whole-word with phonetics to produce a combined reading program. In whole-word, the context has been removed, namely, that rules applied to one word can no longer be transferred to interpreting another, thus preventing the child from building an aggregate system of reading expertise. In his 1955 landmark book, *Why Johnny Can't Read*, Rudolph Flesch remarks that teacher's colleges throughout the world soon began receiving textbooks on how to teach reading using whole-word. The results were predictably disastrous. San Diego Unified School District in Southern California, for example, experienced a 50% dive in the median reading skills of its students in just one year (1990-1991) after adopting the catastrophic method. [453]

Today we have a veritable epidemic of dyslexia and illiteracy. Another industry has grown up around these 'special needs' kids to help them with their 'psychological' problems. "Their eyes move in funny patterns," some counsellors remark (Could this be evidence of a brain disorder?) In actual fact, the poor mite can't learn a huge vocabulary since his brain has to learn all the different pictures that constitute the words of his language. The result is bad spelling, despair, and perhaps most damaging, a stigmatising psychological label that the child is somehow 'mentally impaired' – a label the child will carry with him for the rest of his life.

Today, red marks on exam papers are regarded as 'demeaning' and possibly to blame for some of the 'mental disorders' from which today's children apparently suffer. The child is thus not consistently corrected

---

[452] Eakman, Beverly K, *Cloning of the American Mind...*, op. cit. p.380-381

[453] "A Closer Look – Special Education", *Right to Read Report*, January 1994, Vol.1, No.8, pp.1-3

either on their writing or speech. When the child comes into contact with words he hasn't memorised, particularly ones that are near look-alikes, he begins to exhibit what teachers believe is a typical learning disability. Educator Eakman:

"Take for example two random sentences taken from a typical textbook:

- *"Thomas Jefferson was the first president to be inaugurated in Washington."*
- *"As the Spirit of St Louis touched down on the turf, the crowds surged toward it."*

Using the currently voguish 'whole language'... approach, based on sight memory and context clues alone, a student by seventh grade [13 years old] typically will read these lines as follows:

"Thomas Jefferson was the first president to be assassinated in Washington."

"As the Spirit of St Louis rolled along the surf, the cowards surged towards it."

Naturally this student will do poorly on academic tests. Because of the nature of his errors, the rest of the selections will make no sense to him. The student wonders why Thomas Jefferson was assassinated. The rest of the paragraph seems to indicate the man lived on a good while. Did the Spirit of St Louis have water-landing gear? Why did cowards go up to it instead of away from it? Passed on from grade to grade, this student will eventually throw up his hands in exasperation because nothing in any of his classes makes any sense. What kind of self-esteem do you think he will have?" [454]

Illiteracy, according to a number of studies, has been found to be a decisive factor in former prisoners returning to a life of crime.[455] After all, if you cannot read properly, or have low academic standards and poor scholastic achievements, the employment options are not tremendously welcoming. Michael Brunner, a Research Fellow from the US National Institute of Justice, and author of *Retarding America: The Imprisonment of Potential*, reports that an overwhelming number of prisoners are not 'learning impaired' but actually quite intelligent. Once taught how to read

---

[454] Eakman, Beverly, K, *Cloning of the American Mind*, op. cit. p.382
[455] Brunner, Michael, *Retarding America: The Imprisonment of Potential*, Halcyon House, 1993

285

properly using the phonics method, their self-confidence and esteem rise significantly and they find renewed determination to turn their lives around once they are released. Brunner calls the teaching of reading by the whole-word method 'programmed retardation'.[456]

A 1989 *US News & World Report* article noted that American schools are actually encouraged to brand children as learning disordered (LD) so they can qualify for the supplementary federal funds earmarked for the handicapped.[457]

THE MATHEMATICS SCANDAL

Mathematics is another example of a discipline that relies on a progressive mastery of skills. So if a student drops the ball early on by not grasping some of the fundamental rules and principles, their progress will quickly falter and halt. Today, many kids are allowed to use calculators in class without grasping the basic skills of addition, subtraction, multiplication and division, which underpin further progress. Maths embodies personal initiative and problem-solving, which is the bugaboo of the Teacher's College ethic of dumbing down. The context is once again removed, so a student who struggles with algebra, for instance, fails at the first hurdle if they are not taught the context of why they must learn the discipline. They cannot conceptualise what they are doing, but rather perform the tasks by rote. If they do not understand a particular step, large classes often prevent the teacher from giving an individual helping hand. The student does not want to appear stupid by asking for help in front of his classmates. In *Retarding America,* Brunner hits the nail on the head:

"What brings about the delinquency is not academic failure per se, but a sustained frustration which results from continued failure to achieve selected academic goals. When frustration can find no resolution into constructive or productive activity, one response... is aggressive, anti-social behaviour. Other responses are regression, resignation. These have been well documented from clinical research conducted with both animals and humans....

The anti-social aggression that Pavlov was able to create in the laboratory is being created in tens of thousands of classrooms across

---

[456] Ibid.

[457] "Labeling Away Problem Kids", *US News and World Report*, 13th March 1989, pp.51-61

America.... All the ingredients necessary to create... anti-social aggression through sustained frustration are present: There is an unachievable goal... because the means of achieving it... are absent. The student nevertheless is continually pressured to achieve it by teachers, parents and peers.... Finally the student not only has no alternative for achieving the goal, but... is not allowed to leave the failure-producing environment as a result of compulsory attendance laws. For those who do learn to read [mainly those with good visual memories], *they cannot grasp the magnitude of resentment and hostility that is generated in non-readers over time, due to unrelenting frustration from which there is no escape. For many, this frustration explodes into delinquency or... violent forms of social aggression."* [458]

As further generations of illiterates or academic failures are produced, these parents themselves understand the frustrations their children are undergoing. They too see no purpose behind academic striving because it didn't work for them either. Those students who do excel are often vilified by the majority of under-achievers, so it becomes a mark of the damned to do well in class. 'Teacher's pet', 'You little pus' and other denigrating epithets can actually cause a bright pupil to down-regulate themselves in order to avoid catching flak in the playground during break. Thus, conforming to your under-achieving peers becomes a necessity of survival and popularity. And all of us want to survive and be popular.

HISTORY, GEOGRAPHY, ETC.
Other subjects are also blighted. As politically correct history books began to flood American schools, major human events became marginalised in the footnotes, while the liberation movements of homosexual rights, minority sexual preferences, and those of African-, Native-, Asian- and female Americans were brought to the fore to satisfy the social agendas of Teacher's College. Walter McDougall of the Foreign Policy Institute, a Pulitzer-prize winner, believes that education today is nothing but an ongoing effort *"to mandate an alternate reality.... There is no question that* [school history books today] *presume to explain US history by ignoring Lockean individualism, disparaging George Washington and defending... pornography on the Internet."* [459]

Elsewhere in the world, revisionism has been well underway. Hollywood routinely produces realistic-looking movies that have

---

[458] Brunner, Michael, op. cit.
[459] Eakman, Beverly, op. cit. p.389

reinvented key events in history. Many of the social policies, which brought with them the encouragement of individualism, personal endeavour and scholastic achievement, have been severely disparaged and misreported, not only in the liberal press, but also through TV documentaries, films, debates and, yes, school textbooks. Eakman remarks:

"In 'United States History: In the Course of Human Events', the Aztecs are portrayed as victims of the Spanish conquerors; cannibalistic practices likened to other 'advanced cultures' of the time (moral equivalence). The Renaissance [a noteworthy period of personal initiative] *gets seven lines of text; the Enlightenment gets six lines; the Reformation gets none at all! George Washington* [America's first patriot] *is likened to a boring fellow of ordinary talent who is more symbol than fact. Even a terrorist like César Chavez gets more praise – and more space – than George Washington. Indeed the name of George Washington as a designation for schools is now being removed in several localities because he once owned slaves, another good excuse to excise an important historical figure from the American culture.*

...Take another series, entitled 'History of Us', put out by Oxford University Press and approved for use in fifth-, sixth- and seventh-grade classrooms nationwide.... This 10-volume series by former journalist Joy Hakim... [has] *not a semblance of objectivity. Even the publisher admits – and arrogantly supports – Hakim's bias: 'She* [Hakim] *is very negative about Reagan, but she believes that history is going to agree with her,' said an Oxford University press spokesperson. Who cares what history 'is going to agree with' somewhere down the road? Do the blatantly political beliefs of an individual belong in a child's history book?"*[460]

Geography too is so badly taught that, during my research on this subject in the United States over a ten-year period, it was actually quite rare to find a 15- to 20-year-old who could name seven countries on the continent of Europe. Many would quote by rote the nations that had been discussed in recent news items on CNN, such as Iraq, Israel or Libya.

The level of indoctrination that goes on in the media is of course well known. In spite of earnestly declaring in debates that 'Not all Muslims are terrorists', 'all Catholic priests are not paedophiles' and 'blacks are not exclusively muggers, social security fraudsters and drug-dealers', the

---

[460] Ibid. p.390

stereotypes are apologetically hammered home through careful selection of the news items covered. Very few 'good news' items are broadcast, reinforcing a feeling of social despair that 'the world is going to hell in a handbasket'.

IN CONCLUSION

If a child is doing poorly at school, either with general academics, or specifically with their reading, maths, etc., the following questions should be asked:

- How effective is the level of discipline you apply to your child?
- Does your child do what you say, or is s/he rebellious?
- Does your child's teacher have control of the class?
- Has your child been taught to read using phonics or the whole- word method?
- Does your child eat junk/processed food, such as burger meals, fried foods, kebabs, fizzy drinks and sugar-laden foods?
- Does your child drink adequate amounts of water?
- Does your child take nutritional supplementation?
- Does your child have food allergies?
- Does your child live in a toxic environment?
- Does your child exhibit any physical problems, such as migraine headaches, asthma, constant colds, depression, listlessness or eczema?
- Does your child mix with the wrong crowd?
- Does your child speak well?
- Is your child naughty?
- Is your child a leader or a follower?
- Is your child a good or bad influence on others?

These and other questions can determine where the potential problems lie. While teachers often do a great job, some don't, and it is important to identify teacher problems, if they exist. Equally, it is important not to pathologies into an illness kids just being kids. My research shows that many of the problems children face today result from poor diet, poor parental discipline, poor teacher discipline and an aberrant and politically skewed curriculum designed to dumb children down and teach them to 'fit in' with the amoral new globalist society that is struggling to be born. The point is, all these elements, with the possible exception of world politics, can be controlled by the parents, if the parents have the will to make their voices heard.

Schizophrenia

"I have never seen anyone who was able to change his or her self-perception of 'sick' to 'well' while on drugs." Dr Alan Goldstein, professor of psychiatry, Temple University, Philadelphia

Throughout this book, we have thus far examined psychiatry's view of mental illness and how it is traditionally treated. That there are those who can be described as 'disturbed' or 'mentally deranged' is of course beyond doubt. Author Bruce Wiseman:

"Since the first eyebrow was raised at the sight of erratic behaviour, society has had to deal with the problem of the madman. And it <u>is</u> a problem. Anyone who thinks otherwise has never lived around insane people nor had his life disrupted by their actions.

They destroy in the name of some imagined wrong, they refuse to maintain their physical needs and, even if they simply mope, their presence almost inevitably makes life miserable for those around them.

Most families feel considerable relief when they 'put away' the son, daughter or relative who has been screaming obscenities day and night or who believes all are poisoning him. For this reason, mothers, fathers and others at wit's end have welcomed psychiatric services with open arms over the past two centuries. Why wouldn't they? Any offer to remove insanity from one's midst sounds good when one is pressed to the limit of his emotional and financial resources. This has been the foremost function of psychiatry since its inception – to remove the mentally disturbed from streets and shaken homes so the functioning majority can get on with the business of living." [461]

SYMPTOMS: 'Schizophrenia' as a diagnosis is aberrant, as the symptoms often attached to it vary considerably. Schizophrenia loosely correlates to society's traditional view of the deranged person. Symptoms variously linked to schizophrenia include dermatitis, inflammations of the mucous membranes, chronic diarrhoea and mental problems, including depression, irritability, anxiety, confusion, migraine headaches, sleep disturbance, delusions and hallucinations. Some have likened serious cases of schizophrenia to a nightmare from which there is no awakening. Certainly, to the sufferer, what they are experiencing seems real and

---

[461] Wiseman, Bruce, op. cit. p.55

terrifying enough. LSD-induced schizophrenia, which may feature encounters with monsters and demons, as well as gross mental disperceptions and time distortions, at least has the comfort of the clock. After the allotted number of hours, the effect wears off. But for the classic schizophrenic, whose condition has come upon him by degrees, there is a continuing and harrowing nightmare.

The problem with the label 'schizophrenia' is that many cannot agree on what constitutes 'the disease'. There are a hundred causations that may cause the behavioural patterns that can later be diagnosed as 'schizophrenia'. Often, the practitioner needs to wade through histamine, copper, zinc and mercury tests to see if there are abnormal levels of these agents in their patient's system. Psychiatry, as we have already learned, believes that *"...a return to full pre-morbid functioning in this disorder is not common..."* – in other words, the condition is almost always incurable.

As already seen, there may be a number of reasons why someone will start to behave abnormally. In the previous section on ADD/ADHD, we learned that four factors could come into play in changing behaviour: nutritional deficiency, blood sugar imbalances, toxins in the diet and environment, and food allergies. With schizophrenia, things can often be more straightforward. Many nutritionists and orthomolecular psychiatrists hold the view that, in many cases, we might be dealing with nothing more than the continuing reign of a miserable condition known as pellagra, believed for many years to have been banished to the history books.

NUTRITIONAL LINK – THE PELLAGRA CONNECTION
Pellagra was a fatal disease that threw terror into Europe and the United States during its ravages in the 18th and 19th centuries. Noted originally in the 18th century as a European condition that appeared to be linked to corn diets among the impoverished, pellagra's symptoms were as exotic as they were fatal. Named 'pellagra' (the Italian for 'rough skin'), sufferers of this disease were affected by dermatitis, inflammations of the mucous membranes, chronic diarrhoea and mental problems, including depression, irritability, anxiety, confusion, migraine headaches, delusions, hallucinations and dementia.

Many doctors being trained around the end of the 1800's were specialising in the new medical science - microbiology. And so inevitably, new disease syndromes were analysed as microbiological illnesses. For instance, Titius, a prominent German bacteriologist, pronounced pellagra infectious, even though he had never been to the afflicted areas and had a cursory knowledge of the condition. Other doctors began treating pellagra as infectious, and so the remedies of the day employed against infection were used to appalling effect - quinine, arsenic and strychnine.

The Italian researcher Ceni claimed that a fungus growing on mouldy corn was responsible for releasing poison into the patient, thus causing the disease. Ceni's work inspired others to come up with their own proprietary bacteria, which then created a new problem: the sheer volume of papers being written on these new 'infectious agents' for pellagra were consuming prodigious amounts of time to study and refute, thus preventing any possibility that closed minds could be opened to other potential causal factors. The European microbe-hunting bonanza continued, and a cure for pellagra remained as remote as ever.

And then in 1902, an isolated first case was noticed in Georgia, USA. Then in 1906, a rash of pellagra cases occurred in Alabama in a hospital for the insane. Eighty-eight patients contracted the condition and most subsequently died. Soon cases were appearing everywhere, even in some major metropolitan areas of the United States.

Convinced that they were facing a grave new public health threat, the Public Health Service of the US government swung into action. It set up a pellagra institute in South Carolina and appointed Claude Lavinder to head up the research. Lavinder was convinced that pellagra was microbe-driven, but became frustrated when his experiments failed to produce a spread of the disease in animals. In 1909, a national conference on pellagra was convened, again in South Carolina. Once again, pellagra's links with corn diets and poverty were reiterated. The prevailing mood of the conference was that pellagra was either airborne or infectious in nature. The following year, John D Long replaced Lavinder as head of the PHS's pellagra lab. Long's theories on pellagra were influenced by the well-known British doctor, Louis Sambon, who also believed pellagra to be infectious:

"So great was the horror of the disease that a diagnosis of pellagra was synonymous with a sentence of social ostracism. A severe case of eczema was enough to start a stampede in a community, and 'pellagrins' sometimes covered their hands with gloves and salve, hoping to conceal their condition.

Many hospitals refused admission to pellagra patients. One in Atlanta did so on the grounds that it was an incurable disease. At another hospital in the same city, student nurses went on strike when they were required to attend to pellagrins. Physicians and nurses at Johns Hopkins Hospital in Baltimore were forbidden even to discuss the pellagra cases that might be there. Fear of the disease spread to schools and hotels too....

Tennessee began to isolate all its pellagra patients. The state board of health declared pellagra to be a transmissable disease and required physicians to report all cases.... Exhibits on pellagra were prepared for the public, creating fear of the disease along with interest in it... There was pressure for a quarantine in Kentucky, and pellagra patients at the Western Kentucky Asylum of the Insane were isolated... Isolation did not prevent the spread of pellagra, but only heightened the panic over it." [462]

The turn in the disease came in 1914. Two important things happened that year. Britain declared war on Germany, and the United States Public Health Service appointed the unknown Dr Joseph Goldberger as head of its pellagra team. By this time, a quarter of a million people had perished from the pellagra epidemic in the United States.

Goldberger arrived in the South and, although a bacteriologist by profession, immediately began noticing obvious indications that pellagra was not infectious. He saw that even when pellagrins were kept in close confinement, their doctors and nurses did not contract the condition. He also noticed the different diets shared by the two groups. The poor ate the staple diet of corn, while the more affluent doctors, nurses and other hospital staff ate meat and vegetables. Dr Goldberger then set about changing the diets of pellagrins and was able to rid the disease entirely from hospitals, prisons, asylums and orphanages, demonstrating that the occurrence of pellagra was related to a deficiency of fresh green material in the diet. Goldberger approached this problem by the use of brewer's yeast, which would completely prevent and cure pellagra. Further studies years later would show that the factor in brewer's yeast that was most active in the curative effect was niacin, Vitamin B3.

What happened next amazed even the stoic Goldberger. The *New York Times* published the story of Goldberger's success with pellagra,

---

[462] Etheridge, E W, *The Butterfly Caste: A Social History of Pellagra in the South*, Greenwood Publishing Co, 1972, p.11

explaining his hypothesis concerning poor diet and nutritional deficiency. As a result, Goldberger began to draw intense criticism from his peers, most notably from psychiatry and the virus hunting microbiologists. They accused Goldberger of propagating a dangerous and reckless philosophy in the light of so lethal a disease. A doctor at one medical conference drew considerable applause when he described the newspaper publicity on Goldberger's work as 'pernicious', expecting people to believe that such a lethal epidemic was solely the result of poor diet.[463]

Goldberger continued to receive major criticism from his peers, culminating in the most vicious attacks in 1916. Finally becoming exasperated, Goldberger, his wife and 14 workers decided to perform a series of rather extreme experiments for the benefit of the log-jammed medical establishment. They injected themselves with samples of blood, mucus, faeces other bodily fluids from the pellagrins. None of them contracted pellagra. The medical establishment was less than impressed and the attacks continued. As a result, Goldberger's dietary recommendations to end pellagra were completely ignored for the next twenty years, resulting in hundreds of thousands of further needless deaths. Many pellagrins who developed the mental anguishes associated with the condition were pronounced insane and shut away in asylums. Here they were subjected to electric shock treatment, powerful sedative drugs and prefrontal lobotomies in the hopes of rendering them controllable.

Goldberger continued trying to break the establishment's intransigence on pellagra up until his death in 1929. His work was continued by his faithful colleague Dr W Henry Sebrell. Cases of pellagra were still being reported up to the onset of World War 2 in 1939, even in spite of the fact that Vitamin B3 (niacin) had been isolated as the missing pellagra factor in the mid-1930's.

Soon after the end of World War 2, it was finally admitted by the European and American medical establishments that pellagra had, all along, been a chronic metabolic deficiency disease brought on by an absence of green material in the common diet.

---

[463] Etheridge, E W, ibid.

DR ABRAM HOFFER

Dr Abram Hoffer, the leading mental health expert from Canada we met earlier, claims a 90% cure rate for schizophrenia. Hoffer's definition of a cure for this condition is:

- Free from symptoms
- Able to socialise with family and community
- Paying income tax!

In other words, after *a return to full pre-morbid functioning in his disorder*, the patient is able to retake his place in society and have a life. Hoffer remarks of one such case:

"In October of 1990, a 24-year-old woman arrived at my office. Six months earlier she began to hallucinate and became paranoid. During three weeks in hospital she was started on a tranquilliser. For several months after a premature discharge, she almost starved until a retired physician took her into her home to feed her. When I saw her she still suffered visual hallucinations, but no longer heard voices. I started her on 3 grams of niacin [Vitamin B3] and three grams of Vitamin C daily. Three days later she was much better. By February 1991 she was well. Today, she is still well and lives with her sister." [464]

NIACIN – VITAMIN B3

Hoffer pioneered the use of mega-doses of Vitamin B3, in the form of niacin or niacinamide. Hoffer and Pfeiffer's therapeutic dosage for B3 is between 2-4 grams a day, a level over 100 times the recommended daily allowance for the nutrient, which, at excessive doses over Hoffer's recommendations, can cause liver damage.[465] Having recorded over 4,000 cases and published the results of double-blind trials, Hoffer is convinced vitamin therapy, including high doses of B3, is an effective treatment to schizophrenia. His ten-year follow-up studies on schizophrenics treated with and without vitamin therapy demonstrate that significantly fewer of the vitamin-treated patients were admitted to hospital or suffered suicides.

"The idea that diet could overcome mental problems struck me as preposterous," admitted psychiatrist Frederic Flack, whose 'schizophrenic' daughter Rickie narrowly escaped a recommended lobotomy after

---

[464] Pfeiffer, Carl & Patrick Holford, op. cit. p.113

[465] Hoffer, A, "Safety, side-effects and relative lack of toxicity of nicotinic acid", *Schizophrenia*, 1969, 1:78-87

undergoing years of institutionalisation, electroshocks, drug treatments and restraints. She was finally cured by Dr Carl Pfeiffer using nutrition. Pfeiffer confided to Flack that other prominent psychiatrists had secretly turned to him for nutritional treatment when it was their child or loved one who needed help.

The actual mechanism by which niacin works for many cases of schizophrenia is still not known. Hoffer postulated that the body, in the absence of sufficient B3, creates adrenochrome from adrenalin. Adrenochrome is a chemical known to cause hallucinations. Niacin also stimulates the production of histamine and helps detoxify excess copper, inappropriate amounts of which are related to mental illness. Niacin also assists in converting essential fatty acids into prostaglandins, which in turn help to regulate neurotransmitter hormones in the brain. Hoffer's schizophrenic treatment includes:

> **Vitamin B3 – niacin (no-flush**[466]**) or niacinamide 1,000mg (1 gram) twice a day**
> **Vitamin B1 (thiamine), 100mg a day**
> **Vitamin C, 1 gram after each meal**
> ***Food For Thought* dietary regimen**
> **The basic supplement program (see 'A Guide to Nutritional Supplements')**

---

[466] Niacin invariably causes a blushing of the skin, along with prickly sensations, for about 30 minutes. 'No flush' niacin, bound with inositol, is also available. However, when 500-1,000mg of niacin is taken regularly, flushing stops.

Autism

Dr Joseph Mercola reports: *"Autism is a spectrum of disorders that range in severity from bizarre, violent behaviour to an inability to communicate or interact socially, along with repetitive patterns of behaviour. Estimates of the prevalence of the syndrome in Britain range from 10 cases per 10,000 of the population with 'classic' autism, to 9.1 cases per 1,000 showing some signs of autistic behaviour. The National Autistic Society estimates that there are about 500,000 people with autism in Britain, 120,000 of them children. According to one recent study, there has been a tenfold increase among children between 1984 and 1994."*[467]

AUTISM AND VACCINES – THE LINK
Much has been made in recent times of the potential for vaccines to cause autism. The world is currently experiencing a veritable autism epidemic, with one American child in 130, for instance, developing the condition.

Two main areas to consider are the problems caused by vaccine fillers, and the effects of vaccinations on the bowel and other organs.

VACCINE FILLERS
Vaccines can contain the following: .01-.025% each of formaldehyde, mercury (or substitute #6-pheno-oxyethanol, a protoplasmic poison), aluminium, paint thinner, coolant, antifreeze, dye, detergent phenols, solvent, borax, disinfectant, MSG, glycerol, sulfite & phosphate compounds, polysorbate 80/20, sorbitol, polyribosylribitol, betapropiolactone, Amphotericin B and other chemicals, plus hydrolysed gelatin, casein, dead animal tissue and blood (e.g. cow, chick embryo, monkey, sheep, pig, dog, etc.), aborted human foetus cells, mutated (more virulent) human viruses, contaminant animal viruses (e.g. SV40, which causes cancer in humans), bacteria, bacterial endotoxins and antibiotics.

A parent might reasonably question how smart it is to inject *any* of the above into her infant, whose blood-brain barrier may not yet have fully developed. An immune system reaction might indeed be provoked, but perhaps not the kind for which the mother and father might be hoping.

---

[467] www.mercola.com

To date, the US National Vaccine Injury Compensation Program or NVICP, established in 1986, has paid out in excess of $1 billion in injury awards to Western vaccine-recipients. And there are quite literally thousands of cases pending. This despite the fact that the former Health and Human Services Secretary Donna Shalala narrowed the definition of vaccine damage to such an extent that only immediate and severe reactions can now qualify. Seizures, disorders, brain damage, ataxia, paralysis, learning difficulties and deaths that occur many days or weeks following these vaccinations are now excluded.

Added to this, doctors have little incentive to report themselves to the government's Vaccine Adverse Event Reporting System or VAERS, prompting former director of the US Food and Drug Administration, David Kessler, to confess that *"...only 10% of vaccine injuries are ever reported."* [468] Lisa Jillani, of People Advocating Vaccine Education, has observed the growing number of children now suffering from 20/21st century behavioural disorders:

"So the injuries can even conservatively amount to tens of thousands of children, while doctors continue to diagnose and treat mysterious new illnesses and maintain the 'one in a million' adverse reaction myth taught in medical schools." [469]

MERCURY – MAD AS A 'HATTER'

Ever since hatters went mad from inhaling the vapours of the mercury-based compounds used to stiffen felt in the top hats they made, the warning sirens have always sounded with mercury. In vaccines, however, we are told mercury is safe. In the US, the Environmental Protection Agency's 'safe' level for mercury ingestion is set at .1mcg/kg/day (that's a tenth of a microgram). Now witness the assault that comes against a child in the early period of its life, when its immune system is still developing and has not reached its full protective potential:

Day of Birth – Hepatitis B – 12mcg mercury (thimerosal)
30 times the safe level
At 4 Months – DPT and other shots – 50 mcg mercury
60 times the safe level
At 6 months – Hepatitis B, Polio – 62.5mcg mercury
78 times the safe level

---

[468] *Dayton Daily News*, 25th May 1993

[469] Boykin, Sam *A Shot in the Dark* 1998 www.creativeloafing.com

At 15 months – Further shots – another 50mcg mercury
41 times the safe level

The London *Sunday Times* reports: *"The number of vaccinations given to babies and children in Britain and America has increased significantly. In the United States the number given before the age of two has risen from 8 in 1980 to 22 now. In Britain in 1970, most children received diphtheria, tetanus, polio, whooping cough and BCG for tuberculosis; about half were also immunised against measles. In 1972 rubella was added; MMR in 1988, Hib (Haemophilus influenza type b), against a form of meningitis in 1992, MMR as a second dose in 1996, and meningitis C in 1999.*

The MMR first dose is given between 12 and 15 months, with diphtheria and tetanus and the second dose of MMR at three to five years. MMR does not contain thimerosal, though other child vaccines do. Thimerosal was introduced in the 1930's as a preservative and went into common use without review by America's Food and Drug Administration (FDA) because it was assumed to be safe." [470]

THIMEROSAL BECOMES ORGANIC MERCURY
Dr Tim O'Shea: *"Once it is in nerve tissue, thimerosal is converted irreversibly to its inorganic form. Thimerosal is a much more toxic form of mercury than one would get from eating open-sea fish; it has to do with the difficulty of clearing thimerosal from the blood.*

Thimerosal is converted to ethylmercury, an organic form that has a preference for nerve cells. Without a complete blood-brain barrier, an infant's brain and spinal cord are sitting ducks. Once in the nerve cells, mercury is changed back to the inorganic form and becomes tightly bound. Mercury can then remain for years, like a time-release capsule, causing permanent degeneration and death of brain cells." [471]

O'Shea also reports that the body normally clears mercury by fixing it to bile, but before six months of age, infants don't produce bile. The result: mercury can't be excreted.

---

[470] *The Sunday Times,* 27th May 2001
[471] www.thedoctorwithin.com

299

THIMEROSAL SIDE-EFFECTS INCLUDE:

Aphthous, stomatitis, catarrhal gingivitis, nausea, liquid stools, pain, liver disorder, injury to the cardiovascular system and haematopoietic system, deafness, ataxia, headache, paresthesia of the tongue, lips, fingers and toes, other non-specific dysfunctions, metallic taste, slight gastrointestinal disturbances, excessive flatus, diarrhoea, chorea, athetosis, tremors, convulsions, pain and numbness in the extremities, nephritis, salivation, loosening of the teeth, blue line on the gums, anxiety, mental depression, insomnia, hallucinations or central nervous system effects.

Exposure may also cause irritation of the eyes, mucous membranes and upper respiratory tract. Acute poisoning may cause gastrointestinal irritation, renal failure, fine tremors of extended hands, loss of side vision, slight loss of coordination in the eyes, speech, writing and gait, inability to stand or carry out voluntary movements, occasional muscle atrophy and flexure contractures, generalized myoclonic movements, difficulty understanding ordinary speech, irritability and bad temper progressing to mania, stupor, coma, mental retardation in children, skin irritation, blisters or dermatitis. Exposure may be fatal.[472]

FORMALDEHYDE

Another ingredient commonly found in vaccines is the preservative formaldehyde. Here are the published side-effects:

Eye; nasal; throat and pulmonary irritation; acidosis; acute sense of smell; alters tissue proteins; anemia; antibodies formation; apathy; blindness; blood in urine; blurred vision; body aches; bronchial spasms; bronchitis; burns nasal and throat; cardiac impairment; palpitations and arrhythmias; central nervous system depression; changes in higher cognitive functions; chemical sensitivity; chest pains and tightness; chronic vaginitis; colds; coma; conjunctivitis; constipation; convulsions; corneal erosion; cough; death; destruction of red blood cells; depression; dermatitis; diarrhoea; difficulty concentrating; disorientation; dizziness; ear aches; eczema; emotional upsets; ethmoid polyps; fatigue; fecula bleeding; foetal asphyxiation (and they say they don't know what could cause SIDS?)

Flu-like or cold like illness; frequent urination with pain; gastritis; gastrointestinal inflammation; headaches; haemolytic anaemia; haemolytic haematuria; hoarseness; hyperactive airway disease; hyperactivity; hypomenstrual syndrome; immune system sensitiser; impaired (short) attention span; impaired capacity to attain attention; inability or difficulty swallowing; inability to recall words and names; inconsistent IQ profiles;

---

[472] www.mercola.com, search under 'autism'.

inflammatory diseases of the reproductive organs; intestinal pain; intrinsic asthma; irritability; jaundice; joint pain; aches and swelling; kidney pain; laryngeal spasm; loss of memory; loss of sense of smell; loss of taste; malaise; menstrual and testicular pain; menstrual irregularities; metallic taste; muscle spasms and cramps; nasal congestions; crusting and mucosae inflammation; nausea; nosebleeds; numbness and tingling of the forearms and finger tips; pale, clammy skin; partial laryngeal paralysis; pneumonia; post nasal drip; pulmonary oedema; reduced body temperature; retarded speech pattern; ringing or tingling in the ear; schizophrenic-type symptoms; sensitivity to sound; shock; short term memory loss; shortness of breath; skin lesions; sneezing; sore throat; spacey feeling; speaking difficulty; sterility; swollen glands; tearing; thirst; tracheitis; tracheobronchitis; vertigo; vomiting blood; vomiting; wheezing.

If your child is autistic and was vaccinated, these two vaccine ingredients alone cause exactly the type of damage from which your child is suffering.

AUTISM – THE NUTRITIONAL APPROACH

That autistic children respond well to megavitamin therapy has been known for decades. Nevertheless, many drug treatments given to autistic children and adults revolve around keeping them quiet and out of trouble. Dr Catherine Spears, a paediatric neurologist and Dr Allan Cott of New York found treatment with B6 and zinc to be highly affective. Spears reported that *all* her autistic patients responded to the treatments, which included a change of dietary regimen. Parents, teachers and professionals all noted differences and improvements in behaviour and speech. Dr Henry Turkel reports:

"Wendy was 3 years old when her parents realised she was not developing normally. At 48 months, her mental age was 21 months. She achieved an IQ of 44 and was classified as retarded. When 4 years old, then testing with an IQ of 49, she began megavitamin therapy. Her attention span went from 10 to 15 seconds to ten minutes. Within three months, she began to speak in complete sentences. After six months of treatment, her IQ score had jumped to 72. By the age of 8, her IQ score was 85, classifying her as no longer retarded, with low-average ability – a 40 point shift in four years."[473]

---

[473] Turkel, H et al, "Intellectual improvement of a retarded patient treated with the 'U' series", *J. Orthomo. Psychiatr.*, 13(4), pp.272-276

B6, ZINC AND MAGNESIUM

Dr Bernard Rimland took these successes and ran his own study. His sixteen patients showed marked improvements with B6, magnesium and Vitamin C supplementation. Twelve demonstrated regressions when the nutritional elements were replaced with placebos. Supplementing with magnesium at half the levels of B6 proved even more effective. After a battle, his findings were published in the *American Journal of Psychiatry*.[474] Following Rimland's success, five further studies were conducted, all showing positive results with the zinc, magnesium and B6 combination.

In cases where retardation is accompanied with facial swelling, frequent colds and middle ear infections, pyroluria should be suspected. Tissue swells with deficiencies in zinc and B6, preventing the auditory tubes from draining adequately into the throat. Tests for low Immunoglobulin (IgA) will also indicate susceptibility to infection.

'LEAKY GUT'

Often children appear to develop normally through to age 3 and then, after repeated ear infections, which are treated with antibiotics, seem to cease normal development. Bernard Rimland found that many of the children exhibiting these problems may have Leaky Gut Syndrome, where food proteins have entered the bloodstream through the intestinal wall as a result of damage to the intestinal lining. Treatment with antibiotics, which can further damage the gut, can allow more food proteins to enter the bloodstream, thus creating more allergic reactions. Rimland investigated the link between allergies and autism by testing the effects of removing wheat, milk or sugar from the diets of hundreds of autistic children. About 50% improved from the removal of any one of these.[475] Proteins, such as gluten and casein, can be obnoxious to an early, developing immune system in a child, which can develop antibodies against the invading 'toxins'. These antibodies can then go on the rampage causing any of several burgeoning auto-immune disorders, such as MS, arthritis and type-1 diabetes.

---

[474] Rimland, B et al, "The effect of high doses of Vitamin B6 on autistic children: a double-blind, crossover study", *Am. J. Psychiatr.* 135, 1978, pp.472-475
[475] Rimland, B, et al, "Comparative effects of treatment on child behaviour", *Inst. For Child Behaviour Research*, Pub 34b, January 1988

MILK – HERE WE GO AGAIN

Dr Joseph Mercola reports: *"Findings from two animal studies indicate autism and schizophrenia may be linked to a person's inability to properly break down a protein found in cow's milk. The digestive problem might actually lead to the disorders' symptoms, whose basis has long been debated. This research was done by a physiologist at the University of Florida Dr. J. Robert Cade.*

When not broken down, the milk protein produces exorphins, morphine-like compounds that are then taken up by areas of the brain known to be involved in autism and schizophrenia, where they cause cells to dysfunction. The animal findings suggest an intestinal flaw, such as a malfunctioning enzyme, is to blame. Preliminary findings from that study - which showed 95 percent of 81 autistic and schizophrenic children studied had 100 times the normal levels of the milk protein in their blood and urine - have been presented at two international meetings in the past year but have not yet been published.

The researchers also noted that all milk products must be excluded from the diet. This includes such things as ice cream, yogurt and whey. Even natural flavourings in food must be avoided unless the processor can guarantee beyond a shadow of a doubt that caseinate, the main protein in milk, is not included. We now have proof positive that these proteins are getting into the blood and proof positive they're getting into areas of the brain involved with the symptoms of autism and schizophrenia." [476]

OTHER PROBLEMS

Reuters reported on the 13th June 2001: *"Dr. Ted Kniker has been investigating the theory that poorly degraded food proteins leak from the gut into the blood, having a drug-like effect that changes brain activity. In the first part of his study, Kniker, of the San Antonio Autistic Treatment Center in Texas, found that 5 out of 28 children and adults with autism showed improvements in their symptoms after elimination of dairy products and wheat glutens from their diets.*

In the second part of the study, the researchers eliminated several other foods, including buckwheat, soy products, tomato, pork and grapes from the patients' diets. Symptoms changed dramatically in 39.3% of patients during the second phase of the 3-month intervention period.

---

[476] www.mercola.com

Eight out of 28 patients showed clear improvements, as measured by a variety of quantitative scoring methods, including the Autistic Treatment Evaluation Checklist.

Kniker argues that autism is not usually a defect in brain development, but is more likely to be a brain dysfunction that is secondary to extraneous factors, such as dietary factors, immune dysfunctions, infections or toxins.[477]

ADVICE TO PARENTS WITH AUTISTIC CHILDREN

For those parents wishing to seek alternative help for their children with autism, a great place to start is the Institute of Optimum Nutrition, a British organisation based in south-west London (Tel: +44 208 877 9993). ION will be able to advise you or your co-operative doctor on a megavitamin regimen that will maximise nutritional supplementation while at the same time helping to remove heavy metals and restore health to your child. There is great news for those suffering from this condition. An autistic patient may also benefit from the following:

> ➤ **Have an allergy test and restrict sensitive food items, such as wheat, dairy, egg whites, etc. as appropriate**
> ➤ **Adopt the *Food For Thought* dietary regimen**
> ➤ **Vitamin B6, 100mg, am and pm**
> ➤ **The basic supplement program (see 'A Guide to Nutritional Supplements')**
> ➤ **Remove sugar and other junk/processed foods from the diet**
> ➤ **Discuss gradual removal of mercury amalgam fillings with a co-operative dentist**[478]

---

[477] Reuters, 13th June 2001
[478] Kellner-Read, Bill, *Toxic Bite*, Credence Publications, 2002

Depression and Suicide

In her opening address, the World Health Organisation's Director General Dr Gro Harlem stated: *"...initial estimates suggest that about 450 million people alive today suffer from mental or neurological disorders.... Major depression is now the leading cause of disability globally."* [479]

There is of course no question that depression blights the lives of millions around the globe. A million people commit suicide every year, with between 10 to 20 million suicides attempted annually.[480] Suicide in the US for males between the ages of 35-49 is the number three cause of death, outstripping even diabetes, iatrogenic death (physician-induced) and motor vehicle accidents.

Canada has a particularly bad problem with depression and suicides, with a person killing themselves every two hours. Hospital records for 1998/1999 show that females were hospitalised for attempted suicide at one and a half times the rate of males. Around 9% of those hospitalised for a suicide attempt had previously been discharged more than once following an attempt on their own life in that same year.[481] Physicians wrote out 3 million prescriptions for Paxil (paroxetine) alone, one of the most common anti-depressant medications. Sales for Paxil in 2000 exceeded those in 1999 by 19%.[482]

DEPRESSION SYMPTOMS: Feelings of doom, the inability to take action, listlessness, and that thick lead blanket of despair wreck the lives, not only of the sufferer, but their family, friends and co-workers too.

HISTADELIA

On the physical front, nutrient deficiencies, glucose intolerance and allergy are extremely common in those suffering from depression. One major cause is an excess of the neurotransmitter hormone histamine – a condition known as histadelia. Dr Carl Pfeiffer asks: *"Do you sneeze in bright sunlight? Cry, salivate and feel nauseous easily? Hear your pulse in your head on the pillow at night? Have frequent backaches, stomach*

---

[479] WHO World Health Report 2001,
www.who.int/whr/2001/main/en/chapter2/002g.htm
[480] Ibid.
[481] Canada Health Reviews:
www.statcan.ca/Daily/English/020124/d020124b.htm
[482] *National Post*, 29th March 2001, Vol.9, No.129

and muscle cramps? Do you have regular headaches and seasonal allergies? Have abnormal fears, compulsions and rituals? Do you burn up food rapidly and sometimes entertain suicidal thoughts? ...If a majority of these apply to you, you may benefit from a low-protein, high complex carbohydrate diet (fruits and vegetables), 500mg of calcium, am and pm, 500mg methionine am and pm and a basic supplement program. Avoid supplements containing folic acid as these can raise histamine levels." [483]

Some of our most loved stars, such as Marilyn Monroe and Judy Garland, were likely histadelics. Drawing from over 30 years' experience, Pfeiffer estimates that at least 20% of schizophrenics are histadelics and these are often the problem patients in psychiatric hospitals, since they do not respond to the usual drug treatments, electroshock or insulin coma 'therapy'.

Blood histamine levels can be analysed and often, the compulsive obsessions, blank mind, easy crying and confusion may highlight an underlying chemical addiction to cane sugar, alcohol or drugs. Histadelics experience high saliva discharge and rarely have cavities. Often they are seen wiping saliva from the corners of their mouth. Excess histamine presents rapid oxidation in their body, and their high metabolic rate and subsequent attractive body shape are sometimes potential indicators for the underlying condition. Marilyn Monroe was often heard to remark to photographers: *"You always take pictures of my body, but my most perfect feature is my teeth – I have no cavities."*

A high sex drive characterises the histadelic, who achieves orgasm and sustains it easily. Drug addicts and alcoholics also tend to be histadelic. Heroin and methadone for instance are both powerful histamine-releasing agents. A severe insomnia also characterises the condition, and sufferers often use heavy doses of sedatives in order to get to sleep. The sedatives themselves often become an addiction problem, further compounding the plight suffered by those with depression.

DEPRESSION – THE NUTRITIONAL LINK
Traditional psychiatric treatments are mostly useless for the histadelic depressive. Electroshock, examined in detail in Part 1, traumatises the patient further. Lithium in lower doses of 600-900mg is partially effective, but does not have greater efficacy at higher dosages. Anti-depressant

---

[483] Pfeiffer, Carl & Patrick Holford, op. cit. p.103

drugs are simply mood ameliorators and can be addictive. Nor do histadelics respond to B3 mega-doses usually recommended for schizophrenics. B9 (folic acid) definitely worsens the condition.[484]

What has been shown to work however are treatments which modify how the body releases and detoxifies histamine. Calcium supplementation releases the body's stores of histamine and the amino acid methionine detoxifies histamine through methylation, the body's usual method of breaking down the neurotransmitter. Laboratories can test for histamine levels in the blood and this is often one of the first best steps a practitioner can take to determine if histamine is a player in their patient's depression.

Maes et al also found that serum levels of zinc in 48 unipolar depressed subjects (16 minor, 14 simple major and 18 melancholic subjects) were significantly lower than those in the 32 control volunteers.[485]

HELPING THOSE WITH SUICIDAL TENDENCIES

The major problem with those suffering from chronic depression is suicide. Today, such family members are often consigned to psychiatric care, which, as we have seen, can create problems of its own for the patient. Research group Truehope states:

"One of the particularly tragic outcomes of a mood disorder is suicide. Over 90% of suicide victims have a significant psychiatric illness at the time of their death. These are often undiagnosed, untreated, or both. Mood disorders and substance abuse are the two most common. Around 15-20% of depressed patients end their lives by committing suicide." [486]

In times gone by, caring family members gathered around and gave the depressed relative the assurance and attention to talk things through. Often drug addiction or substance abuse were key factors. Today, with the fracturing of the family unit, the denigration of religion, and the

---

[484] Pfeiffer, Carl & Patrick Holford, op. cit.

[485] Maes, M, et al, "Hypozincemia in Depression", *J. Affect. Disord.*, 31, 1994, pp.135-140

[486] Truehope Ltd., *Defining a New Model for the Care of the Mentally Ill*, www.truehope.com; Robins, E, *The Final Months: A Study of the Lives of 134 Persons*, Oxford University Press, NY: 1981; Conwell, Y, et al, "Relationships of Age and Axis 1 Diagnoses in Victims of Completed Suicide: A Psychological Autopsy Study", *American Journal of Psychiatry*, 153, pp.1001-1008

separation of many families from each other with the hectic pace of 21st century life, psychoanalysis has simply taken over the task of counselling that used to be carried out by caring relatives or the neighbourhood minister. I strongly believe that this has had a deleterious effect on our society, in view of the medications prescribed which appear to have a quieting effect, but underneath are propagating a roiling of the emotions.

I further believe that a neighbourhood pastor/minister, or the equivalents in the other religions, also have a pivotal role to play in maintaining the mental stability of their parishioners. It simply has not worked the psychiatric way, with psychiatrists themselves, as we have seen, committing suicide more often than the public they are supposed to be treating. Later in this book, we will examine motivation and the spiritual issues connected with taking action, which have been so able to assist those suffering from depression in regaining control of their lives and starting forward once again.

COMBINING NUTRITIONAL
GOOD SENSE WITH COUNSELLING

In our current times, more than ever, it is essential for the depressed to have an understanding friend or relative with them constantly. Ideally this should be someone the depressed person looks up to, and from whom they can take guidance. Measures should be taken to remove influences that can have a depressing effect on the patient. These include newspapers, TV news, video and computer games, heavy metal, rap, pop and other 'culture' music. Instead, positive influences, serene surroundings, such as countryside outings and an active, outdoors lifestyle with plenty of exercise, far removed from those settings which have surrounded the patient during their bouts of depression, are ideal for setting the tone for recovery.

Negativity is an emotional, spiritual force which has a compounding effect on the body. Religious writings, such as the Bible, concentrate on eradicating negativity from a person's life and instead replace it with a model that offers an explanation of where that person fits in the overall scheme of things. Since Nietzsche apparently killed God, man has become his own deity. This little god has not been doing very well in administering his own creation, over which he seems to exercise so little control. We're born. We live. We die. Then what? It's enough to drive anyone to depression.

And then we see the constant onslaught of bad news. During my lectures, I invite the audience to go home and comb through a daily national newspaper with a red marker pen and put a big red 'X' next to every article that is bad news. Then I ask them to do the same for the TV listings. Then go back through the newspaper and put a big blue 'X' next to every single article that is absolutely NONE OF THEIR BUSINESS. This will give a stark indication of how much junk we take into our brains for absolutely no achievable gain.

What we focus on becomes our reality. Ecuador does not feature in most people's lives in the West, because very few people go there and we don't focus on it. Yet out street, our workplace, our family, our cars – these are part of our focus and so describe our physical context. *When we understand that we become what we focus on, then we need to change the focus.* It isn't hard to see how someone fixated on splatter films and Satanism is going to have a negative focus in that direction – with all the concomitant effects this will stir up.

On the physical side, the following may be of benefit to the depressive:

- ➢ **A low-protein, high complex carbohydrate diet (fruits and vegetables) (see *Food For Thought* dietary regimen)**
- ➢ **Vitamin B6, 50mg, am and pm**
- ➢ **Zinc (gluconate), 25mg, am and pm**
- ➢ **Calcium, 500mg, am and pm**
- ➢ **Magnesium, 200mg, am and pm**
- ➢ **Manganese, 10mg, am and pm**
- ➢ **Methionine, 500mg, am and pm**
- ➢ **The basic supplement program. (Histadelics should avoid supplements containing folic acid as these can raise histamine levels)**
- ➢ **Exercise and rest**

Phobias, Paranoia and Copper

"All our research, everything in our clinical experience over the past twenty-five years, has convinced us that you can improve your emotional state by improving your nutrition: by making sure that every body cell receives optimal amounts of every essential nutrient."
Cheraskin, Ringsdorf and Brecher, authors of *Psychodietetics*

Previously, with depression, we examined the effects of high levels of the neurotransmitter histamine, which is used by the brain to regulate water usage, tears, mucus, saliva and other bodily secretions. Equally, low levels of this neurotransmitter may also create problems that are often linked to schizophrenia. This condition is known as histapenia.

SYMPTOMS: Undue suspicion and paranoia of people. The ability to withstand pain well. Hirsutism (heavy growth of hair). Hard to achieve orgasm with sex. Canker sores. Phobias and fears. Abnormal sensory perceptions – seeing and hearing things. Ringing in the ears. Excessive dental fillings. An absence of headaches and allergies.

Low histamine is often accompanied by high levels of copper, two factors in themselves which may produce abnormal behaviour. Many studies done over the years have gauged the correlation between excess copper and behavioural abnormalities. Dr Michael Briggs from Wellington, New Zealand, for instance, postulated that many cases of schizophrenia could in fact merely be copper poisoning. Dr Carl Pfeiffer studied the connection between histapenia, copper and behavioural problems with his patients for many years. He reports that a sub-group of around 50% of his schizophrenic patients were high in copper. Pfeiffer also noted that low levels of zinc and manganese were also implicated and that excess copper depresses histamine and can be implicated in copperised pipes which bring water into the household. Abnormal lead and mercury levels are also well known to produce schizophrenic symptoms.

HISTAPENIA-PELLAGRA-ESTROGEN LINK
Several studies have seen a link between pellagra, the classic Vitamin B3 deficiency disease, and excess copper. Doctors Finddlay and Venter discovered that pellagra patients were also high in copper. Dr Krishnammachavi discovered this connection in India in 1974 and found

that Vitamin B3 appeared to regulate copper levels in the body.[487] Vitamin C deficiency also seemed to raise copper levels, which in turn produced a vicious spiral, since excess copper is known to destroy Vitamin C. Thus a combined deficiency in B3 and C works to elevate copper levels in the body, which in turn destroy further supplies of Vitamin C.

HISTAPENIC MODALITY: Excess or dominant levels of the female sex hormone estrogen in the body, which brings on the classic menopausal symptoms such as hot flushes, depression and mood swings, is also known to raise copper levels in the body, which in turn deplete Vitamin C. In my book *Health Wars*, we examined the connection between heart disease and depletion of Vitamin C in the body (scurvy), brought on by the dissolving of collagen, a tough, fibrous material which clads the cardiovascular system, giving it structure and form. In the 1960's, when the first contraceptive pill, Envoid, was introduced, healthy young women began perishing from thrombosis. The contraceptive pill, with its elevated levels of estrogen, raises copper levels and depletes Vitamin C. This excess of copper in turn depresses levels of histamine. Low levels of histamine produce inadequate levels of saliva, which in turn fail to protect the teeth from bacterial decay.

By restoring the balance of nutrients in the body, histamine can be brought to normal levels and the patient will experience relief from their symptoms. Any patient suffering from phobias, fears, hallucinations, or exhibiting many of the symptoms described earlier, can obtain a blood test to track levels of copper and histamine to determine whether they are histapenic. Dr Pfeiffer states that histapenic patients may benefit from the following:

> ➢ **Niacin, 500mg, am and pm (may cause blushing)**
> ➢ **Folic acid (B9), 1,000mcg each am**
> ➢ **B12 injection, weekly or daily supplementation**
> ➢ **L-Tryptophan, 1,000mg at bedtime**
> ➢ **Zinc and manganese daily**
> ➢ **The *Food For Thought* dietary regimen, but increase protein in diet**
> ➢ **The basic supplement program (see 'A Guide to Nutritional Supplements')**

---

[487] Krishnammachavi, K, *Am. J. Clin. Nutr.*, 1974, 27:108-111

Pyroluria

Zinc and Vitamin B6 deficiencies give rise to a common physical illness, often mistaken for a mental disease, known as pyroluria. This disease occurs when a large number of chemicals called pyrroles are manufactured by the body, which act as 'anti-nutrients' – that is, they bind to zinc and aldehyde chemicals, such as pyridoxine (B6), rendering them unavailable to the body. Pyrroles can be measured in the urine and a simple test can be used to determine whether the patient has a problem in this area.

SYMPTOMS: Withdrawn and likes isolation. Has set routines and becomes uncomfortable when these are disrupted. Pronounced 'fruity' breath and body odour. Has no dream recall. Constant colds and infections. Irregular menstrual cycle. Impotency. Upper abdominal pain as spleen and liver become engorged periodically with catabolic red cell debris. Sometimes walks stooped to ease the pain. Miscarriages with male babies. Compulsively creative. Insomnia. White spots on fingernails. Stretch marks on skin. Morning nausea and constipation. Pale skin which does not tolerate sunlight. Hypersensitive to light. May become emotionally exhausted.

Many of us can experience one or several of the above. But a patient exhibiting a range of these symptoms should incur suspicion that they might be suffering from pyroluria. Carl Pfeiffer recalls one patient at his famous Princeton Bio-Center clinic in New Jersey:

"Since she was 11, Sara's life had been a nightmare of mental and physical suffering. Her history included chronic insomnia, episodic loss of reality, attempted suicide by hanging, amnesia, partial seizures, nausea, vomiting and loss of periods. Her knees were so painful (X-rays showed poor cartilages) and her mind so disperceptive that she walked slowly with her feet wide apart like a peasant following a hand plough drawn by tired oxen.

Psychiatrists at three different hospitals gave the dubious, 'waste-basket' labels of 'schizophrenia', 'paranoid schizophrenia' and 'schizophrenia with convulsive disorder'. At times, her left side went into spasms with foot clawed and fist doubled up. Both arm and leg had a wild, flaying motion. Restraints were needed at these times. Psychotherapy was ineffective and most tranquillisers accentuated the muscle symptoms. Sara tested positive for pyroluria and was given B6 and zinc.

Urinary kryptopyrrole was at times as high as 1,000mcg%, the normal range being less than 15. She was diagnosed as zinc and B6 deficient and treatment was started. Over three months, her knees became normal, the depression subsided, as did the seizures, her periods returned, the nausea vanished and so did the abdominal pain. She has had no recurrence of her grave illness, finished college and now works in New York. She takes zinc and B6 daily. When under stress of any kind, she increases her intake of Vitamin B6." [488]

DREAM RECALL

Those suffering from a deficiency in Vitamin B6 cannot recall their dreams. Contrary to many theories, it is this author's opinion that dream recall is normal and an essential part of cleansing and rebooting the mind in readiness for the coming day.

Science knows almost nothing about sleep, other than the physiological observations it has made about this curious part of our lives over the years. About one third of our existence is spent between the sheets, so to speak, and yet the precise reasons why we dream remain unknown.

Aside from all the soothsaying, dream interpreters and the like, many will testify that they feel more refreshed, more mentally alert and stable, more emotionally balanced, if they dream regularly. Some have reported that they feel humbled and more 'a part of something wonderful that I don't really understand'. Certainly, if dreaming can make a population more humble and part of something 'wonderful', then I for one am all for it, in view of how things are in our society today.

On the nutritional side, lack of dream recall can be cured simply by supplementing Vitamin B6 in increments (not exceeding 800-1,000mg a day). Clinics can measure B6 and zinc deficiencies very easily, often by analysing liver enzymes, which elevate in the absence of B6.

SKIN, BALDNESS, NAILS AND DENTISTRY

Pyrolurics often have pale skin due to lack of skin pigmentation. Some, who have never been able to tan, can do so after zinc and B6

---

[488] Pfeiffer, Carl & Patrick Holford, op. cit. 118

supplementation. Local depigmentation (vitiligo) does not respond to B6 and zinc.[489] Baldness and lack of eyelashes and brows may often respond to zinc and B6, as can greying hair, which has been known to reverse to the original colour with zinc therapy.

Nail-biting can also be a result of zinc and B6 deficiency. Thin, brittle and weak nails strengthen in time with zinc and B6 and the nutritional supplement regimen we will shortly be discussing in the end section. Once nails are strong, nail-biting often ceases of its own accord. Small, white spots on the nail may disappear with zinc treatment, but larger discolourations sometimes have to grow out with the nail.

Crowded incisors and a narrow upper dental arch are also an indication of the pyroluric. Gums may also be red and retracted, indicating the presence of pyorrhoea where there is a zinc deficiency. Drs. Curson and Losee find both copper and cadmium to be high in the enamel of decayed teeth when compared with that of healthy teeth. Persons suffering from tooth decay will benefit from (obviously) giving up sucrose, white flour and white rice and supplementing with B6 and zinc over and above the basic supplement program.

Pfeiffer and Holford believe that about 10% of the population may be pyroluric, which symptoms are evident when stress becomes predominant. Pyrolurics may benefit from the following:

> **Vitamin B6, 100mg, am and pm**
> **Zinc (derived from zinc gluconate), 35mg, am and pm**
> **Manganese, 10mg, am and pm**
> **The *Food for Thought* dietary regimen**
> **The basic supplement program (see 'A Guide to Nutritional Supplements')**

---

[489] Dr W Henry Sebrell discusses a doctor in Miami who was treating vitiligo with niacin therapy. Regrettably no further information exists as to dosage or outcome. Neem cream is also a traditional, natural way to treat skin depigmentation.

Hypoglycaemia – Chaotic Blood Sugar

The brain runs on glucose, claiming up to 30% of the body's production of the essential sugar. 'Blood sugar' levels are vital to the correct functioning of both brain and body. When this delicate balancing act is disrupted, chaotic blood sugar levels, or hypoglycaemia, throw both the body and mind into turmoil. It is estimated that 1 in 4 of us may suffer from some form of glucose intolerance or hypoglycaemia.

SYMPTOMS: Trembling, anxiety, fatigue, wobbly if hungry, confusion, irritability, palpitations, cold hands and feet, low blood pressure, blackouts, angry outbursts, violence, depression, forgetfulness, road rage and an inability to concentrate.

SWINGS AND ROUNDABOUTS

When the body has not been fed for some time and blood sugar fuel runs low, the body becomes hungry, inviting the person to consume more nutrients for fuel. The brain triggers the release of adrenalin, which in turn provokes the liver into releasing stored glucose in the liver (glycogen) to use as fuel. The use of stimulants and the excessive intake of high glycaemic carbohydrates (bread, sugar, pasta, etc.) however disrupt this elegant fuel control system.

Tea, coffee, sucrose, chocolate, junk food, cigarettes and other 'mood enhancers' are constantly reported being available in mental institutions. These also stimulate the production of adrenalin and fool the body into releasing glucose from the liver (glycogen) before it is required. Blood sugar levels soar. Frequent intakes of these foods however cause the pancreas to over-produce insulin, the hormone responsible for transporting glucose into the cells. The result is that excess amounts of the sugar hormone produced causes blood sugar levels abruptly to dive. Symptoms of glucose intolerance set in and a vicious cycle is created as more sugar is craved to relieve the symptoms. The end result of this cycle is chaotic blood sugar (hypoglycaemia), exhausted pancreas and adrenal glands, and the accompanying physical and mental symptoms described earlier. Type 2 diabetes is the inevitable result when the body becomes resistant to the insulin as a safety measure.

THE SWEETEST POISON

When it comes to identifying the most common poison we willingly use against ourselves, an amazing feat resulting in millions of deaths worldwide every year, there really is no contest. The perpetrator is as unlikely a candidate as any you might wish to name, and its unmasking is probably all the more horrifying because this substance has burrowed its way into our civilisation like a parasite, draped in the false colours of comfort and familiarity. It has an entire industry behind it as usual, hell-bent on marketing the stuff any way it can. It's whiter than heroin, sweeter than your fiancée, more soluble than the National Debt, and more pernicious than nicotine because, like a true demon, this little beauty comes in a million disguises and always dresses like a friend.

We grew up being brainwashed with all the sayings: " Sugar and spice and all things nice." "Sweetheart", "Sugar-plum" – all painting the white stuff in a great and cuddly light. But seeing as we are in the mood for some truth, let's take a hard look at the 's' word, and also its partners-in-crime, the 'sweeteners' aspartame and saccharin. Are you nervous about shattering some highly refined illusions?

Dr William Coda Martin was the first publicly to label sucrose a poison. Martin's definition came about after he determined the classical definition of a poison was *"...any substance applied to the body, which causes or may cause disease."* [490] So what is sucrose? Obviously the first task we must carry out is identifying exactly what sugar is. Once again, we have to do our homework and pre-empt the vocabulary – so let's define our terms. There are a number of 'sugars' around. Here are the main ones:

Glucose – found with other sugars, but occurs naturally in fruits and vegetables. A number of core foods we consume are converted by our body into glucose, or blood sugar as it is sometimes called, which is the form in which this highly efficient energy source is made available to our life-systems. Glucose is always present in our bloodstream and is a key material in the metabolic functions of all plants and animals.

Dextrose - known as 'corn sugar', is manufactured from starches.
Fructose - natural sugar found in fruits.
Lactose – milk sugar
Maltose – malt sugar
Sucrose – refined sugar manufactured from sugar cane and beet.

---

[490] Martin, William Coda, *When is a Food a Food – and When a Poison?* Michigan Organic News, March 1957, p.3

The last, sucrose, is the white stuff that goes into the tea, coffee, soft drinks and sodas, and shows up in everything from tomato ketchup to Ding-Dongs, doughnuts and Twinkies. There are few manufactured or processed foods today that do not contain either sucrose, aspartame or saccharin. Sugar's prevalence for 300 years has made the sweet-hearts in the sugar industry wealthy beyond most people's imaginations. Naturally, the sugar barons are willing to do or say just about anything to keep their products bathed in the safe and neighbourly light that result in us scoffing it down by the bushel-load.

SUGAR BOMBING

Excess sugar is initially stored in the liver in the form of glycogen. As more sugar is stuffed into our sagging bodies daily, the liver swells like a balloon to accommodate it[491], waiting in vain for the garbage truck to take it out of the body (detoxification/elimination). The truck almost never arrives because we do not detoxify our bodies (sugar has also been linked constipation[492]). Finally, reaching its limit, the liver has had enough and pours the sucrose toxins it has accumulated back into the bloodstream in the form of fatty acids, which are then taken to storage bins in the inactive areas of the body, namely the belly, thighs, hips, breasts and the backs of our upper arms (triceps area).

Once the inactive storage areas are filled to capacity, the body begins distributing the metabolite acids into the active organs, such as the heart and kidneys.[493] These fats accumulate as rapidly as the sucrose continues to pour in, impairing the functioning of vital organs, causing hormonal imbalance[494], creating lethargy, abnormal blood pressure as the circulatory and lymph systems are invaded, depleting vital Vitamin C reserves, threatening the cardiovascular system.[495] An overabundance of white cells occurs, leading to the slowing down of tissue formation. The system is nearing collapse at this point, but still the sugar keeps a-coming....

---

[491] Goulart, F S, *American Fitness*, "Are You Sugar Smart?" March-April 1991, pp.34-38
[492] Goulart, F S, ibid.
[493] Yudkin, Kang and Bruckdorfer, *British Journal of Medicine*, "Effects of High Dietary Sugar", #281, 1980, p.1396
[494] Yudkin, J, *Nutrition and Health*, "Metabolic Changes Induced by Sugar in Relation to Coronary Heart Disease and Diabetes", Vol.5, #1-2, 1987: pp.5-8
[495] Pamplona, Bellmunt, Portero and Prat, *Medical Hypotheses,* "Mechanisms of Glycation in Atherogenesis", #40, 1990, pp.174-181

How about the cellulite, varicose veins and the rotten teeth?[496] [497] How about the kids bouncing off the walls with mineral depletion, ADD and ADHD because sucrose robs minerals, impairs brain function, resulting in increased emotional instability, concentration difficulties, hyperactivity and violence in the classroom[498] [499], ending up no doubt with a Ritalin or Prozac prescription, black eyes from fighting, detention, lousy grades... and conceivably a school shooting or two....[500]

Glutamic acid, the key to proper brain function, is derived from a diet rich in unrefined plant dietary. Glutamic acid is broken down by B vitamins into compounds that regulate stop and go functions in the brain. B vitamins however are manufactured by symbiotic bacteria inhabiting our intestines. As the sucrose bombing continues, these bacteria are killed by the toxic sugar metabolites, resulting in a severe depletion of our B-vitamin production. This in turn impairs brain function. The results in adults can traverse the awesome spectrum from sleepiness and the inability to calculate or remember, through to dizziness[501], heightened PMS symptoms[502] and possibly finishing with those famous murderous impulses, resulting in your lawyer's "Twinkie Defence".[503]

---

[496] Cleave and Campbell, *Diabetes, Coronary Thrombosis and the Saccharine Disease*, John Wright and Sons, Bristol, UK: 1960

[497] Glinsman, Irausquin and Youngmee, "Evaluation of Health Aspects of Sugars Contained in Carbohydrate Sweeteners", Report from FDA's Sugar Task Force, Center for Food Safety and Applied Nutrition, Washington DC: 1986, p.39

[498] Schauss, Alexander, *Diet, Crime and Delinquency*, Parker House, Berkeley, CA: 1981

[499] Goldman, J et al, "Behavioural Effects of Sucrose on Preschool Children", *Journal of Abnormal Child Psychology*, #14, 1986, pp.565-577

[500] *Journal of Abnormal Psychology*, #85, 1985

[501] *Journal of Advanced Medicine*, 1994 7(1): pp.51-58

[502] *The Edell Health Letter*, September 1991; 10:7(1)

[503] *"On 27 November 1978, Dan White, a former San Francisco city supervisor who had recently resigned his position, entered San Francisco's city hall by climbing through a basement window and then shot and killed both mayor George Moscone and supervisor Harvey Milk. After White's subsequent trial for the murders, a new term entered the American lexicon: 'Twinkie defence'. This phrase came to represent the efforts of criminals to avoid responsibility for their actions by claiming that some external force beyond their control had caused them to act the way they had, and it arose from the successful defence mounted by White's legal team that White's eating of Twinkies and other sugar-laden junk foods had diminished his mental capacity."* http://www.snopes.com/errata/twinkie.htm. Author's note: Interesting that White's defence team argued that their client's junk-food diet was *evidence* of his depression *not the cause of it*, as the papers subsequently reported.

And so, as the human becomes the sugar equivalent of the Frankenstein monster, pancreatic and adrenal functions become inhibited by excess sucrose-triggering, resulting in the impairment of pancreatic enzymes such as trypsin and chymotrypsin, vital for arresting healing processes and preventing cancer growths.[504] Sugar may lead to cancer of the breast, ovaries, prostate and rectum.[505] It has been implicated in colon cancer, with an increased risk in women[506], and is a risk factor in biliary tract cancer.[507] Sugar can cause appendicitis[508], increase the risk of Crohn's Disease and ulcerative colitis[509], and can exacerbate the symptoms of multiple sclerosis.[510] Excess sugar consumption has also been linked to Parkinson's and Alzheimer's Diseases.[511] Complete removal of sugar from the diet has seen stunning recoveries from cancer, diabetes and heart illnesses.

SACCHARIN

Saccharin has long been a traditional alternative for those on diets, aware of the damage done to both teeth and general health by a chronic consumption of sugar. But saccharin itself, far from being the panacea for those addicted to the taste concepts of sucrose, has been dogged from the outset with its own health concerns.

Saccharin is a synthetic, white crystalline powder, which, in its pure state, is over 500 times as sweet as sugar cane. In its commercial state, it is 350 times as sweet, meaning of course that you need 350 times less of the stuff to approximate the same level of sweetness usually provided by

---

[504] Appleton, Nancy, *Healthy Bones*, Avery Publishing Group, NY: 1991; see also Day, Phillip, *Cancer: Why We're Still Dying to Know the Truth*, Credence Publications, England: 2001

[505] *Health Express*, "Sugar and Prostate Cancer", October 1982, p.41

[506] Bostick, Potter, Kushi, et al, "Sugar, Meat and Fat Intake, and Non-Dietary Risk Factors for Colon Cancer Incidence in Iowa Women", *Cancer Causes and Controls #5*, 1994, pp.38-52

[507] Moerman, Clara et al, "Dietary Sugar Intake in the Etiology of Biliary Tract Cancer", *International Journal of Epidemiology*, Vol. 22, #2, 1993, pp.207-214

[508] Cleave, T, *The Saccharine Disease*, Keats Publishing, New Canaan, CT: 1974, p.125

[509] Cleave, T, *Sweet and Dangerous,* Bantam Books, New York: 1974, pp.28-43; also Persson, B G et al, "Diet and Inflammatory Bowel Disease", *Epidemiology*, Vol. 3, #1, January 1992, pp. 47-51

[510] Erlander, S, *The Disease to End Disease*, "The Cause and Cure of Multiple Sclerosis", No. 3, 3rd March 1979, pp.59-63

[511] Yudkin, J, *Sweet and Dangerous*, Bantam Books, NY: 1974, p.141

commercial sucrose. Saccharin's compound is $C_6H_4CONHSO_2$, declaring itself to be that most deceitful of terms - a 'carbohydrate'. Yet it has no nutritive value and is not digested by the body. Dr Elizabeth M Whelan explains some of the problems saccharin has experienced:

"Saccharin, which has been in use as an alternative to sugar since the early 20th century, officially assumed the 'carcinogen' title in March 1977, when a rodent study in Canada produced an excess of bladder tumours in the male animals. This finding immediately triggered the threat of the so-called "Delaney Clause", a Congressionally mandated provision that requires the Food & Drug Administration to ban – literally 'at the drop of a rat' – any synthetic food chemical shown to cause cancer when ingested by laboratory animals.

When millions of weight-conscious Americans got the word that their only available low-calorie sweetener was going to be banned (cyclamates had been banned in 1970 for similar reasons), they were outraged – and immediately bought up almost every little pink packet in the land. Congress responded to this outrage by protecting saccharin from the Delaney Clause and allowing it back on the market with a health-warning label. Saccharin's reputation was further tarnished however when the US National Toxicology Program, referring again to the Canadian rat study, elected to put saccharin on its 'cancer-causing" list – formally declaring it an "anticipated human carcinogen."[512]

Evidence indicates that saccharin is a weak carcinogen in animals. Its potential for tumour mischief in humans however remains the subject of some heated debate. In May 2000, the upbeat United States National Institute for Environmental Health Services removed saccharin from its list of suspected carcinogens. Three years earlier though, a board of independent experts, which included the Center for Science in the Public Interest and the California Department of Health, had voted to err on the side of caution to keep saccharin 'a suspected carcinogen'.

The food industry has expended considerable resources attempting to get saccharin off the hook. Consumers appeared to have their own ideas. The food giants were encouraged by the many citizens who came forward to complain that every alternative to sugar was being systematically victimised as a carcinogen, as had been the case with cyclamate and

---

[512] Whelan, Elizabeth M, *The Sweet and the Sour News about Saccharin*, American Council on Science and Health, 17th May 2000

aspartame. America's Food & Drug Administration, usually quick to follow its own policy of applying the Delaney Clause and banning even suspected carcinogens from public use, relented in the face of public pressure, but mandated that saccharin should carry a warning label.

Dr Samuel Cohen, a pathologist at the University of Nebraska, is probably America's foremost authority on saccharin and its chemical ramifications. In answer to the investigative panel's queries on how exactly saccharin causes cancer, Cohen replied that when the sodium form of saccharin combines with rat urine, it creates crystal-like stones in the bladder of the creature. These stones in turn damaged the organs of the animal, leading to the potential for cancer.[513] Cohen however cast doubt on saccharin's danger to humans when he explained the significant differences between rat and human urine and how they would chemically react with the crystalline sweetener.

ASPARTAME
Today saccharin remains as controversial as ever, and the debate over whether or not it represents a cancer hazard to the public continues to rage. And yet, people who have turned to another alternative to saccharin and sugar over the past 20 years, have become equally dismayed at a parallel fur-fight over aspartame, decked out in the garb of a light blue sachet, which began adorning restaurant and diners the world over under the brand names Nutrasweet, Equal, Spoonful and Equal-Measure.

Aspartame was discovered by accident in 1965 by James Schlatter, a chemist working for G D Serle Company, who was testing anti-ulcer compounds for his employers. Aspartame's original approval as a sweetener for public consumption was blocked by neuroscientist Dr John W Olney and consumer attorney James Turner in August 1974 over concerns about both aspartame's safety and G D Serle's research practices. However, aspartame duly received its approval for dry goods in 1981 and its go-ahead as a sweetener for carbonated beverages was granted in 1983, despite growing concerns over its neurological effects.[514] In 1985, G D

---

[513] Cohen's testimony is interesting as it dovetails with John Beard's findings that cancer is a healing process (survival response) that has not terminated. These healing processes are understood to be caused by damage done to the body by carcinogens. Therefore, a carcinogen can be deemed to be any material that causes cellular damage to the body, initiating a healing process carried out by stem-cell trophoblast.

[514] Two FDA scientists, Jacqueline Verrett and Adrian Gross, reviewed data from three studies which highlighted alleged irregularities in G D Serle's research procedures. The two government scientists declared that the irregularities they had uncovered were

Serle was purchased by biotech giant Monsanto, and Serle Pharmaceuticals and The NutraSweet Company were created as separate corporate identities.

According to researcher Alex Constantine in his essay entitled "Sweet Poison", aspartame may account for up to 75% of the adverse food reactions reported to the US FDA, due primarily to its reported ability to affect neurological processes in humans. Dr Olney found that an excess of aspartate and glutamate, two chemicals used by the body as neurotransmitters to transmit information between brain neurons, could kill neurons in the brain by allowing too much calcium to collect in the neuron cells to neutralise acid. This neurological damage led Olney to label aspartate and glutamate 'excitotoxins', in that they, according to Olney, 'excite' or stimulate the neural cells to death.[515]

Side-effects laid at the door of aspartame include multiple sclerosis, Alzheimer's disease, ALS, memory loss, hormonal problems, hearing loss, epilepsy, Parkinson's disease, AIDS dementia, brain lesions and neuroendocrine disorders. Risks to infants, children and pregnant women from aspartame were also underscored by the Federation of American Societies for Experimental Biology, a research body that traditionally follows FDA policy and adopts a softly-softly approach to chemical problems. The Federation declared: *"It is prudent to avoid the use of dietary supplements of L-glutamic acid by pregnant women, infants and children. The existence of evidence for potential endocrine responses... would also suggest a neuroendocrine link and that... L-glutamic acid should be avoided by women of childbearing age and individuals with affective disorders."*[516]

Phenylalanine: The amino acid L-phenylalanine, used by the brain, comprises 50% of aspartame. People suffering from the genetic disorder phenylketonuria (PKU) cannot metabolise phenylalanine and so an excess of this amino acid builds up in parts of the brain, leading to a decrease of serotonin levels, bringing on emotional disorders and depression.

Methanol: Also known as wood alcohol, the poison methanol is a 10% ingredient of aspartame, which is created when aspartame is heated

---

serious enough to warrant an immediate halt to aspartame's approval for use. *Food Magazine*, "Artificial Sweetener Suspicions", Vol.1, No.9, April/June 1990.
[515] *The Guardian*, London, UK, 20th July, 1990
[516] *Food Magazine*, ibid.

above 86°F (30°C) during, for example, the preparation of processed foods or the sweetening of hot beverages. Methanol oxidises in the body to produce formic acid and the deadly neurotoxin, formaldehyde, also used as a prime ingredient in many vaccinations. Methanol is considered by America's Environmental Protection Agency (EPA) as *"...a cumulative poison, due to the low rate of excretion once it is absorbed. In the body, methanol is oxidised to formaldehyde and formic acid; both of these metabolites are toxic."*[517]

A one litre carbonated beverage, sweetened with aspartame, contains around 56mg of methanol. Heavy consumers of soft drinks sweetened with aspartame can ingest up to 250mg of methanol daily, especially in the summer, amounting to 32 times the EPA warning limit.

Dr Woodrow C Monte, Director of the Food Science and Nutritional Laboratory at Arizona State University, was concerned that human response to methanol was probably much higher than with animals, due to humans lacking key enzymes that assist in the detoxification of methanol in other creatures. Monte stated: *"There are no human or mammalian studies to evaluate the possible mutagenic, teratogenic, or carcinogenic effects of chronic administration of methyl alcohol."*[518]

Monte's concern about aspartame was so great that he petitioned the FDA through the courts to address these issues. Monte requested that the FDA *"...slow down on this soft drink issue long enough to answer some of the important questions. It's not fair that you are leaving the full burden of proof on the few of us who are concerned and have such limited resources. You must remember that you are the American public's last defense. Once you allow usage* [of aspartame], *there is literally nothing I or my colleagues can do to reverse the course. Aspartame will then join saccharin, the sulfiting agents, and God knows how many other questionable compounds enjoined to insult the human constitution with government approval."*[519]

Ironically, shortly after Dr Monte's impassioned plea, Arthur Hull Hayes, Jr., the Commissioner of the Food & Drug Administration, approved the use of aspartame in carbonated beverages. Shortly after, he

---

[517] *Extraordinary Science*, Vol.7, No.1, Jan/Feb/Mar 1995, p.39
[518] *The Guardian*, "Laboratory Animals Back from the Dead in Faulty Safety Tests", April/June 1990
[519] Ibid.

left the FDA to take up a position with G D Serle's public relations company.[520] In 1993, the FDA further approved aspartame as a food ingredient in numerous process foods that would always be heated above 86°F, as part of their preparation.

Dr Joseph Mercola is no lover of aspartame. The well-known nutrition and health researcher itemises another catalogue of woes that have come to punctuate aspartame's hopeless legacy as a food additive:

"In 1991, the National Institutes of Health listed 167 symptoms and reasons to avoid the use of aspartame, but today it is a multi-million dollar business that contributes to the degeneration of the human population, as well as the deliberate suppression of overall intelligence, short-term memory[521] and the added contribution as a carcinogenic environmental co-factor.

The FDA and Centers for Disease Control continue to receive a stream of complaints from the population about aspartame. It is the only chemical warfare weapon available in mass quantities on the grocery shelf and promoted in the media. It has also been indicated that women with an intolerance for phenylalanine, one of the components of aspartame, may give birth to infants with as much as a 15% drop in intelligence level if they habitually consume products containing this dangerous substance."[522]

DIETARY APPROACHES
A person suffering from hypoglycaemia or type 2 diabetes may benefit from the following:

> **Cut out junk foods, especially sodas and soft drinks, sucrose, high glycaemic carbohydrates, such as pasta, bread, grains and sweet potatoes. Switch instead to the *Food for Thought* dietary regimen described in the section and book of the same name.**

---

[520] Ibid.

[521] The FDA instigated hearings in 1985 on aspartame at the request of Senator Metzenbaum, when a sample case was heard, in which a woman's memory suffered almost complete collapse until she ceased taking aspartame-laced products.

[522] Mercola, Joseph, www.mercola.com. See also: Steinman, D, *Diet for a Poisoned Planet*, University of California study, p.190

- ➢ Increase water intake to four pints a day
- ➢ Regular exercise (at least one hour a day, four times a week)
- ➢ Zinc (gluconate), 25mg a day, am and pm
- ➢ Vanadium or chromium picolinate, 200mcg a day, taken every other day, two weeks on, two weeks off
- ➢ Manganese, 10mg, am and pm
- ➢ The basic supplement program (see 'A Guide to Nutritional Supplements')

Allergies

We have examined some of the problems of allergies and how they affect the mind. Common food intolerances, such as those for wheat (gluten), milk (casein), chocolate, eggs, oranges and other salicylates may disrupt hormone levels, resulting in mental symptoms that can range from depression to schizophrenia and the classic 'straitjacket' problems.

SYMPTOMS: Many of these later problems, described as mental illnesses, may begin early in childhood and show up as eczema, infantile colic, rashes, fits and temper tantrums, excessive mucus formations, frequent, rapid colds, hyperactivity, speech difficulties, anxiety, seasonal allergies and coeliac disease (malabsorption of food). In *Health Wars*, we examined the problems brought on by infants fed cow's milk during their first two years' of life. This is a vulnerable period for a small child, whose immune system usually has not fully developed until the third year. Assaulting the child with multiple vaccinations, foreign and often hostile proteins, such as those found in wheat and cow's milk, can lead to all sorts of problems, such as autism and type 1 diabetes, especially when the child has not been adequately breast-fed to ensure the full spectrum of immune bodies are taken in.

Once the immune system is formed, there may be imperfections in how the system performs when assaulted with particles the body identifies as toxins. Damage and scarring to the intestinal wall by gluten/gliaden in wheat, barley, rye and oats, for instance, destroys the finger-like villi which absorb nutrients, leading to coeliac disease, where the food can pass unprocessed through the small intestine. Leaky gut syndrome, where undigested food particles permeate the damaged intestinal wall and enter the bloodstream, is typified by systemic poisoning and a chronic-fatigue reaction of lethargy, listlessness and depression.

Experimental double-blind studies and control trials conclusively show that wheat, milk, cane sugar, eggs (often the whites), tobacco and food additives are the chief culprits. In one control study, 96 patients diagnosed as suffering from alcohol dependence, major depressive disorders and schizophrenia were compared with 62 control subjects selected from adult hospital staff members for possible food/chemical intolerances. Those suffering as 'depressives' were found to be the highest suffering from allergies: 80% were found to be allergic to barley and 100% were allergic to egg white. Over 50% of the alcoholics were found to be allergic to egg white, milk, rye and barley. Of the schizophrenic group, 80% were found to be allergic to both milk and eggs. Only 9% of the control group were found to suffer from any allergies.[523]

Schizophrenics, routinely treated with drugs, were randomly assigned milk- and gluten-free diets while on the locked ward. They were discharged nearly twice as rapidly as control patients assigned a high-cereal diet. Wheat gluten secretly added to the cereal-free diet undid this effect, showing that wheat gluten was a player in the behaviour of these schizophrenic patients.[524]

ELIMINATION/CHALLENGE TESTING

Removing problem foods and then reintroducing them one by one under controlled conditions to see if the problems reoccur is known as elimination/challenge testing. This should always be done under clinical supervision, especially when side-effects may be quite severe, such as fits, asthma, severe depression and violent, psychotic episodes.

THE ANTIHISTAMINE EFFECT

We examined the effects of histadelia, or excess histamine, in the body, and its association to mental illness. It is interesting to note that many psychiatric medications are very similar in their chemical profiles to antihistamines, and indeed are designed to suppress brain histamine receptors. Tricyclic and antidepressant drugs, such as imipramine (Tofranil) and Amitriptyline, are in this group. Other drugs, such as chlorpromazine and promazine, are designed to inhibit histamine production and promazine is used to treat allergies. This seems to confirm the role of histamine excess in related emotional disorders and therefore Pfeiffer, Holford and Hoffer encourage physicians to adapt their patients' diets before resorting to potentially debilitating medication. Carl Pfeiffer has also devoted much of his professional research time to examining B6 (pyridoxine), zinc and manganese deficiencies, and their role in restoring his patients to health:

"Several vitamins are noted for their effectiveness in reducing allergic symptoms. Vitamins C and B6 are probably the most effective. Dr William Philpott has used both of these vitamins intravenously to turn off allergic symptoms provoked by testing for allergies. The patients on adequate Vitamin C will have fewer allergic symptoms. B6 should be

---

[523] Pfeiffer, Carl & Patrick Holford, op. cit. p.139
[524] Ibid.

given to the point of nightly dream recall and the minerals calcium and potassium should be plentiful in the diet. Zinc and manganese are also needed by the allergic patient. Elimination of the offending foods may be needed for several months. For multiple food allergies, in which this approach would severely limit the diet, a four-day rotation diet in which each food is eaten only once every four days should be tried. If this approach is unsuccessful, intradermal allergy testing to determine the degree of allergy and the neutralising dose of each allergen is recommended." [525]

Most patients suffering from food allergies also have pyroluria, where excessive pyrrole chemicals are found in the urine, binding Vitamin B6 and zinc. Since coeliac damage to the intestinal wall may result in malabsorption of nutrients into the body, while often allowing undigested food proteins into the blood creating allergy, healing of the intestinal system is vital to a restoration of the patient to full nutritional homeostasis.

Those suffering from allergies may benefit from the following:

> **Allergy testing to determine foods to which the patient is sensitive**
> **Adopt the *Food for Thought* dietary regimen**
> **Avoid foods that trigger allergies**
> **Methionine, 500mg, am and pm**
> **Calcium, 500mg, am and pm**
> **Magnesium, 400mg a day**
> **Zinc, 25mg, am and pm**
> **Manganese, 10mg, am and pm**
> **Essential fatty acids**
> **Vitamin B6, 100mg, am and pm (enough for nightly dream recall. No more than 1,000mg a day!)**
> **Vitamin C, 1g – 2g, am and pm**
> **The basic supplement program (see 'A Guide to Nutritional Supplements')**

---

[525] Ibid.

Alzheimer's, Senile Dementia

Mental impairment problems are devastating our cultures today, and yet this has not always been the case. Clearly, toxicity issues are at the fore. As many as a third of all hospital beds in the UK are taken up with geriatric patients suffering a host of disorders, a large proportion of them institutionalised because of senility. The cost to healthcare runs into the billions.

With mental impairment problems, the following questions should be asked and the conditions addressed FIRST:

➢ Is the patient eating organic, whole, non-pesticide-laden food?
➢ Is the patient nutritionally deficient?
➢ Is the patient drinking up to 4 pints of clean, fresh water a day?
➢ Does the patient have chaotic blood sugar levels?
➢ Is the patient on any psychiatric medication which might be giving the appearance of senility or slow cognitive ability?
➢ Does the patient suffer from food allergies?
➢ Does the patient live in a toxic environment?
➢ Does the patient eat junk food and drink sodas?
➢ Has the patient been mentally unchallenged for a period of time?

MEMORY PROBLEMS – POTENTIAL CAUSES
Several factors influence memory:

➢ Use it or lose it!
➢ Blood supply to the brain
➢ Nutritional intake, especially minerals such as zinc and manganese, vitamins, especially the 'B' group, and essential fatty acids
➢ Food allergies
➢ Toxins
➢ Abnormal blood sugar levels

USE IT OR LOSE IT!
In my view, retirement is the single most damaging thing for a person, when they are persuaded to end their productivity and bow out of the work ethic until they expire. It is in the nature of humans to produce and be

mentally active. Depression, listlessness and despair often set in when brains are put in mothballs and the person vegetates in a chair in front of the TV for the rest of their lives. The secret of a long life, as George Burns once said, *"...is to keep breathing!"* But stay productive also. In *Health Wars*, we take a look at cultures who routinely live past 100 and remain active. If you are 70-80, start looking around for another career! Think of the skills and knowledge you have amassed that could benefit others. If your brain is busy and well fed, it is a happy brain. And so will you be too.

BLOOD SUPPLY TO THE BRAIN
One of the most common medical conditions we suffer from over the age of 50 is atherosclerosis, or plaque in the arteries. In *Health Wars*, we devote two chapters to affairs of the heart and the cardiovascular system, showing that heart disease, in almost all its forms, may be traced back to nutritional deficiencies, including an early form of scurvy.

SCURVY
Scurvy occurs when collagen breaks down in the body. Collagen is a fibrous material the body uses to clad arteries, veins and capillaries, as well as organs and the skin, to give them structure. Collagen is a lot like the steel girders you see when builders are erecting a new skyscraper. Each collagen fibre has been calculated to be far tougher and stronger than an iron wire of comparable width. In the absence of adequate nutrition, specifically Vitamins C, E and the essential amino acid lysine, collagen begins to dissolve. When sailors went off to sea and eschewed their usual diet of fruits and vegetables in favour of the non-perishable foodstuffs used during long voyages, scurvy invariably set in within a matter of weeks and the sailors literally fell apart. The cure was to recommence consumption of living, whole fruits and vegetables rich in the nutrition required to repair the collagen and nourish the whole body.

ATHEROSCLEROSIS
With heart disease, the process is much slower, sometimes taking years to develop. Like scurvy, a chronic Vitamin C deficiency causes the beginning of a collapse in the arterial walls, necessitating a healing process to commence, in the form of lipoprotein(a) fats which the body attempts to use to bond the thousands of tiny breaches in the arterial walls.

These lipoproteins are Nature's perfect Band-Aid. They are extremely sticky and form the atherosclerotic deposits associated with advanced forms of heart disease today. Cardiovascular medicine, unaware or willingly ignorant of the underlying nutritional deficiency cause of atherosclerosis, focuses its attention on vilifying the lipoprotein's LDL (low-density lipoprotein) cholesterol content as one of the primary *causes* of heart diseases, when it is in fact the healing (survival response) precursor, *brought on by a chronic Vitamin C deficiency.* Today the drug industry has mobilised a multi-billion-dollar business of anti-cholesterol drugs, which have wrought devastating results in cardiac patients, necessitating a further $20 billion drug program to combat all the side-effects.[526]

Most people have accumulated Lp(a) in their arteries after age 50, bringing on the usual problems with sticky blood, thrombosis, atherosclerosis and high blood pressure. Strokes too are caused when Lp(a) clogs the brain artery, impairing vital blood flow to the brain. And it is here that our interest in memory loss focuses. Impaired blood flow to the brain will cause death or partial paralysis. Patrick Holford writes:

"When cells are starved of oxygen, they switch to a more primitive mode of operation called anaerobic respiration. The cells begin to decide and spread – unless they are nerve cells.... Nerve cells can't regenerate. So what happens to them? They just stop working. The result is senility."[527]

ALUMINIUM AND TOXIC METALS

Another common finding in premature senile dementia, known as Alzheimer's disease, is an entanglement of nerve fibres. When these nerve clusters are found in the frontal and temporal regions of the brain, they are frequently saturated with aluminium.[528] Many theories abound on how this aluminium accumulates. Aluminium can be taken into the body through the water supply, cooking utensils, toothpastes (the tube), aluminium foil packaging, soft drinks and antacids. Detoxification regimens, such as those expounded on in *Food For Thought* and *Health Wars*, will assist the body in ridding itself of unwanted accumulations of heavy metals. Chelators, natural substances that attach themselves to toxic elements and escort them out of the body, are used to remove aluminium.

---

[526] Sellman, Sherill, *Hormone Heresy*, GetWell Int'l, Inc. 1998; also Seaman, Barbara, *The Doctors' Case Against the Pill*, Hunter House, USA, 1995, p.7
[527] Pfeiffer, Carl & Patrick Holford, op. cit. p.176
[528] Martyn, C, et al, "Geographical relation between Alzheimer's disease and aluminium in drinking water", *Lancet*, 14th January 1989

Excess amounts of the following metals are known memory disruptors and inhibitors:

Lead: leads to hyperactivity and aggression. Taken in from traffic fumes and industrial pollution. Chelated using Vitamins C, B1 and zinc.
Aluminium: leads to memory loss and senility. Derived from cooking utensils,, water, etc. Chelated using zinc and magnesium.
Cadmium: leads to aggression and confusion. Derived from cigarettes. Chelated with Vitamin C and zinc.
Copper: leads to anxiety and phobias. Derived from water piping. Chelated with zinc.
Mercury: leads to headaches and memory loss. Derived from pesticides, some vaccinations and mercury amalgam dental fillings. Chelated with selenium.

FOOD ALLERGIES
Those with memory impairment problems may also be suffering from the effects of food allergies, as discussed earlier. An allergy test may determine an underlying, treatable food allergy problem, which may be contributing to the patient's condition.

PELLAGRA
As discussed in the section entitled 'Schizophrenia', an old nutritional problem named pellagra may be haunting us still. Pellagra is a niacin (B3) deficiency which will result in the four 'D's – dizziness, diarrhoea, dementia and death. Vitamin B3 is essential for oxygen ultilisation in the body. It is incorporated into the coenzyme NAD (nicotinamide adenosine dinucleotide). Low amounts of B3 will invariably bring on symptoms that can be interpreted as dementia, Alzheimer's, etc.[529]

BOOSTING THE MEMORY
Those suffering memory impairment have a veritable arsenal of nutritional weapons at their disposal, as we shall see.[530] The neurotransmitter acetylcholine is the brain hormone responsible for memory retention. Experiments done at Palo Alto Hospital in California showed that drugs which boost production of acetylcholine produced 'supermemories'. Natural nutrients however can effectively boost acetylcholine production. These are choline, glutamine, DMAE, a nutrient found in fish, and its salt, Deanol. Pyroglutamate is also excellent, and

---

[529] For more information on pellagra, see *Health Wars*.
[530] See section entitled 'A Guide to Nutritional Supplements'

many 'memory' supplements on the market today contain a mix of these nutrients which work better when used synergistically.

ELDERLY NUTRITIONAL FAILURES

A US study in 1975 failed to find one geriatric patient with a normal nutritional profile.[531] Alzheimer's and senility in general may be no more than decades of sub-optimal nutritional abuse, combined with a slow toxicity through foods and the environment. Boosting the nutritional intake of the elderly is of course rarely done in care homes and hospitals, where nutritional education among doctors and nurses is sadly lacking. The regimen at the end of this section will be beneficial for all who are suffering from these types of problems.

SELF-POISONING THROUGH PERSONAL CARE AND HOUSEHOLD PRODUCTS

Household and personal care products contain chemicals, which, over time, can build systemically in the body, causing mental impairment and other serious health problems. A special section on these is included at the end of the book (see 'Environmental Toxins'). Shampoos, conditioners, make-up, antiperspirants, mouthwash, baby oil, fly spray and a dozen other offenders are used by the population daily with scant regard for the long-term hazards, which are only now becoming known.

> - **A diet rich in fish oils and fresh vegetables and fruit (see *Food For Thought* dietary regimen)**
> - **Eliminate all junk or processed foods**
> - **Change out potentially harmful personal care and household products for safe alternatives (see 'Environmental Toxins')**
> - **Vitamin C, 2,000mg, am and pm, along with hydroxylated and methoxylated bioflavonoids (Vitamin P)**
> - **Thiamine (B1), 100mg a day**
> - **L-carnitine (Vitamin B_T), 400mg, three times a day**
> - **Deanol – 100mg a day**
> - **DMAE – 500mg a day**
> - **Supplements containing 'smart' nutrients, such as 5-HTP, pyroglutamate, glutamine, phosphatidylcholine and pantothenic acid (B5).**

---

[531] Pfeiffer, C & Patrick Holford, op. cit. p.178

- ➢ **Essential fatty acid intake. Omega 6 fat intake should be twice that of Omega 3's. (see 'A Guide to Nutritional Supplements') These can be taken in supplement form or by grinding up one measure of sunflower seeds, sesame and pumpkin seeds and two measures of flax seeds, taking two tablespoons of this mixture every morning. Ensure you buy fresh seeds.**
- ➢ **Removal of dental amalgams (not all at the same time!)**
- ➢ **4 pints of clean, fresh water a day (2 litres)**
- ➢ **A basic nutritional supplement program boosts oxygen to the cells and prevents deficiency in any one of over 60 different nutrients (see 'A Guide to Nutritional Supplements')**

Disease Round-up

ANOREXIA

This eating disorder has gained prominence over the past twenty years. Characterised by a lack of appetite, almost invariably accompanied by psychological stresses and significant weight-loss, patients literally begins to starve themselves. Traditional treatments have included psychotropics such as chlorpromazine, sedatives, anti-depressants and electroshock. British child singing star Lena Zavaroni was given a lobotomy for her anorexia at Cardiff Hospital. She died two weeks later of an infection.

SYMPTOMS: Loss of appetite, weight loss, impotency in males, nausea, skin lesions, depression, anxiety amenorrhoea. Anorexia is also exacerbated by the subject having a compulsion to be lean and thus fashionably attractive.

In the 1980's, Professor Bryce-Smith reported in Britain's *Lancet* that anorexics were invariably zinc-deficient. Studies were showing that zinc-deficient animals lost their desire for food and that the small intestinal mucosa were abnormal as a result.[532] When force-fed a diet that is zinc-deficient, anorexics can become seriously ill.[533] With lack of nutrient absorption invariably accompanying the condition, a downward spiral is created when loss of food creates a deepening zinc deficiency which in turn further suppresses appetite, creating more zinc deficiency.

Bryce-Smith and Dr Simpson treated a 13-year-old girl who was anorexic, tearful and depressed. After treatment with a basic supplement program, antioxidants and zinc, she had recovered to 'normal' within two months, was cheerful again, and had increased her body weight by almost 45%.[534]

Hambridge and Silverman advise that "*...whenever there is appetite loss in children, zinc efficiency should be suspected.*"[535] Researcher Bakan concluded that "*...the symptoms of anorexia and zinc deficiency are similar in a number of respects.... It is proposed that clinical trials be*

---

[532] Akar, *Lancet*, 13th October 1984, p.874
[533] Flanagan, *J. Nutr.* 114, 493-502: 1984
[534] Bryce-Smith & Simpson, *Lancet*, 11th August 1984, pp.350-351
[535] Hambridge & Silverman, *Arch. Dis. Child.*, 48, 567: 1973

undertaken to test its effectiveness in treatment.[536] Horrobin et al discovered that *"...there is substantial evidence to suggest that anorexia nervosa is due to a combined deficiency of zinc and EFA's* [essential fatty acids]*"* [537]

Many other studies confirm the connection between zinc deficiency and appetite loss. Normalising of menstruations also occurred with anorexics supplemented with zinc.[538] Cigarette smoking and other substance abuse have also been linked to eating disorders.[539] Ward concluded from his trial that *"...the urinary element of a 21-year-old female suffering from anorexia nervosa exhibits highly significant decreases in Ca, Co, Cr, Cu, Fe and Zn, when compared to an age-matched female control. Zinc, and possibly calcium imbalance, is shown to be associated with anorexia nervosa."* [540]

Safai-Kutti reported: *"During a follow-up period of 8-56 months, 17 out of 20 patients increased their body weight by more than 15%. The maximal weight gain was 57% after 24 months of zinc therapy. The most rapid weight gain was 24% over 3 months. None had weight loss after the administration of zinc therapy. None of our patients developed bulimia."* [541]

BULIMIA
SYMPTOMS: The patient binge-eats and follows with self-induced vomiting, the use of laxatives, diuretics, strict fasting and compulsive exercise in order to avoid gaining weight. Not all bulimics are anorexic. The patient often complains of a lack of control when around food. Other factors to consider with anorexia and bulimia are hypoglycaemia (glucose intolerance), food allergies and candiadasis. The patient should seek qualified nutritional and emotional counselling while undergoing treatment.

Anorexics and bulimics may benefit from:

---

[536] Bakan, *Med. Hyp.*, 5, 7: 1979
[537] Horobin, et al, *Med. Hyp.*, 6, 277-296: 1980
[538] Safai-Kutti, *Am. J. Clin. Nutr.*, 44, 581-582: 1986
[539] Jonas & Gold, *Lancet*, 15th February 1986, p.390
[540] Ward, *J. Mircronutr. Anal.*, 2, 211-231: 1986
[541] Safai-Kutti, *Acta. Psychiatr. Scand. Suppl.*, 361, 14-17: 1990

- The *Food For Thought* dietary regimen, adapted to provide a protein-rich, organic, whole-food diet, which includes fruits, vegetables, lentils, beans, ground seeds (sesame, sunflower, flax and pumpkin), quinoa and lightly broiled fish. Avoid all fried foods
- Curtailment of substance abuse, including tobacco and street drugs
- Avoid junk food, sodas, and confectionary
- Good counselling from someone the patient trusts and respects
- Zinc (gluconate), 25mg, am and pm
- A full-spectrum liquid amino acid supplement
- Vitamin B6, 100mg, am and pm
- Pancreatic (digestive) enzyme supplement
- The basic supplement program

ADDICTIONS

A classically undernourished person seeks a 'lift' to improve how they feel. Often substance abuse or addictions are the result. Repetitive behaviour carried out in a state of emotion will establish the cycle as a comfort zone in the brain, especially if the addictive activity results in a perceived improvement of mood. "Alcohol makes me forget..." is an improvement of mood to the alcoholic, who might be seeking refuge from emotional, financial or professional problems.

Once the addiction sets in, there are biochemical and nutritional implications that need to be dealt with, along with the psychological factors. These are best treated side by side.

SYMPTOMS: Insomnia, nightmares, violent mood swings, feelings of doom, hallucinations, craving for sweets and alcohol, fluctuating weight, hypoglycaemia, extreme anxiety and nervousness. Once again a downward spiral is created when alcohol or drug abuse depresses appetite, which leads to malnutrition, which leads to a need to improve mood, which leads to alcohol and drug abuse, which leads to a further depression of appetite, and so on.

Addiction and Hypoglycaemia

Alcoholics and drug addicts invariably have chaotic blood sugar (hypoglycaemia). Carl Pfeiffer reports that in 1973, a group of 200 alcoholics were tested for glucose intolerance. 97% of them came up positive.[542] Those addicted to alcohol, drugs (recreational or pharmaceutical) and junk foods can manipulate their blood sugar and hence mood with their habits. This creates a dependence on the substances to improve mood (see section on Hypoglycaemia).

Addiction and Allergies

Often the addict can test positive for allergy with the substance to which they are addicted or drawn. Pfeiffer, Philpot and Kalita discovered that over 75% of tobacco smokers showed a positive allergy for tobacco on skin tests.[543] Typically all addicts require a normalisation of blood sugar, a nutrient-dense, organic diet (the majority eaten raw to preserve amino acids and enzymes) and optimum supplementation.

Libby and Stone pioneered the use of mega-doses of intravenous Vitamin C in detoxifying heroin and methadone addicts. 30-85 grams a day were administered to 30 heroin addicts with 100% success.[544] Pawlek achieved significant results using 3 grams of Vitamin C and high doses of niacin (up to 2 grams/day).[545] Alkali-forming diets are essential for the recovering alcoholic. In 1973, Blackman gave 19 heroin addicts sodium and potassium bicarbonate every half an hour for two hours, followed by a two-hour break, and repeated the cycle until withdrawal had been completed. The volunteers reported that withdrawal symptoms were either completely or considerably reduced.[546]

Narconon

The highly successful Narconon program claims a 70% success rate with substance abuse withdrawal and detoxification over two years. The program makes the point that withdrawal is not the same as detoxification. Drug residues may stay within the body for several months after withdrawal before the patient is 'clean'. Optimum nutrition and the guidelines below are used by Narconon to assist the patient in a full and, as far as possible, hassle-free detoxification. Kirsty Alley, star of Cheers, was formerly an alcohol and cocaine addict who recovered through the Narconon program.

---

[542] Pfeiffer, Carl & Patrick Holford, op. cit. p.165
[543] Ibid.
[544] Libby, A F & I Stone, "The Hypoascorbemia-Kwashiorkor Approach to Drug Addiction Therapy: Pilot Study", *Orthomolecular Psychiatry*, 6(4),300-308:1977
[545] Pfeiffer, Carl & Patrick Holford, op. cit. p.166
[546] Ibid.

The three-step program used by Narconon involves:

1) Withdrawal from addictive drugs and substances. The patient is given a comprehensive mineral and vitamin program, sometimes the latter is administered intravenously. This is backed up with a special magnesium and calcium drink, which assists in eliminating the cramps, twitches and nerve pain which often accompany opiate withdrawal.

2) Purification involves the use of a combination of niacin (Vitamin B3) saunas and exercise to sweat out the drug and substance residues. Niacin is steadily increased up to 2,000mg a day, accompanied with a comprehensive exercise regimen and prolonged sessions in the sauna. The patient is constantly drinking purified water to hydrate their system.

3) Full 24-hour counselling support is given during the program duration.

Breaking Patterns – The Carrot and the Stick

Addictions and habits also have another angle to them which must be dealt with, namely patterns. The human brain uses patterning in order to establish behaviour it believes will assist it in surviving. Any behaviour repetitively carried out over a 15- to 30-day period in a state of positive emotion will be established by the brain as a pattern, otherwise known as a 'comfort zone'. Unfortunately bad patterns, or addictions, can begin this way. The key to patterning revolves around understanding that the brain's most dominant human dynamic is survival. The two key elements the brain uses to survive are:

➤ The need to avoid pain (the stick)
➤ The desire to gain pleasure (the carrot)

Pleasure

These elements are invariably used, for example, in advertising, where a client's product is advertised to the public with tremendous pleasure linked to it; in practising a skill, over and over, in order to master it; educating a child at home using pain and pleasure, scolding if naughty, rewarding if good. Animals, such as dogs, are also trained the same way, where they are taught repetitively to carry out an action, and are then rewarded each time they perform it satisfactorily, or scolded if they do not. The dog will link fetching a stick to the pleasure of receiving a food treat, and will then perform the task when required.

Ivan Pavlov and Vladimir Bekhterev experimented with dogs, where they were able to induce salivation at the ring of a bell. Donald Ewen Cameron used electroshock to 'de-pattern' his subjects, attempting to change their behaviour. Repetitive patterning may have been installed in a person quite accidentally. A person tries smoking because he has heard it is 'cool' and relaxes you. He coughs and chokes over the first few, but PERSISTS. Thereafter his body 'learns' the technique, because the behaviour has been repeated persistently for a period of time in a state of emotion.

Pain

Right from birth, our brain has been evaluating survival threats in the outside world and linking pain or pleasure to the various activities in which we engage. If we fall off our bike and hurt ourselves, our brain may be reluctant to try the activity again as it seeks to avoid pain in order to survive. A number of activities can cause people 'brain-pain'. Here are a few:

- ➢ Speaking in public
- ➢ Parachuting
- ➢ Bungee-jumping
- ➢ Viewing sharks underwater while in a cage
- ➢ Handling snakes
- ➢ Handling cockroaches
- ➢ Dieting
- ➢ Giving up smoking
- ➢ Giving up alcohol
- ➢ Giving up drugs
- ➢ Moving out of a comfort zone

Some of these, such as parachuting, bungee-jumping and swimming with sharks are perceived as a survival threat by the brain, and so our trusty, cerebral organ will give us the appropriate, uncomfortable, emotional state to warn us from undertaking the activity. Giving up things, such as cigarettes, drugs, alcohol or certain types of food, moves us out of the mental comfort zones our brains created when we repeated this behaviour persistently in a state of emotion. Thus the brain has been educated to perceive that ceasing these activities constitutes a survival threat.

Breaking the Pattern

It is quite straightforward a matter to re-educate the brain into dumping unwanted addictions and habits (mental patterns) and installing beneficial ones. The method is a three-step process:

➤ Gain leverage on the problem
➤ Break the unwanted pattern/habit/addiction
➤ Install the new pattern/habit

Step 1 - Gaining Leverage on the Problem

How badly do you want to give up smoking or drugs? So badly that you will do anything? Gaining leverage is all about getting the mind to the point of critical mass where you are prepared to do whatever it takes to dump the habit or addiction. How many people tried to diet when they didn't want to? Or attempted to quit smoking when their heart wasn't in it? It is absolutely necessary to *gain leverage* on your habit prior to breaking the pattern associated with it. Below are some questions you might find helpful in gaining the necessary leverage on your situation:

➤ In order to arrive at the solution, have I examined the problem?
➤ Do I actually know what I want out of life?
➤ Am I willing to move out of my comfort zone?
➤ Am I prepared to cease routinely doing what I know is harming myself and others?
➤ What do I *have* to change in my life?
➤ Am I prepared to change these things RIGHT NOW?
➤ What do I think I am doing correctly at the moment?
➤ What will be the consequences to myself and others if I DON'T change?

The problem with bringing 'positive thinking' to bear on an addiction is simple – you have to think! As most nail-biters, drinkers, drug-takers or smokers will tell you, the brain will automatically trigger the pattern to indulge these activities without conscious thought. Positive thinking is crucial for gaining leverage on the problem, but alone won't often achieve the goal. Two other steps are required.

Step 2 - Breaking the Pattern

Nail-biters will pop down to the pharmacy for some of that revolting gunk they paint on their nails. Next time the brain decides to trigger their nail-biting pattern, they end up with a mouthful of the noxious liquid. This causes the brain some pain. When done repeatedly in a state of emotion over a period of time, the brain will forget the old pattern.

I was a cigarette smoker for 15 years and was able to quit using a bag of lemons! Every time I felt like a cigarette, I would cut a lemon in half and squeeze it into my mouth instead. The brain didn't think much of this pattern-breaking method. Neither did my eyelids, which flickered several hundred times a second! Over a period of time though, the brain finally gave up with the smoking pattern, as the lemons were causing it too much consternation and ....pain.

Breaking patterns is also dependent on location. If you go to a bar or pub and that is where you smoke and drink, you must break the pattern of going there if you want to drop these activities. If you want to change your eating habits, often the restaurant which serves the food that gets you into trouble beckons all the more! Avoid it and set up a new regime or pattern that avoids old routines or haunts. The brain only needs time and repetition in order to learn a new way.

Step 3 – Installing the New Pattern

World-class motivator Anthony Robbins has a great system for teaching pattern installations, which I highly recommend. Installing new and beneficial patterns enables a person to 'customise' their lifestyle and remove the junk patterns at the same time. All it takes to do this is persistence, persistence, persistence and persistence! Simply link mental pain and anguish to the pattern or activity you wish to banish, then link a huge amount of pleasure to the incoming pattern and then *keep doing this for the required period of time*. While I was quitting smoking, I used to drive around in my car with an unlit cigarette hanging from my lips, so I could smell the tobacco and feel the texture of the cigarette in my mouth while I was imagining diseased lungs in hospital buckets, coughing paroxysms, a tight chest and burnt clothing. Thus I was linking extreme pain to my cigarette habit.

After routinely torturing my brain with these images for around five minutes or so at a time, I would then take the cigarette, break it, and spend ten minutes linking a huge amount of pleasure to NOT SMOKING! I breathed in the clean air, felt how wonderful it was to be a non-smoker, and revelled in the success of the victory. And sure enough, after a number of attempts at getting me to repeat the pattern (for which it received the obligatory lemon), I proved to be more persistent than my brain, which

342

subsequently caved in under the assault of lemons and fresh air and accepted the new pattern of NOT SMOKING.

Notice that you can also teach your brain to build a pattern that will override your brain's natural survival instinct and indulge in a dangerous activity, if that is what you want. Soldiers are trained to think coolly under life and death, survival situations. People do swim with sharks and bungee jump and sky-surf and hunt snakes. If this is really what you think you have been called to Earth to do, then patterning can achieve it... and much more besides.

Revision
Old patterns go, but the brain still files them away to see if they can be used at a later date. Some ex-smokers still crave cigarettes if they are in a location-sensitive part of their old pattern, in a state of emotion, and then get a whiff of tobacco smoke. Repeat steps 1-3 every three months or so following the ceasing of a pattern to hammer home to the brain just how things are going to be from now on.

In summary then, those suffering from addictions may benefit from the following:

> **Adopt the *Food for Thought* dietary regimen**
> **Thiamine (B1), 150mg a day**
> **Niacin (B3), 500mg, am and pm**
> **Pantothenic acid (B5), 500mg, am and pm**
> **Vitamin B6, 100mg, am and pm**
> **Vitamin C, 10 grams a day, spread throughout the day**
> **L-glutamine powder, 5 grams, am and pm**
> **Essential fatty acids, including GLA**
> **The basic supplement program (see 'A Guide to Nutritional Supplements')**
> **Break the addiction pattern**

CRIMINAL VIOLENCE AND ANTI-SOCIAL BEHAVIOUR
A number of studies highlight glucose intolerance, heavy metal poisoning and junk diets to be the leading causes of violent behaviour in our culture today. As a result of refined diets and an excess of sugar and other high glycaemic foods, the offender experiences chaotic blood sugar levels, glucose intolerance and 'reactive' hypoglycaemia - the rebound low

343

experienced after sugar levels have plunged following the resultant increased production of insulin.

Bernard Gesch of Natural Justice, a UK-based charity, is championing the move towards improving nutrition in prisons, as well as society. A former probation officer, Gesch is adamant that the most central strategy towards discontinuing a culture's flirtation with social violence must be to feed the people properly:

"What we're trying to do is introduce something new into the criminal justice system, that is, the existence of the human brain."[547]

Gesch believes that exposure to neurotoxins, such as lead, cadmium, aspartame and food additives, together with nutritional deficiencies and a constant intake of low-nutrient-density, sugary junk foods are all it takes to get the riot police out:

"There are many chemicals around us that are known to affect behaviour. Our environment is increasingly polluted. Our food supply has fundamentally changed. In the same way that we don't notice ageing, how would we notice the effects of gradual changes in our diet and environment?" [548]

The Cycle of Violence
Consider that all behaviour is controlled by the brain, which is completely dependent on nutrition. Consider that a disrupted or chaotic supply of glucose, the only fuel the brain accepts, has a marked effect on behaviour, and that junk food is directly responsible. Consider also that anti-nutrients, such as lead and cadmium, directly affect brain function. And then recognise that when criminals are 'brought to justice' and then imprisoned, the same low nutrient-density food, drugs, cigarettes and pollution accompany the inmate and continue the deleterious effects. Then he is released into the same society to ingest the same junk food, take the same drugs and stimulants and experience the same hopeless behaviour patterns.

In the UK, Gesch's South Cumbria Alternative Sentencing Options Scheme (SCASO) required young offenders to undergo 'nutritional rehabilitation' as part of their processing. Tests recorded the levels of

---

[547] Pfeiffer, Carl & Patrick Holford, op. cit. p.157
[548] Ibid.

vitamins and minerals as well as toxins, blood sugar and an overall assessment of the inmate's dietary habits. *Every subject tested had abnormal glucose intolerance on a five-hour glucose tolerance test.* Zinc deficiency was also extremely prevalent.[549]

Finnish researcher Virkkunen studied 69 repeat offenders for reactive hypoglycaemia. With no exceptions, *all had glucose intolerance.* A later study showed abnormal insulin activity among all violent re-offenders who participated.[550]

In the US, behavioural expert Professor Stephen Schoenthaler placed 3,000 inmates on a low saturated fat, high-fibre diet which restricted sugary, refined foods. The results were extraordinary. Schoenthaler reported a

- ➢ 21% reduction in anti-social behaviour
- ➢ 25% reduction in assaults
- ➢ 75% reduction in the use of restraints
- ➢ 100% reduction in suicides[551]

Another study confirmed that amending the diet indeed has startling consequences in behaviour modification. The project reported a 44% reduction in anti-social behaviour with the most significant reductions occurring with repeat, serious offenders.[552]

Toxic Metals
A combination of the previously noted dietary problems, coupled with measurable increases in lead and cadmium in the subjects tested, demonstrated pronounced delinquency, impaired intellectual performance and a predisposition to commit violence. These pollution problems have been repeatedly measured in studies around the world.[553] Perhaps more

---

[549] Holford, P, "Crime – Nourishment or Punishment?" *Optimum Nutrition*, Vol. 8.2 (ref 82): 1995

[550] Virkkunen, M, *Neuropsychobiology*, 3,35-40 & 8,30-34: 1982

[551] Schoenthaler, S J, "The Northern California diet-behaviour program: An empirical evaluation of 3,000 incarcerated juveniles in Stanislaus County Juvenile Hall", *Int. J. Biosocial Res.*, 5(2),99-106: 1983

[552] Ibid.

[553] Freeman, R, Gamys, V P, & L E Smythe, "Lead burden of Sydney schoolchildren", University of New South Wales, January 1979; Needleman, H L, Davidson, I, Sewell, L E, et al, "Sub-clinical lead exposure in Philadelphia schoolchildren: Identification by dentine lead analysis", *New Eng. J. Med.*, 290, 245-248: 1974; Thompson, G O, et al,

startling is the fact that the amount of lead and cadmium required to affect behaviour is around 1% of that needed to produce physical symptoms of poisoning, so the link between the two effects has been more difficult to pinpoint.

Perhaps the most damning aspect of social violence comes from the fact that, in spite of the heap of science demonstrating quite unequivocally that nutrition has this quieting effect, and that even adding orange juice to the diets of inmates has been known to produce a staggering 47% reduction in antisocial behaviour among juvenile offenders[554], still nothing is done, either by government, the prison services, the food industry or the medical establishment centrally to correct the problem. Can violence be described as an economic necessity? After all, prisons are quite the boom industry in America, while newspapers and the entertainment industry rely on a steady diet of violence, rape and anti-social behaviour to fill their columns and screens for the gossip-hungry and violence-titillated public. To all 'public servants' and politicians out there, desiring to make their mark and do something to leave society in a better state than that in which they found it, the jury is in – now what will you do?

Food Allergies and Violence

Is the reader any longer surprised that the same problems stirring up hyperactivity and a dive in intellectual performance among our youth are those which blight our streets and nations today? Food allergies, such as milk and wheat intolerance, digestive problems, disturbed sleep and reactions to food additives are ever part of the root cause. Menzies discovered that of 25 children with tension fatigue complications, 84% had abnormal EEG and 72% had digestive problems specific to the diets they were consuming.[555] Gesch summarises:

"75% of our referrals were for violent offences, many of whom were multiple offenders.... Of those kept on the combined social and nutritional

---

"Blood lead levels and children's behaviour: Results from the Edinburgh lead study", *J. Child. Psycho. Psychiatr.*, 30(4), 515: 1989; Pihl, R O and F Ervin, "Lead and cadmium in violent criminals", *Psychol. Rep.*, 6(3), 839: 1990

[554] Schoenthaler, S J, "Diet and delinquency: A multi-state replication", *Int. J. of Bio. Res.*, 5(2), 73: 1983

[555] Menzies, I C, "Disturbed children: The role of food and chemical sensitivities", *Nutr. Health*, 3, 39-45: 1984

regime, none re-offended with [violence] *by the end of the 18-month pilot study.*"[556]

The cost of this amazing supplement 'treatment'? Between £4-£10 a month. The cost of keeping a juvenile in detention? Over £2,000 a month.

Once again, a fundamental reappraisal of society's basic relationship with its food and environment is the key to overcoming the social mayhem experienced in so many parts of the world today. The majority of the conditions which give rise to violent behaviour can be treated simply and effectively with nutritional and lifestyle changes. This will of course adequately explain why the Hunzas and other 'isolated' groups around the world have no track record of violence or anti-social behaviour in their cultures due to their nutrient-dense diets, clean environment and socially responsible attitudes. As Harvard professor Ernest Hooten once remarked: *"Let us go to the 'ignorant savage', consider his way of eating, and be wise."*[557]

EPILEPSY, FITS AND CONVULSIONS

The two elements that are frequently deficient in those suffering from convulsions and epilepsy are magnesium and manganese. To date, four studies have shown a correlation between low levels of manganese and epilepsy.[558] Once supplementation starts, the subject appears to suffer less. Manganese supplementation is ideally carried out within the framework of the basic supplement program (see 'A Guide to Nutritional Supplements') and a change to the *Food For Thought* diet.

Manganese is available in many foods normal to a healthy diet, but junk foods are noticeably deficient in this vital mental mineral. Magnesium injections have been known instantly to suppress convulsions.

---

[556] Gesch, B, "Natural justice: A pilot study in evaluating and responding to criminal behaviour as an environmental phenomenon: The South Cumbria (England) Alternative Sentencing Options (SCASCO) project", *Int. J. Biosocial Med. Res.*, 12(1), 41-68

[557] Hooten, Ernest A, *Apes, Men and Morons*, Putnam, New York: 1937

[558] Dupont, C l, & Y Tanaka, "Blood manganese levels in children with convulsive disorder", *Biochem. Med.* 33(2):246-55, 1985; Papavasilou, P S, et al., "Seizure disorders and trace metals: manganese tissue levels in treated epileptics", *Neurology*, 29:1466, 1979; Sohler, A and C C Pfeiffer, "A direct method for the determination of manganese in whole blood: Patients with seizure activity have low blood levels", *J. Orthomol. Psychiatr.*, 8(4):275-280, 1979; Tanaka, Y, "Low manganese level may trigger epilepsy", *Journal of the American Medical Association*, 238:1805, 1977

Vitamin B6 and zinc are also key nutrients that can be employed to treat fits and convulsions.

Those suffering from these problems are advised to have an allergy test to see if food allergies are playing a role. Also a hair mineral analysis should be carried out to discover if there are any deficiencies. Once these are corrected, the fits usually cease.

> - The *Food For Thought* dietary regimen
> - Vitamin E, 800IU a day
> - Vitamin B6, 100mg, am and pm
> - Manganese, 10mg, am and pm
> - The basic supplement program (see 'A Guide to Nutritional Supplements')

PARKINSON'S DISEASE

SYMPTOMS: Parkinson's is a motor system disorder marked by a destruction of the cells which produce the neurotransmitter hormone dopamine. Symptoms include muscle rigidity, impaired movement, problems with balance and coordination, sexual disinterest, tremors and agitation. Traditional treatment includes drugs, which replace the brain's dwindling supply of dopamine and minocycline, which may prevent dopamine cell damage by blocking the production of nitric oxide.[559]

Potential Causes

Aspartame: The infamous artificial sweetener has been found to trigger or worsen cases of Parkinson's. As discussed earlier, aspartame contains a number of modalities which can cause mental degeneration. The sweetener is the bane of food regulatory agencies around the world which receive a high percentage of their total complaints from people experiencing aspartame reactions.[560]

Faulty metabolism of iron in the body.[561]

Homocysteine: Raised levels of this protein metabolite are found in Parkinson's patients, who have a corresponding lack of folate in the body. One study reports:

"While previous studies have shown that levels of homocysteine are elevated in people with Parkinson's disease, the precise role of

---

[559] Proceedings from the National Academy of Sciences, 4th December 2001, 98:14669-14674

[560] Day, Phillip, *Health Wars*, op. cit.

[561] *Nature Genetics*, February 2001, 27:209-214

348

homocysteine in the development of the disease has remained unclear. This study strongly suggests that elevated homocysteine levels can indeed render neurons vulnerable to Parkinson's disease. This study establishes that a diet with low folic acid levels increases homocysteine levels and the homocysteine, in turn, renders neurons in the brain vulnerable to dysfunction and death." [562]

Exposure to pesticides and petroleum-based, hydrocarbon solvents. [563]

Those suffering from Parkinson's may benefit from the following:

> **An allergy test**
> **A diet rich in fish oils and fresh vegetables and fruit (see *Food For Thought* dietary regimen)**
> **Vitamin E, 800IU a day** [564]
> **Deanol – 100mg a day**
> **DMAE – 500mg a day**
> **Supplements containing 'smart' nutrients, such as 5-HTP, pyroglutamate, glutamine, phosphatidyl choline and pantothenic acid (B5)**
> **Cease eating junk foods, sugar and artificial sweeteners**
> **Cease using personal care and household products with potentially harmful ingredients and switch to safe alternatives (see 'Environmental Toxins')**
> **Essential fatty acid intake. A basic nutritional supplement program boosts oxygen to the cells and prevents deficiency in any one of over 60 different nutrients (see 'A Guide to Nutritional Supplements')**
> **Discuss the replacement of any mercury amalgam fillings with a co-operative dentist**

TARDIVE DISKINESIA (TD)

This condition is a side-effect of psychiatric medication, which can cause the patient's extremities to move spasmodically. Lips, tongue, jaw, fingers, toes and legs twitch or 'dance' as a result of nerve complications. Some doctors, such as world TD expert Dr William Glazier, believe that up

---

[562] *Journal of Neurochemistry*, January 2002;80:101-110
[563] Annual Meeting of the American Academy of Neurology in San Diego, CA, USA, 9th May 2000; *Neurology*, September 2000;55:667-673.
[564] *Arch. Neurol.* 1997;54:pp.762-765

to 70% of long-term psychiatric drug users risk getting symptoms of TD. Seymour Rosenblatt, in his *Beyond Valium*, explains how psychiatry first became aware of the condition:

"One day we noticed something peculiar. Some patients developed a strange, wormlike tongue movement. It was hardly noticeable – a twitch of the tongue tip – but you could see it when they held their mouths open. As the days passed, the symptoms grew worse. Their lips began rotating in a chewing movement. Soon the whole mouth was thrusting and rolling, the tongue flicking out like the tongue of an anteater.

What kind of strange behaviour was this? It grew worse. It afflicted their arms and legs. They began to writhe slowly, purposelessly, a few of them developing a to-and-fro rocking motion.

Little did we know it, but we were in the process of observing the first serious drawback of antipsychotics [medication].... *It swept through the hospitals like an epidemic. One after another the patients were stricken. Soon we had almost 50% of our mental patients chewing and grimacing in a horrible grotesquerie.*

What was the cause? We didn't know. Families of the afflicted patients went running to the doctors. 'What have you done to poor Joe?' they demanded. 'He's writhing so badly we can't stand the sight of him!'"[565]

Rosenblatt later discovered that drugs such as Thorazine were blocking the nerve receptors. The receptors were not getting their usual transmitter messages. They were firing less often and a state of lethargy ensued. TD is often thought to be irreversible. Patrick Holford and Carl Pfeiffer, on the other hand, report that TD patients respond well to dietary changes, along with intakes of zinc, manganese, Vitamins C, E, B3 & B6 and Deanol, as well as evening primrose oil. These are required by the body to turn essential fats into prostaglandins, which affect nerve impulse transmissions.[566] A TD patient should be encouraged to follow all the basic steps of diet and nutrition explained in this book for the optimum chance of restoring loss or impaired function to their nervous system.

---

[565] Rosenblatt, Seymour & Reynolds Dodson, *Beyond Valium – The Brave New World of Psychochemistry*, Putnam's, New York: 1981, pp.164-165
[566] Pfeiffer, Carl & Patrick Holford, op. cit. p.30

SLEEP DISORDERS

Sleep comes upon us when levels of the neurotransmitter serotonin rise while circulating levels of adrenalin decrease. Serotonin is partially made from the protein constituent (amino acid) tryptophan, currently banned for general sale because of a contamination introduced through its production by genetic engineering. Many believe this was done deliberately to save the patented sleeping pill market, as tryptophan is remarkably effective in getting us to snooze. Interesting that now the nutrient has been declared safe, it is still banned!

If you are not getting your share of shut-eye, you may benefit from the following:

- **Change to the *Food For Thought* dietary regimen**
- **Avoid junk and sugary foods**
- **Avoid food additives**
- **Vitamin B6, 100mg, am and pm**
- **Zinc, up to 50mg a day**
- **Avoid all stimulants after 4pm**
- **L-tryptophan, 1,000mg, am and pm**
- **Eat calcium and magnesium-rich foods (avoid dairy! Leafy green vegetables are ideal, along with nuts and seeds)**
- **Remove worries and stress, as far as possible**
- **The basic supplement program (see 'A Guide to Nutritional Supplements')**

Environmental Toxins

In *Cancer: Why We're Still Dying to Know the Truth*, I devote an entire chapter to potential and actual carcinogens in the personal care and household products marketplace which have seriously affected health for decades. These toxins can also have a direct and cumulative effect on cognitive ability and 'mental health'. The problems stem from governments' inability financially to test and effectively regulate these chemicals with the limited budgets they have available. Compounding this problem are the conflicts of interest that exist between chemical manufacturers and the government regulatory agencies themselves, making independent, objective adjudication of these drugs and chemicals a near impossibility.

Agencies, such as Britain's Environment Agency and America's Environmental Protection Agency exist, so far as the public is concerned, for no other reason than to ensure that we can raise our families and work at our jobs in, as far as possible, a contamination-free environment. All technologically advanced nations have such environmental agencies, and yet every year, people still die by the hundreds of thousands, polluted and poisoned by these substances. So what has gone so very wrong?

The major problem stems from the rate at which new chemicals and chemical products are pouring onto the world's markets. Government agencies, already so tightly controlled financially with annual budget constraints, simply do not have the resources to test more than a dozen or so each year. Therefore they must rely heavily on industry-sponsored reports on product safety *from the manufacturers themselves*, which naturally opens up a wide arena for abuse. Agencies such as the EPA threaten dire fines on pharmaceutical and chemical companies found indulging in any foul play to ram potentially unsafe products through regulation. But prosecution of such cases by government on a realistic scale is rare since litigation consumes prodigious amounts of taxpayers' money.

Worse, the very government regulatory agencies themselves, such as the US Food & Drug Administration and Britain's Medicines Control Agency (MCA), which are supposed to protect the public from potentially dangerous products coming onto the market, are horribly compromised because of personal investments or ties with the chemical/drug industries. A *USA Today* analysis of financial conflicts at 159 US Food and Drug

Administration advisory committee meetings from 1st January to 30th June 2000 finds that:

> ➢ At 92% of the meetings, at least one member had a financial conflict of interest.
> ➢ At 55% of meetings, half or more of the FDA advisers had conflicts of interest.
> ➢ Conflicts were most frequent at the 57 meetings when broader issues were discussed: 92% of members had conflicts.
> ➢ At the 102 meetings dealing with the fate of a specific drug, 33% of the experts had a financial conflict.[567]

"The best experts for the FDA are often the best experts to consult with industry," says FDA senior associate commissioner Linda Suydam, who is in charge of waiving conflict-of-interest restrictions. But Larry Sasich of Public Citizen, an advocacy group, says, *"The industry has more influence on the process than people realise."*

Britain's Medicines Control Agency fares little better with its track record for impartiality when it comes to regulating the drug industry. According to a *Daily Express* investigation, key members of the Committee on Safety of Medicines and the Medicines Commission themselves have heavy personal investments in the drug industry. Yet these committees are the ones which decide which drugs are allowed onto the market and which are rejected!

According to the report, two thirds of the 248 experts sitting on the Medicines Commission have financial ties to the pharmaceutical industry. Drug regulators such as Dr Richard Auty have £110,000 worth of holdings with AstraZeneca. Dr Michael Denham owns £115,000 worth of shares in SmithKline Beecham. Dr Richard Logan has up to £30,000 shares in AstraZeneca, SmithKline Beecham and Glaxo Wellcome. Logan's role with the committee involves examining cases where a drug might have to be withdrawn from the market for safety reasons.

David Ganderton was an advisor for nine years with the CSM panel who used to work for AstraZeneca. His current shareholding with this drug company is worth £91,000. Other members of the committees with substantial holdings for example include Dr Colin Forfar, with £22,000

---

[567] *USA Today* article by Dennis Cauchon, *FDA Advisers Tied to Industry*, 25th September 2000, http://www.usatoday.com/news/washdc/ncssun06.htm

with Glaxo Wellcome and Dr Brian Evans owning £28,000 worth of shares with Glaxo Wellcome.[568]

The Daily Express report goes on to tell us: *"Tom Moore, a former senior executive with AstraZeneca, told the Sunday Express that the drug companies go out of their way to build strong links. He said, "Their objective is to get as close as possible. They are an extremely powerful lobby group because they have unlimited resources."*

The [drug] *companies provide* [members of CSM and other regulatory committees with] *trips abroad to conferences, large research grants that can keep a university department employed for years, and consultancies that can boost an academic's humble income."*

What remote hope can there be of proper, unbiased, objective research on nutrition? Many of these government regulators will eventually leave their posts to take up positions with the companies they once regulated. This makes excellent strategic sense for the chemical industry, which can use the expertise of such talent to smooth the way through their products' regulation and approval procedures.

PERSONAL CARE AND HOUSEHOLD PRODUCTS

Poor regulation, self-regulation and a blizzard of confusing and contrary scientific data have resulted in a tragically large number of chemicals making it into our personal lives with little or no warnings attached. Most people have no idea, for example, what the personal care products they use every day are doing to them. As an example, in 1990, 38,000 cosmetic injuries were reported in the US that required medical attention.[569] Health concerns are continuously being raised about ingredients in shampoos, toothpastes, skin creams, and other personal care products. In fact, researchers in Japan, Germany, Switzerland, and the US say many ingredients in personal care products may be related to premature baldness, cataract formation, environmental cancers, contact dermatitis and possible eye damage in young children. We'll find out what some of these substances actually are in a moment and why these researchers have every reason to be concerned.

---

[568] *Daily Express,* micro edition, 6th August 2000

[569] Steinman, D & Samuel S Epstein, *The Safe Shopper's Bible,* pp.182-183, ISBN 0020820852; also Consumer Product Safety Commission (CPSC), Product summary report: Washington DC, 1990

The National Institute of Occupational Safety and Health has found that 884 chemicals available for use in cosmetics have been reported to the US Government as toxic substances.[570] So why are these potentially harmful ingredients allowed in personal care products?

In 1938 the US Government created a legal definition for cosmetics by passing The Federal Food, Drug and Cosmetic Act. Cosmetics were defined as products for *"cleansing, beautifying, promoting attractiveness, or altering the appearance."* In this definition, a cosmetic is defined *"in terms of its intended purpose rather than in terms of the ingredients with which it is formulated."*[571] In other words, although the Food and Drug Administration classifies cosmetics, incredibly it does not regulate them. According to a document posted on the agency's Internet homepage, *"...a cosmetic manufacturer may use any ingredient or raw material and market the final products without government approval."*[572]

On 10th September 1997, Senator Edward M. Kennedy of Massachusetts, while discussing an FDA reform bill, stated, *"The cosmetic industry has borrowed a page from the playbook of the tobacco industry, by putting profits ahead of public health."* Kennedy further stated, *"Cosmetics can be dangerous to your health. Yet this greedy industry wants Congress to prevent the American people from learning that truth. Every woman who uses face cream, or hair spray, or lipstick, or shampoo, or mascara, or powder should demand that this arrogant and irresponsible power-play by the industry be rejected. A study by the respected, non-partisan General Accounting Office reported that more than 125 ingredients available for use in cosmetics are suspected of causing cancer. Other cosmetics may cause adverse effects on the nervous system, including convulsions. Still other ingredients are suspected of causing birth defects. A carefully controlled study found that one in sixty users suffered a cosmetic related injury identified by a physician."*[573]

---

[570] Steinman, D & S Epstein, *Safe Shopper's Bible*, op. cit.
[571] Consumer Health and Product Hazards/Cosmetic Drugs, Pesticides, Food Additives, Volume 2 of The Legislation of Product Safety, edited by Samuel S Epstein and Richard D Grundy, MIT Press, 1974
[572] http://vm.cfsan.fda.gov/~dms/cos-hdb1.html
[573] This statement is quoted from Senator Kennedy's office on http://www.senate.gov/~kennedy/statements/970910fda.html

In 1998, Peter Phillips and *Project Censored* listed the year's top 25 censored stories. The number 2 censored story (as detailed in his book) was titled "Personal Care and Cosmetic Products May Be Carcinogenic."[574]

Shocking news indeed. Let's take a brief look at a few of the ingredients that top the list of potentially harmful compounds that are present in products we use every day.

Sodium Lauryl Sulfate (SLS)
SLS is a very harsh detergent found in almost all shampoos and more than a few toothpastes. Pick up a cross-section of these products next time you visit the supermarket and you will find SLS or SLES in pride of place under the ingredients label. SLS started its career as an industrial degreasant and garage floor cleaner. When applied to human skin it has the effect of stripping off the oil layer and then irritating and eroding the skin, leaving it rough and pitted. Studies[575] have shown that:

> Shampoos with SLS could retard healing and keep children's eyes from developing properly. Children under six years old are especially vulnerable to improper eye development (Summary of Report of Research to Prevent Blindness, Inc. conference)
> SLS can cause cataracts in adults and delays the healing of wounds in the surface of the cornea.
> SLS has a low molecular weight and so is easily absorbed by the body. It builds up in the heart, liver, lungs and brain and can cause major problems in these areas.
> SLS causes skin to flake and to separate and causes substantial roughness on the skin.
> SLS causes dysfunction of the biological systems of the skin.
> SLS is such a caustic cleanser that it actually corrodes the hair follicle and impairs its ability to grow hair.
> SLS is routinely used in clinical studies deliberately to irritate the skin so that the effects of other substances can be tested.[576]

Ethoxylation
Ethoxylation is the process that makes degreasing agents such as sodium lauryl sulfate (SLS) less abrasive and gives them enhanced

---

[574] Phillips, Peter, *Censored 1998: The News That Didn't Make the News*, Project Censored, 1998 ISBN 1888363649
[575] Vance, Judi, *Beauty to Die For*, Promotion Publishing, 1998
[576] Study cited by *The Wall Street Journal*, 1st November 1988

foaming properties. When SLS is <u>eth</u>oxylated, it forms sodium lau<u>reth</u> sulfate (SLES), a compound used in many shampoos, toothpastes, bath gels, bubble baths, and industrial degreasants. The problem is, the extremely harmful compound 1,4-dioxane may be created during the ethoxylation process, contaminating the product. 1,4-dioxane was one of the principal components of the chemical defoliant Agent Orange, used to great effect by the Americans during the Vietnam War to strip off the jungle canopy to reveal their enemy. 1,4-dioxane is a hormonal disrupter believed to be the chief agent implicated in the host of cancers suffered by Vietnam military personnel after the war. It is also an estrogen mimic thought to increase the chances of breast and endometrial cancers, stress-related illnesses and lower sperm counts.

Leading toxicologist Dr Samuel Epstein reports: *"The best way to protect yourself is to recognize ingredients most likely to be contaminated with 1,4-dioxane. These include ingredients with the prefix word, or syllable PEG, Polyethylene, Polyethylene Glycol, Polyoxyethylene, eth (as in sodium laureth sulfate), or oxynol. Both polysorbate 60 and polysorbate 80 may also be contaminated with 1,4-dioxane."*[577]

Propylene Glycol
Propylene glycol is a common ingredient used extensively in industry as a component of brake fluids, paint, varnishes and anti-freeze compounds. It also appears in many beauty creams, cleansers, makeup and children's personal care products. Judi Vance writes:

"If you were to purchase a drum of this chemical from a manufacturer, he is required to furnish you with a material safety data sheet (MSDS) and it may alarm you to find that this common, widely used humectant has a cautionary warning in its MSDS that reads: "If on skin: thoroughly wash with soap and water."[578]

The American Academy of Dermatologists published a clinical review in January 1991 that showed propylene glycol caused a significant number of reactions and was a primary irritant to the skin even in low levels of concentration (around 5%). However propylene glycol routinely appears

---

[577] Steinman, D & S Epstein, *Safe Shopper's Bible,* op. cit. pp.190-191
[578] Vance, Judy, *Beauty to Die For,* op cit.

in the top three ingredients of a given product, indicating that it is present in high concentration.[579] It has been shown that propylene glycol:

> ➢ Has severe adverse health effects and has been found to cause kidney damage, and liver abnormalities.
> ➢ Damages cell membranes causing rashes, dry skin, contact dermatitis and surface damage to the skin.
> ➢ Is toxic to human cells in cultures.

Diethanolamine (DEA)
Cocamide DEA
Lauramide DEA

A colourless liquid or crystalline alcohol used as a solvent, emulsifier, and detergent (wetting agent). DEA works as an emollient in skin-softening lotions or as a humectant in other personal care products. When found in products containing nitrates, it reacts chemically with the nitrates to form potentially carcinogenic nitrosamines. Although earlier studies seemed to indicate that DEA itself was not a carcinogen, more recent studies show that DEA has the capacity unequivocally to cause cancer, even in formulations that exclude nitrates.[580] DEA may also irritate the skin and mucous membranes.[581] Other ethanolamines to watch out for are: triethanolamine (TEA) and monethanolamine (MEA).

Fluorides (Sodium Fluoride and Hexafluorosilicic Acid)

Fluorides used in the drinking water supplies are a toxic, non-biodegradable, environmental pollutant, officially classified as a contaminant by the US Environmental Protection Agency. Shocking though it may be to contemplate, the reality is, these chemicals are simply hazardous industrial waste - by-products variously from the manufacture

---

[579] The first two or three ingredients listed on a product label usually constitute over half of a formulation. In some products, the first two or three ingredients can constitute 70-90% of the formulation. Ingredients are listed in descending order, going down to 1% concentration. Below 1%, ingredients may be listed in any order.

[580] Epstein, Samuel S, *The Politics of Cancer Revisited*, East Ridge Press, 1998, p.479

[581] Many nitrosamines have been determined to cause cancer in laboratory animals. Nitrosamine contamination of cosmetics became an issue in early 1977. The Food & Drug Administration expressed its concern about the contamination of cosmetics in a Federal Register notice dated 10th April 1979, which stated that cosmetics containing nitrosamines may be considered adulterated and subject to enforcement action.

of phosphate fertilisers and aluminium smelting - which are disposed of in the public water supply.[582]

Alcohol

A colourless, volatile, flammable liquid produced by the fermentation of yeast and carbohydrates. Alcohol is used frequently as a solvent and is also found in beverages and medicine. As an ingredient in ingestible products, alcohol may cause body tissues to be more vulnerable to carcinogens. Mouthwashes with an alcohol content of 25 percent or more have been implicated in mouth, tongue and throat cancers, according to a 1991 study released by the National Cancer Institute. Also a disturbing trend in accidental poisonings has been attributed to alcohol consumption from mouthwashes. After the NCI figures were published, Warner Lambert, manufacturers of the mouthwash Listerine (previously 26.9% alcohol), announced a new version of their product with significantly less alcohol.[583]

Alpha Hydroxy Acid (AHA)

An organic acid produced by anaerobic respiration. Skin care products containing AHA exfoliate not only destroy skin cells, but the skin's protective barrier as well. Long-term skin damage may result from its use.

Alumin(i)um

A metallic element used extensively in the manufacture of aircraft components, prosthetic devices, and as an ingredient in antiperspirants, antacids, and antiseptics. Aluminium has long been linked to Alzheimer's disease.[584] Use of aluminium pots and pans to cook food and the use of aluminium cans for soda, as well as the unnecessary cultural penchant for spraying aluminium directly into our lymph nodes as underarm antiperspirant all give grave causes for concern.

Animal Fat (Tallow)

A type of animal tissue made up of oily solids or semisolids that are water-insoluble esters of glycerol and fatty acids. Animal fats and lye are the chief ingredients in bar soap, a cleaning and emulsifying product that may act as a breeding ground for bacteria.

---

[582] For more information on the important subject of water fluoridation, see *Health Wars* – 'Water Under the Bridge'.
[583] Winslow, Ron, *Wall Street Journal*, 23rd April 1991, p.B1
[584] See section on Alzheimer's disease.

Bentonite

A porous clay that expands to many times its dry volume as it absorbs water. Bentonite is commonly found in many cosmetic foundations and may clog pores and suffocate the skin. Bentonite is used by fire fighters to suffocate forest fires by eliminating the oxygen available.

Butane

Aerosol propellant. Flammable and in high doses may be narcotic or cause asphyxiation.

Animal Collagen

An insoluble fibrous protein that is too large to penetrate the skin. The collagen found in most skin care products is derived from animal carcasses and ground up chicken feet. This ingredient forms a layer of film that may suffocate the skin.

Dioxin (see also Ethoxylation and 1,4-Dioxane)

A potentially carcinogenic by-product that results from the process used to increase foam levels in cleansers such as shampoos, tooth pastes, etc., and to bleach paper at paper mills. Dioxin-treated containers (and some plastic bottles) sometimes transfer dioxins to the products themselves. It has been shown that dioxin's carcinogenicity is up to 500,000 times more potent than that of DDT. [585]

Elastin of High-Molecular Weight

A protein similar to collagen that is the main component of elastic fibres. Elastin is also derived from animal sources. Its effect on the skin is similar to collagen.

Fluorocarbons

A colourless, non-flammable gas or liquid that can produce mild upper respiratory tract irritation. Fluorocarbons are commonly used as a propellant in hairsprays.

Formaldehyde

A toxic, colourless gas that is an irritant and a carcinogen. When combined with water, formaldehyde is used as a disinfectant, fixative, or preservative. Formaldehyde is found in many cosmetic products and conventional nail care systems.

---

[585] Steinman, D & S Epstein, *Safe Shopper's Bible,* op. cit. p.342

Glycerin

A syrupy liquid that is chemically produced by combining water and fat. Glycerin is used as a solvent and plasticiser. Unless the humidity of air is over 65%, glycerin draws moisture from the lower layers of the skin and holds it on the surface, which dries the skin from the inside out.

Kaolin

Commonly used in foundations, face powders and dusting powders, kaolin is a fine white clay used in making porcelain. Like bentonite, kaolin smothers and weakens the skin.

Lanolin

A fatty substance extracted from wool, which is frequently found in cosmetics and lotions. Lanolin is a common sensitiser that can cause allergic reactions, such as skin rashes, sometimes due to toxic pesticides present in the sheep's wool. Some sixteen pesticides were identified in lanolin sampled in 1988. [586]

Mineral Oil

A derivative of crude oil (petroleum) that is used industrially as a cutting fluid and lubricating oil. Mineral oil forms an oily film over skin to lock in moisture, toxins, and wastes, but hinders normal skin respiration by keeping oxygen out. Used in baby oils.

Petrolatum

A petroleum-based grease that is used industrially as a grease component. Petrolatum exhibits many of the same potentially harmful properties as mineral oil.

Propane

Aerosol propellant. Is flammable and in high doses may be narcotic.

Salt

Very drying, irritating, and corrosive.

Talc

A soft grey-green mineral used in some personal hygiene and cosmetics products. Inhaling talc may be harmful as this substance is recognised as a potential carcinogen. Talc is widely recognised to be one of

---

[586] National Academy of Sciences' concern over lanolin contamination: NRC, 1993, p.313

the leading causes of ovarian cancer.[587] It is used by many around the genital area and can also be found on condoms.

So what do you do? Where can you go to get hold of safe personal care products that are effective and of high quality?

TAKING CONTROL OF THE JUNK

Samuel Epstein MD is a world-renowned authority on the causes and prevention of cancer. He was named the 1998 winner of the Right Livelihood Award (also known as the 'Alternative Nobel Prize'). Dr Epstein has devoted the greater part of his life to studying and fighting the causes of cancer. He is Professor of Occupational and Environmental Medicine at the School of Public Health, University of Illinois Medical Center at Chicago, and the chairman of the Cancer Prevention Coalition. He is arguably one of the world's leading toxicologists.

As the author of *The Politics of Cancer* and *The Breast Cancer Prevention Program*, he advocates the use of cosmetics and other products that are free from suspected carcinogens. Based on Dr Epstein's research and recommendations, he has awarded one company the 'Seal of Safety' from the Cancer Prevention Coalition. This company, Neways International, manufacturers and distributes its own personal care products, which are free of potentially harmful ingredients. Dr Epstein is enthusiastic about the groundbreaking work Neways has done in this area: *"Neways has pioneered and succeeded in providing consumers with cosmetics and toiletries free of cancer-causing and harmful ingredients and contaminants. I warmly congratulate them on their accomplishments."*

During the course of our work on this and other research projects, Credence researchers have had an opportunity to work with Neways technical personnel and examine the Neways product line. I myself flew to Utah to examine their production plant at Salem and talk with their executives at length. As a result of Credence's investigations, like Dr Epstein, we do not hesitate, as an independent, non-affiliated organisation, to recommend Neways' carcinogen-free personal care products and nutritional supplements to all who are looking to make a change for the better.

---

[587] Steinman, D & S Epstein, *Safe Shopper's Bible*, op. cit. p.259

Tom Mower, President of Neways, lays out the focus of his organisation: *"Neways is in the business of helping people detoxify their bodies. Knowing the chemical constituents of your personal care products and their effects on your body enables you to understand how toxic culprits can contaminate your body. Ingredients like sodium lauryl sulfate (SLS), diethanolamine (DEA), triethanolamine (TEA), propylene glycol, fluoride, and alcohol have been identified by experts as known or potential carcinogens that can be found in ordinary personal care products.*

So Neways provides shampoos without sodium lauryl sulfate. We have lotions without propylene glycol, bubble bath without DEA or TEA, toothpastes without saccharin or fluoride, and mouthwash without alcohol. We use toxin- and carcinogen-free products that give consumers something more than clean skin or fresh breath - they provide peace of mind."

See our *Contacts! Contacts! Contacts!* section for further information on how to obtain non-toxic substitutes for toothpastes, cosmetics, detergents, polishes, sprays and deodorants, or whole bathroom change-out kits. Don't use insecticides. Press for clean, non-fluoridated tap water. Most importantly, as we will find out in an upcoming section, we must 'think clean' with our diet. The new lifestyle we must adopt must be a sensible, easy-to-follow regimen, and we must know why we are following it.

Eliminating the Pied Piper
The Science of Natural Hygiene

Dr Herbert M Shelton, one of Natural Hygiene's leading proponents, described the science as *"...that branch of biology which investigates and applies the conditions upon which life and health depend, and the means by which health is sustained in all its virtue and purity, and restored when it has been lost or impaired."*

Natural Hygiene recognises that the human body is subject to natural laws, which, if broken, will invariably produce disease. It also appreciates that the body, with all of its wondrous workings, is an organism that is constantly striving for wellness. The words 'Natural Hygiene' imply a cleanliness of the body that is achieved through natural, non-contrived means. No patented potions. No weird rituals. No monopoly on hidden or arcane knowledge. Natural Hygiene is a way of eating and living practised under various different names and disguises by hundreds of thousands around the world who are enjoying long, disease-free lives as a result of applying some very simple but telling techniques. Harvey Diamond, whose *Fit For Life* series is a worldwide banner for Natural Hygiene, and whose own life was radically turned around with its application, gives his own summation:

"The underlying basis of Natural Hygiene is that the body is self-cleansing, self-healing, and self maintaining. Natural Hygiene is based on the idea that all the healing power of the universe is within the human body; that nature is always correct and cannot be improved upon. Therefore nature does not seek to thwart its own devices. We experience problems of ill-health (i.e. excess weight, pain, stress) only when we break the natural laws of life." [588]

The science of Natural Hygiene revolves around the following topics:
- Understanding The Body's Natural Digestive Cycles
- Correct Consumption of Fruit
- The Concept of High Water-Content Food
- Correct Food Combining
- Detoxification

---

[588] Diamond, Harvey & Marilyn, *Fit For Life*, Bantam Books, 1985, p.19

THE BODY'S NATURAL DIGESTIVE CYCLES

The basis of Natural Hygiene teaches that the human body's digestive system goes through three eight-hour cycles every twenty-four hours:

Noon – 8pm: **Appropriation** of food (eating and digestion)
8pm – 4am: **Assimilation** of food (absorption and use)
4am – Noon: **Elimination** (excretion of waste products)

It is not hard to see these cycles in action. It is also uncomfortably clear when these cycles are thrown into confusion and turmoil by, for example, eating a pizza late at night or eating a big breakfast.

APPROPRIATION

The body prefers the Appropriation Cycle to happen on time, commencing at noon. Those who rise late in the morning can easily make it through to noon without any food, because the body is currently in the Elimination Cycle and isn't yet ready for food. After the commencement of the Appropriation Cycle however, once afternoon arrives, we become uncomfortable if we do not eat anything. Our body craves nourishment during Appropriation and will let us know of its needs in no uncertain terms if we are remiss in supplying it the necessary fodder. The most important rule during Appropriation is *to eat only when your body is hungry*. It is therefore important to cut out all stimulants, such as sugar, coffee and tea, which can manipulate blood sugar levels and trick the body into becoming hungry for food it doesn't need.

ASSIMILATION

The Assimilation Cycle mostly occurs at night, and ideally must, like Britain's RailTrack, leave on time. Assimilation (nutrient extraction and use) at night makes all the sense in the world as the body is resting and the digestive system can crank into gear and do its thing with the minimum of interruption. Night-time is naturally not a good time for Appropriation (eating and digestion) because of the horizontal angles involved. During Assimilation at night however, the body extracts nutrients in our intestines, which are twelve times the length of our trunks, designed as they are to keep high-water-content, unrefined plant dietary food in their clutches until all the nutrients are withdrawn. If you leave three hours between your last meal and when you go to bed, a properly combined supper, along the lines we will be examining, will already have left the stomach and be well on its peaceful way through the alimentary tract for its squeezing and extracting by the time you lay your head down on your pillow. During the night, your body is putting all those nutrients to work replenishing your systems, replacing damaged cells and allowing the blood and lymph systems to pick up waste and take it to the garbage collection points in preparation for the Elimination cycle the following morning.

If however you commit the cardinal sin and wolf down your cheese and pineapple pizza (with the obligatory jalapenos) immediately prior to going to sleep, you will go to bed feeling like you have swallowed an anvil. Your body is horizontal which means that gravity is working against your stomach and everything therein, inevitably resulting in the desperate need to throw down half a bucket of antacids at 2:30am to douse the mighty conflagration, or else prop your head up on a pillow in a vain attempt to stop the resultant hydrochloric acid reflux bringing those jalapenos and cheese up for a chat.

ELIMINATION
At 4am, Elimination cuts in and the garbage truck arrives to take out the junk. Your body has sorted through the food it has processed, and has rejected the food debris that cannot be absorbed and satisfactorily metabolised into its constituent nutrients for further use. Elimination is simply the removal of waste matter from the body, be it from fibrous, non-metabolised food or other waste products the body generates, which we will examine in a minute. The human body has very efficient systems to accomplish the shedding of waste from the body, using the bowel and urine to excrete the junk the body no longer wants to be involved with. The body also eliminates metabolic toxins, which have accumulated in the body, shunting them out via the underarm, the bowel, the urine, glands at the backs of the knees, glands behind the ears, from the groin area, from the nose, the mouth, the ears and the skin.

Emergency elimination can be dramatic and is carried out by the body when time is of the essence in getting rid of dangerously toxic material before the body's internal systems and health are threatened. Examples of this are diarrhoea, a waterfall of a nose during colds, and of course, vomiting.

Elimination is the most thwarted digestive cycle of the three - an abuse that has led to chronic obesity in our populations and catastrophic ill-health. *The reason is because the Elimination Cycle is almost always sabotaged by us unwittingly eating big, badly combined breakfasts, preventing the body from executing its essential daily function of getting waste out of the body.* Thus the junk stays put and gets filed in all the parts of our bodies where it can do the least harm.

WASTE PRODUCTS

It's a good idea to have a cursory knowledge of waste products with which our bodies have to get to grips on a daily basis. These include:

- ➢ Food detritus
- ➢ Toxic food metabolites and mucoid plaque
- ➢ Catabolic cellular debris
- ➢ Chemical toxins

Food Detritus

...we have already looked at. It's simply the fibrous waste the body cannot absorb to make cell structure. This fibre, as most know, is extremely beneficial in adding bulk to digestion, giving you that 'full' feeling and enabling the colon to move everything comfortably along. Fibre also scours the digestive tract of impacted faecal matter (mucoid plaque) and cleans everything it passes with its Brillo-pad action.

Toxic Food Metabolites and Mucoid Plaque

...are more dangerous compounds and include the mess of partially processed complex animal proteins, the acidic gunk resulting from bad food combining and uric acid from chronic meat-eating unable to be broken down because humans lack the enzyme uricase. The danger of toxic food metabolites is that, with a junk diet, these poisons can accumulate at a more rapid rate than the body can eliminate them. This condition is sometimes referred to as toxaemia or acidosis. Toxic sucrose and milk metabolites are also created since the body lacks renin and lactase enzymes to break down milk proteins and the vitamins and minerals necessary to process the hopeless sucrose. These toxins are of course also acidic and represent a danger to the body.

Clogged colons are one of the major causes of diseases today, not least because a clogged colon cannot efficiently absorb nutrients from the food it is processing. The other problem is that moisture is extracted from food as it is digested, and the resultant mass can become gluey and adhesive, coating the walls of the colon and intestines (mucoid plaque). Modern, processed foods are the worst for accomplishing this.

It has been estimated that an adult consuming an average, animal protein-heavy Western-style diet during their life can have between 7 to 25 pounds or more (3 to 10 kilos) of layered, impacted faecal matter clogging their digestive system. The average Westerner consuming this diet faithfully holds eight full meals of undigested food and waste matter within their digestive system at any one time. The mucoid plaque can be rubbery or hardened material, unable to complete the journey through the intestines. It quickly begins to rot, producing foul odours and gases. This decomposing material is a haven for germs and bacteria, which quickly thrive, producing toxins that can enter the bloodstream and affect the entire body.

Curiously we as humans once again take the Biscuit of Distinction for being the only creature in nature almost always corrupting its natural food supply by processing, boiling, frying, irradiating, roasting and otherwise destroying its valuable nutrition prior to slamming it together in any combination and wolfing it down. This 'bad', nutritionally corrupted food produces its own acidic by-products, including unstable oxidation elements ('free radicals'), which can damage the colon, causing healing processes to commence, potentially resulting in irritable bowel, Crohn's and colorectal cancers. It is a measure of how serious this food-processing and -corrupting problem has become in the West that colorectal cancer is the second leading cause of cancer death for both males and females in many parts of the industrialised world.

Catabolic Cellular Debris
...is toxic waste and results from the ongoing replenishment of cells in your body as tissue is built up (anabolism) or broken down (catabolism) as part of the body's usual life-preserving activities. There is a new 'you' being produced every seven years or so, and Your Inestimable You-Ness can only be manufactured from the nutrients with which you supply your body. If you want to have the body of Aphrodite or Zeus, then supply your body with first-class Olympian (raw material) nutrition and assist it in ridding itself of the old bricks and mortar. If however you don't want to make the effort, then expect to look like Bacchus (does the body of Mars come from eating same?). It has been estimated that old cells are being replaced by new cells at the rate of three hundred to eight hundred billion a day. I don't know. I didn't do the counting. Harvey Diamond explains metabolic imbalance:

"Old cells are toxic (poisonous) and must be removed from your system as soon as possible by one of four channels of elimination: bowels, bladder, lungs and skin. This is a normal, natural process of the body and is not something with which to concern yourself, unless for some

368

reason this toxic waste material is not eliminated at the same rate that it is being produced. As long as there is a sufficient amount of energy at the body's disposal, this waste is eliminated properly.

The second way toxaemia is produced in the system is from the by-products of foods that are not properly digested, assimilated and incorporated into cell structure. As far as your weight is concerned, common sense will tell you that if more of this toxic waste is built than is eliminated, there is going to be a build-up of the excess. This translates as 'overweight'. Adding to the problem, toxins are of an acid nature. When there is an acid build-up in the body, the system retains water to neutralize it, adding even more weight and bloat."[589]

Metabolic imbalance thus occurs when your body is producing more waste than it is eliminating. This waste is acid. The body tries to use retained water and minerals, such as sodium, magnesium, boron, calcium, iron and potassium, to render the system a harmless, slightly alkaline pH (7.4). Minerals, such as calcium and boron, are often leached from the skeleton, eventually resulting in weakened bone structure, poor teeth and a breakdown in cartilage and connective tissue. These problems will invariably lead to osteoporosis and the various forms of arthritis. A heavy animal products consumer can lose up to 90–100mg of calcium a day as the body tries to maintain a healthy alkali balance.

How do we know if we are toxic and acidic? Below are some of the indicators:

> ➢ A constant feeling of sluggishness and being 'off-colour'.
> ➢ Chronic tiredness or chronic fatigue syndrome
> ➢ A susceptibility to infections, colds and flu
> ➢ Stomach and digestive problems
> ➢ Bad breath unrelated to dental problems
> ➢ Body odour that persists after bathing
> ➢ A coated tongue in the morning
> ➢ Poor wound healing
> ➢ Aches and pains or the start of rheumatoid arthritis
> ➢ Suffering from a degenerative disease

---

[589] Diamond, Harvey, ibid. p.30

ENVIRONMENTAL TOXINS

The last category of waste products that concerns us here are general environmental toxins we looked at earlier. These will include chemicals in personal care and household items that are absorbed through the skin and the mouth, which cumulatively collect in our tissues and organs. Other toxins will be tar, nicotine and other poisons from cigarettes, alcohol metabolites from social drinks, drug residues, both pharmaceutical and recreational, vaccination toxins such as formaldehyde, air pollutants, water pollutants, such as fluoride compounds, chlorine, lead, copper and aluminium, food pollutants such as chemicals, drugs and hormones fed to animals we later eat, cosmic radiation, terrestrial radiation, environmental radiation and chemical residues and hormonal anabolics absorbed through our skin by the man-made products we touch and use.

These toxins are naturally missing from the environments of those cultures traditionally living long lives. This does not mean we are doomed to die early because we live in a chemical junkyard of a society; it means we have to be ever mindful of ensuring that we rid toxins out of our environment, use safe products free of these chemical problems, and see that the garbage gets put on the Elimination Truck every day when it comes a-calling. At the moment, Garbage Elimination, Inc. for most of us isn't calling at all.

OPTIMISING THE ENERGY SYSTEM

The body expends a great deal of energy processing food and detoxifying compounds, so the human body is essentially an energy system that needs to be calibrated efficiently. You can give your body an easy time with digestion by properly combining foods (in which case you free up loads of energy for detoxification duties), or you can be a beast to it and slap together all manner of gut-warping culinary treasons. The body, you'll be pleased to hear, is self-calibrating, but this calibration can easily get thrown out of the window if we decide to write our own computer program on how the body should run, and consume junk foods and stimulants.

Hopefully you are now beginning to appreciate how important an efficient, undisturbed Elimination (Detoxification) Cycle is, and why it is essential that the body conserves its energy for carrying out this life-saving and longevity-preserving function.

Your greatest weapon in assisting the body to cleanse itself centres around...

THE CORRECT CONSUMPTION OF FRUIT

At the heart of Natural Hygiene is the science of energy. The great news is that you can manipulate your body's energy usage very simply by the sort of food you consume, and you can start right now. As we have already seen, to assist the body in eliminating toxins and waste during its morning cycle EVERY DAY, the idea is not to introduce anything during the Elimination Cycle that will divert the body from doing its life-saving housework. No traditional breakfasts please. No Aunt Lily's Arkansas Pancakes. No grits or muesli. No British Heart-Attack-on-a-Plate, with the fried eggs, fried bread, sausages, tomatoes, and bacon. The problem is, many folks are culturally prepared to eat a herd of wildebeest in the morning, since it was hammered into us by our obese grannies time and time again that a healthy, farm-fresh breakfast was essential to our optimum welfare. Unfortunately this dangerous rubbish which our grannies fervently believed and took to their eventually failing hearts, is why many of them remained the size they did, up until they died of a toxin-related, food-abuse disease, such as coronary heart disease, stroke or cancer.

If you want the Queen's telegram, and wish to achieve a happy and healthy longevity, bouncing your great-granddaughter upon your firm and functioning knee, then you must admit you aren't going to make it with the West's current food *modus operandi*. The frightening legacy this dietary treachery will give you will be a heart attack, cancer, and the other nightmares we are currently experiencing. If you want to live to be a healthy hundred, find those who routinely live to these ages, and do what they do.[590]

Organic fruit is your man. Clean, light and more mobile than an SAS infiltration unit. Fruit digests in the intestinal tract, not the stomach, and charges through your system in 30 minutes. Fruit contains the monosaccharide sugar fructose, which is completely metabolised and converted to blood glucose, the energy form the body uses to sustain its life-systems. Your brain runs on nothing but glucose, and fruit is your most efficient source of this essential blood sugar. Besides, blood sugar levels rise and normalise after adequate fruit consumption, meaning that your hunger switch is turned off and you eat less food.

---

[590] For a fuller explanation on the various issues surrounding longevity, see *Health Wars*.

Fruit (uncontaminated with pesticides, of course), is rich in hard-working enzymes, vitamins, amino acids, minerals and fibre and is an extremely low-taxing amino acid source in the morning, which makes it ideal for breakfast. And what do amino acids build? That's right. *Proper human proteins.* Fruit is alluring with its shapes and colours, has the most exotic tastes, and is loved by almost everybody. Those few who hate fruit are usually addicted to heavy, processed foods, which they indiscriminately combine with fruit into an apocalyptic jam-preserve, which will produce fermentation, putrefaction, acid residues and the resultant graveyard gas and corpse-like breath. Fruit should always be consumed on an empty stomach *combined with no other foods.* And don't worry about those few days of loose bowels. There is no fever accompanying them. Witness your body having a good clear-out.

Fruits can be described as the perfect food because humans have been found in the past to survive indefinitely on them, all the nutrients required for life being found in a diet of varied fruits which grow on six out of the seven continents on Earth. Within the past seventy years however, commercially grown fruit, cereals and vegetables have lost a significant part of their mineral content due to over-farming.[591] This deficiency can be easily and simply remedied using mineral and antioxidant supplementation, which shall be discussed later.

Here are the Ten Fruit Commandments. Tattoo them on your cookie jar:

> - *Eat fruit <u>on an empty stomach</u> any time during the day*
> - *Always leave 30 minutes after fruit consumption before eating foods other than fruit*
> - *Leave at least 3 hours after a properly combined meal before consuming fruit. This allows the previous meal to leave the stomach and avoids putrefaction and fermentation*
> - *Before noon, consume only fruit*
> - *Never combine fruit with any other foods*
> - *Never eat fruit AFTER a meal as a dessert*
> - *Steer clear of bananas, avocados and dates in the morning. These can be eaten, properly combined, during the Appropriation Cycle, after noon*

---

[591] McCance & Widdowson, "The chemical composition of foods", special report series no. 235/297, Medical Research Council, & MAFF, 1940, 1946, 1960, 1976 & 1991

> *If you get hungry during the morning, eat another piece of fruit and keep munching until the blood sugar levels normalise and your hunger abates*
> *Eat organic fruit only where possible*
> *Do not eat processed, canned or cooked fruit, which normally contain sugars, e-additives and other aliens*

Fruit is the perfect food when eaten on its own. Although sometimes described as an acid, malic acid from apples, for example, actually yields an alkali ash in the body, unless it is combined with other foods, whereupon the usual acid gunk is produced. During the morning Elimination Cycle, fruit is invaluable in assisting in detoxification and the elimination of toxins. The fruit consumer, properly following the above rules, will experience a rapid return of energy, a steady and satisfying weight-loss, and an overall feeling of health and well-being, as these nutrients use the vital juices of fruit to gain instant access to the energy processes of the body. All these benefits just from consuming fruit the right way? YES!! And we haven't even looked at the *really* good tools yet.

If fruit is eaten with, or even after other foods, problems will, more often than not, result. This is because the Fruit Express is trying to get through to its destination quickly, and its clear path is blocked by a Chicken Fried Rice Goods Train lumbering through the colon at walking speed. The resultant wincing collision causes the liquefied fruit juices to combine with China's finest and this fruity morass in your stomach will begin to spoil. Proteins in the chicken putrefy and the rice carbohydrates ferment, resulting in the usual problems. Culturally we have come to view fruit as a dessert, which is nutritional heresy, in that fruit will always charge down the tunnel before hitting the back end of the Beef Risotto you chose to wolf down half an hour earlier. Once again, fruit should always be consumed on an empty stomach for happy smiles and care-free miles.

WATER

The other important consideration is water. Lots of it. The body needs in excess of four pints of water daily (2 litres). Water is used by the body for digestion, detoxifying cells, watering the lungs, keeping the body alkalised and a host of cleaning duties. Water expert Dr Fereydoon Batmanghelidj maintains that asthmas, allergies, diabetes, arthritis, angina, stomach upsets, chronic intestinal complaints and certain other degenerative illnesses are the body's many cries for water, complaints which are dramatically improved with a consistent, long-term intake of fresh, clean water.[592] Dr Batman's best-selling book has helped thousands quash long-term health problems effortlessly and inexpensively. Coffee, tea, sodas, beer and a host of other liquids do not qualify as 'clean, fresh water' for the body, and should not be consumed by any patients experiencing a degenerative condition. Many of these are diuretic (water expelling) in their effect because of their chemical compositions.

Cancer patients especially should be consuming 4 pints of water a day[593] as part of their intake of vital nutrients, provided they do not have any renal (kidney) damage or disease that will cause complications with urine production resulting from the intake of additional water. Flushing the body with CONSISTENT, long-term water consumption is a superb way to assist with detoxification and hydration and is especially important for patients diagnosed with a 'mental illness'. Drink a glass half an hour before a meal and then two glasses around two and a half hours afterwards for optimal digestive effects. The remainder of the day's intake of water can occur throughout the day.

THE CONCEPT OF HIGH WATER-CONTENT FOOD
The greatest tool in Natural Hygiene is to rearrange your diet to include a high percentage of high water-content, whole living, organic, alkali-forming foods in addition to the water you drink. Items like vegetables and fruits contain very high levels of water. A water melon for instance is 98% water. In a perfect world, this fruit water would be bowing under the weight of minerals and vitamins from the soils in which it was grown, and also laced with other nutrients. A significant portion of this mineral content is now missing from the food chain because soils are not currently being replenished with the minerals stripped out of them by successively grown crops. And so supplementation of vitamins and minerals in their correct form must be carried out by us citizens in order to avoid a gradual and deadly mineral deficiency building up to strike us down with disease.

Natural Hygiene is all about keeping the body in balance nutritionally, metabolically, and also constantly replenished with water. 70% of our planet's surface is water, our bodies are 70%-75% water, so it makes sense to eat a diet consisting of at least 75% water-based foods that have not

---

[592] Batmanghelidj, F, *Your Body's Many Cries For Water*, Tagman Press, 2001

[593] A carbon filter attached to a tap/faucet is adequate for producing chlorine- and soluent-free water to drink. This is preferable to plastic-bottled water which can be contaminated with chemicals from the plastic. Water in glass bottles is fine.

been processed and had the water and much of the accompanying nutrients stripped out.

Water is essential to life. On a cellular level, water is used by the body to transport nutrients to the organs and remove the waste products we examined earlier. Our blood comprises a very high percentage of water (blood serum), which the body naturally wishes to replace regularly. The difference between drinking water and fruit and vegetable water is in the nutrient content. Naturally a body fed on a diet comprising 80% unrefined plant dietary (unadulterated, high-fibre, organic fruit and vegetables) is a body being saturated in water-borne nutrition that is instantly and highly bio-available. A body well-watered in this way is a body whose three digestion cycles, APPROPRIATION, ASSIMILATION and ELIMINATION work with consummate ease. A well-watered body is a body which can clean itself on the inside with more precision than a laser.

But we don't eat this way today. Our societies are sick, obese, acidic, feeble, oxygen-starved, dehydrated, disease-ridden, pharmaceutically poisoned havens for mischief. There we are, showering our external bits squeaky-clean every morning with the cheapest chemicals available at the most expensive salon prices, and yet no cleaning is ever done on the insides of our bodies. That is why we are dropping dead of cancer and a whole host of other problems. We don't allow the body to cleanse and properly nourish itself on the inside and even if we do, we don't give it the water it needs to carry out the job. Why? Because the average Western diet we will consume today primarily comprises concentrated and processed foods – *foods which have had the water content stripped out of them*. We eat these foods because we have had the mother-of-all-selling-jobs done on us by Big Food who have sold us on taste. Actually a human doesn't need much selling on taste, but *"...boy, have we've got the taste for sugar, chocolate, and a range of refined foods now, baby!"* as Ted Turner would undoubtedly say. And these have led us, like the Peptic Pied Piper, away from sanity and health, and down the broad path that leads to destruction. The good news? Your body is made in such a way that if you just stop doing bad things to it, it often recovers and becomes healthy and energetic all by itself.

Acid and Alkali Ashes

Q: If we're so rich and smart, how come we're so sick and tired?

A: Because our bodies in the Western world are in a constant state of acid siege.

Dr Ted Morter Jr. has spent a lifetime analysing the effects different foods have on our internal environment. Morter states that the body responds perfectly to every stimulus that is applied to it and each of these body responses is geared towards one aim and one aim only - survival. Sometimes this response is termed 'disease', if it goes against our ideal of what 'health' should be. Morter confirms the fact that the human body likes to dwell in a slight alkali (around pH 7.4). When we acidify our internal environment with certain types of food, the body is forced to neutralise, or 'buffer' this acid using a number of ingenious systems, mostly comprising alkalising minerals, such as sodium, calcium, potassium, magnesium and iron. Urine pH is a great indicator of what is happening inside the body and varies according to how much excess protein is consumed and has to be 'buffered' (neutralised). Note that blood pH must ALWAYS be between 7.35 and 7.45, or else life ends abruptly within a matter of hours.[594]

Foods we eat leave an 'ash' in our system. Rather than the dry flaky stuff that gets all over the carpet when we blow on an old fire, food residues in the body can be solid or liquid, but the 'ash', or residue they leave can either be acid or alkali (and, on the odd occasion, neutral). The main acid generators are proteins, whether derived from animal or other sources. The key problem of course is the high level of proteins humans have been persuaded to eat today.

THE DANGERS OF EXCESSIVE PROTEIN

There is nothing wrong with protein. The body needs it, and we'd all be in a disaster situation without it. But, once again, the human body does not need anywhere near the level most have been conned into consuming. By the way, notice that the main acid-ash-producing foods are all backed by tremendously powerful and wealthy food lobbies with huge advertising budgets – i.e. meat, sugar, grains, coffee and tea, dairy... and yes, even

---

[594] Natural (physiological) acid produced through normal cell respiration is easily expelled in the breath via the lungs. Our blood pH is normally 7.35 when it is carting this acid, in the form of carbon dioxide, to the lungs for elimination. Blood is pH 7.45 after it has been 'cleaned up', the CO_2 removed, and then oxygen is taken on to deliver to your heart and the rest of your body.

orange juice! A quick survey of the TV content of one evening will give you a picture of how many advertising dollars go into persuading the public to become acidic. Where's the alkali lobby for fruits and veggies? There's no big money in these foods in comparison to the previous list, so there is no lobby.

The protein levels most of us eat today are many times greater than the body actually needs (between 20-40g a day are the estimated requirements) and the excess we consume can quite literally kill us. Some of us are slogging down up to 10 times the body's protein requirements and more, in our efforts to consume the hindquarters of three rhinos and drink a swimming pool full of milk with our grain 'cereals' laced with refined sugar every morning. How our systems eventually exhaust themselves and collapse with all the acid generated is a book all on its own. But for our purposes here, the key is to understand the effects of excess protein consumption and how the body tries to deal with it. When the digestive system is hit with a storm of acid derived from excessive protein food metabolism, this acid is potentially lethal and our hard-working body needs to sort the problem in a hurry.

Firstly the brain mobilises mineral buffers to raise the acidic pH of our internal environment towards neutral in an effort to counteract the protein acids.[595] After munching down burgers, chicken, eggs, pasta, cheese, seafood, grains – all accompanied by the inevitable acid-producing coffee, tea, sodas and alcohol, the mineral buffers use alkalising minerals and water to combine with the acid generated by these food ashes to raise their pH, before escorting them out of the body via the kidneys. Notice the body loses these alkalising minerals when they are eliminated along with the acid.

THE AMMONIA BUFFER
More often than not, the mineral buffers alone are not strong enough to render the internal environment a sufficient alkali not to hurt or even damage the kidneys. Fortunately the body has several back-up systems. The one we're interested in is the ammonia buffer. The kidneys begin producing ammonia, a strong alkali (pH around 9.25), which dramatically raises the pH of the excreta, sometimes as high as pH 8.5. Some people will notice that their urine smells of ammonia, and urinating can even hurt, due to the caustic nature of the solution being squirted out. Hence

---

[595] The pH (potential of hydrogen) scale is exponential and runs between 0 for extreme acid and 14 for extreme alkali. 7 is neutral.

the need for our old friend, cranberry juice – an acid – which will then normalise the solution and eliminate the pain (there must be an easier way than all this).

A strong smell of ammonia in the urine may indicate that the body's reserves of alkalising minerals are severely depleted. The body of course can mobilise further supplies of alkalising minerals like calcium, boron, sodium and magnesium, but you won't be happy with where it takes them from (calcium from the bones, etc.). A chronically acidic environment over many years will cause a severe depletion of minerals from the body, resulting in dangers of kidney exhaustion (too much ammonia production and acid damage), osteoporosis, mineral deficiency diseases, and then the auto-immune problems brought on by excess acid lodged in the joints and cartilage, such as arthritis and a host of other complaints.[596] Notice that the body is amoral in this regard. It's just trying to survive what you are doing to it. Morter sums up the body's attitude very succinctly:

"Your body doesn't care if you are sick or healthy. It doesn't plan for the future. Your body doesn't think and it doesn't judge. It doesn't care if you are hurting or if you are happy. All it does is respond to survive. Your body makes thousands of perfect survival responses every instant of your life. You may like the results of these responses and call it 'health'. Or you may not like the results and call it 'ill-health'. Your body doesn't care whether you like the responses or not. Survival of this instant is your body's only goal. Not survival later today, or next week, or next year. Survival now. Your body was designed to survive. It wasn't designed to be sick or well. What it is will be the accumulation of stresses that have been imposed upon it."[597]

Osteoporosis, heart disease, cancer, arthritis, diabetes and a host of the ailments we have been examining in this book <u>can all be traced to the body's attempts to survive</u>. They can also all be traced to an inherent deficiency in the raw materials (vitamins and minerals) required to get the survival job done, food allergies, chaotic blood sugar, toxins and drug damage. The body doesn't care whether you like the results of its survival efforts or not. When you eat, drink, breathe, exercise, rest and think, you elicit a response from your body. So 'health' and 'disease' can be termed

---

[596] Kidney dialysis is used when the kidneys can no longer filter out waste products from the body. Without dialysis for damaged kidneys, the body would become overwhelmed with acid and soon die.
[597] Morter, M T, *An Apple a Day?* BEST Research, Inc. 1997

effects of your body's responses. Diarrhoea, vomiting, colds, flu, arthritis, osteoporosis, diabetes and a host of the mental problems we have been examining may not be anyone's idea of a good time, but these dramatic conditions are the result of the body's response to a stimulus. As Morter says, if you don't like the body's response, change the stimulus.

ACIDOSIS

With this in mind, we can begin to join a few dots. If the body likes to be a slight alkali, and we are eating extremely acidic (processed), malnourished diets because we are told to by our TV, our body's response will be to buffer the resultant acidic gunk and excrete it rapidly. There are many 'diseases', or body responses, that can be evident from the body accomplishing these actions. Heartburn (acid reflux), indigestion, diarrhoea, mineral loss, resulting in mineral deficiency diseases. Calcium loss diseases, magnesium loss diseases, and so on.

And then, because we are chronically dehydrated because we don't drink water and eat high-water content food any more (that's all gone out of fashion), we are plagued by water deficiency ailments, such as constipation, asthma, heartburn, colitis and more ailments than I've got time to write down for you. In addition, your cells really don't go a bundle on being chronically bathed in acid, either inside or outside the cell environment, so there is a potassium buffer response within your cells to raise the pH of your intercellular environment. Cells break down as part of the life and death processes going on in your body all the time, so they add their catabolic acid to the sludge of the fast food nightmare. Now your brain is forced to order the kidneys to excrete more ammonia to alkalise the excreta before the latter's acid begins burning up the delicate tissues of the kidneys, urethra and other components.

By this time, we've normally managed to scoot down to the doctor's waiting room where we can expect to get drugs, which will 'make us feel better' (they treat the symptoms – not cure the underlying cause). GPs are generally unaware of the alkali/acid struggle going on with many diseases, and they are certainly unaware of the nutrition causation, because most of them haven't been trained in nutrition. Drugs given to a patient will themselves elicit their own responses from the body (side-effects), almost all of which will be acidic. High sugar sodas will fool our body into producing acids in preparation to digest a meal that never arrives, so there is even more acid flying around.

Clinical urine analysis is always useful in providing an indicator of what is going on in the body. When I was living in Los Angeles, there was a big thing going on in the tabloids about how freelance reporters were going through the trash of the stars who lived in Beverly Hills and on Mulholland Drive in order to find material for a 'good' story. While I do not condone this sort of parasitic behaviour in the least, going through your body's own trash, using a urine analysis and pH test, yields a lot of useful information. You can learn a lot from the things your body throws away.

A lot of people like to get technical over these issues. They measure protein grams, they measure urine pH, they put themselves through all kinds of strictures, which to me destroy the fun of life. My take is this: simply recognise the signs your body provides that your internal environment is acidic and begin moving it towards alkali by consuming a diet that is 80% alkali-ash-producing foods and 20% acidic. Notice from the lists at the back of the book that almost all fruits and veg are alkali-ash-producing, *and yet many are acidic going in*. Even a humble pear will register pH5.5, and yet pears, along with the malic acid in apples, *have an alkalising effect on the body*. Thus fruits and veggies are the best alkalising tools on the market, containing as they do all the essential minerals the body requires to set up its intricate buffer systems. If your tongue or mouth hurts when you consume fruit, this may be an indicator of how acidic your body is, *before* you begin to do something about it. Start to change your diet gradually using raw-blended or lightly steamed, crunchy vegetables, and your body will appreciate you for your care and gradual education.

ALKALI BODIES ABSORB OXYGEN

Dr Otto Warburg, who received a Nobel Prize in the 1930's, noted that alkaline bodies absorbed up to 20 times more oxygen than acidic bodies. He found that diseased bodies were acidic bodies which repelled oxygen. Conversely he discovered that alkaline bodies are healthy bodies, with a high absorption of life-preserving oxygen. And today, those cultures living long life-spans all have alkalised body systems. The Okinawans, for instance, renowned for their longevity and health, live on their southern Japanese island, which is made predominantly of calcium compounds (coral reef). The water these Japanese citizens consume has been found to contain, per quart, 8,300 mg of dissolved (ionised) calcium and 9,700 mg of non-ionised, non-dissolved calcium for a total of 18 grams of calcium in its various forms. And the Okinawans drink 4/5 quarts a day, and then irrigate their farm soils with it! Researcher Robert Barefoot, who has made a study of the Okinawans, states that by the time he added it up, the Okinawans were getting over 100,000 mg (100g) of calcium in various forms a day and probably violating the RDA over hundredfold for every mineral and vitamin.[598] Yet we are told the RDA for calcium is a miserable 600-1,000mg a day.

When Otto Warburg explained his exciting acid/alkali conclusions to his medical peers over half a century ago, they threatened to revoke his medical licence. Yet experiments with ulcerated breast mass and other tumour material show categorically that malignant cells grow prolifically in acid, anaerobic environments, but shrivel and die in calcium- and oxygen-rich alkalis.[599]

CARL REICH

Dr Carl Reich, noted nutritional research pioneer, demonstrated that Vitamin D was crucial to the absorption of calcium, and that modern man, in addition to being chronically deficient in ionised calcium, also dwelt mostly under artificial light and was not getting enough interaction of full-spectrum sunlight on the cholesterol in his skin to produce abundant Vitamin D through photosynthesis. Artificial light over prolonged periods can abruptly affect mood.[600]

Dr Reich found that when a patient has adequate levels of ionised calcium, his saliva pH range was slightly alkaline at 7.5 to 7.0 (neutral). Body excretions tended to be acidic as the body rids itself of toxins and waste in the ideal way. However, when the body was calcium-deficient, the saliva pH range tended to be acidic, from 6.4 to 4.6, and the body excretions were now alkaline, as the body attempted to mobilise calcium and water to rectify the acid/alkaline balance. Dr James K van Fleet states: *"When the body does not get enough calcium, it will withdraw what little calcium it has from the bones to make sure there is enough in the bloodstream, then the body does its best to bolster the sagging architecture by building bony deposits and spurs to reduce movement and limit activity."* [601] Notice that this is another survival response. Once

---

[598] Barefoot, Robert R, *The Calcium Factor*, an audio briefing. Available at www.exxelaudio.com; also *The Calcium Factor*, published by Deonna Enterprises Publishing, PO Box 21270, Wickenburg, AZ, 85358, USA

[599] Barefoot, Robert, op. cit.

[600] Index 'sunlight' and 'depression'

[601] Van Fleet, J K, *Magic of Catalytic Health Vitalizers*, Parker Publishing, 1980

again, your body does not care whether you hurt or not, it is simply exercising damage control due to an extreme threat situation.

Osteoporosis, arthritis, rheumatism, sclerosis and periodontal disease are all the body's way, not of exhibiting 'disease', but of discouraging and preventing unnecessary movement during a raging mineral deficiency. Calcium lactates, along with magnesium and Vitamin D, are the sure way to help these symptoms, together with a change of lifestyle and diet.

Alkalising the body in children can happen within days with food and supplements. Adults take much longer, sometimes months, and the elderly may take up to a year to start rendering an alkaline result on the saliva test. The good news is, they will be moving in the right direction if they make some dietary and lifestyle changes for the better.

Want to live to be a healthy hundred? Then find someone who is a healthy hundred, like the Hunzas, and do what they do.[602] Diets low in meat and milk, but rich in 80-85% unrefined plant dietary and alkali ash foods, along with full trace mineral supplementation (including calcium/magnesium/ Vitamin D) are diets rich in mineral-saturated, high-water-content *alkalising* foods that will start combating unnecessary dietary acids and start shifting your body's pH values towards health and longevity – it's as simple as that.

It is interesting and poignant to note that the observations outlined in this chapter were encountered over 50 years ago and yet, today, modern disease research still refuses to make nutrition and body acid/alkali a firm priority. Notice the comments made in 1967 by Corinne H Robinson in *Normal and Therapeutic Nutrition*:

"Because the body makes [pH] *adjustments in the regulation of body neutrality, the reaction of the diet is of no practical significance in health.... Those who become concerned about the relative acid or alkalinity of foods have often been misled by false advertising claims of the food quack."* [603]

---

[602] Day, Phillip, *Health Wars*, op. cit.

[603] Robinson, C H, *Normal and Therapeutic Nutrition*, 13th ed. New York: MacMillan & Co., 1967, p.131

If I really had the time, I would find out what Ms Robinson's 'special interests' were when she wrote those words. Never mind. We can't straighten the world out all in one day. ☺

Your Past Does Not Equal Your Future
(Some great mental and physical tips)

We have looked at a tremendous spectrum of subjects so far which affect the way a person feels and looks at the world. In this chapter, I would like to give you some great ideas for turning corners and attracting more happiness and contentment into your life. And what are happiness and contentment, if not knowing where you fit into the greater scheme of things and being able to maintain the all-important *balance*. Put simply, where are you on my famous motivation scale (0-10)? Are you having a good life? Are you winning the human race? Is this really the future you ordered?

THE MOTIVATION SCALE
0 - I am dead. No longer breathing. I am beyond human help.

1-4 – I suffer from abject depression. I cannot take action. I am listless, suicidal, physically unfit/unwell. No one understands me. The world is going to hell in a hand-basket. I am often medicated and sedated. I have bad dreams. I have to take drugs to maintain any semblance of normality. Why do I even bother breathing? My parents/wife/husband do not understand me. I eat junk food and watch disturbing, demonic programs on TV. I have no belief in any future existence beyond my own life. I just don't know where I fit in. I am tormented, demonised and just want all the pain to end. I...er... oh, it doesn't matter.

5-7 – My existence and life bore me. I cannot be bothered with most activities over and above doing those things that are necessary for my survival. I am apathetic. I walk around looking at others and wondering what planet they're from. I hate my boss. I dislike my job. I am non-productive and constantly moan. I'm frequently/permanently broke. I don't often travel and have never enjoyed going abroad. Besides, everyone's a hypocrite, especially foreigners, the church, politicians and those who think they have the answer to what ails me. What's the point in looking after yourself? No one gets out alive anyway. Yes, I use stimulants, cigarettes, alcohol and drugs. DO YOU HAVE A PROBLEM WITH THAT? OK, so I'm hostile and often violent. It's how you have to be to get by. Yes, I'm frustrated. I hate people who have more than I do. I'm probably better off dead.

8-9 – OK. All this makes sense to me. Show me what to do and I'll get busy. Life is good. I am curious and interested about things. I like to research and discover new ways to do good. People say I am pleasant to be around. I am productive. I like helping others. Yes, I have upsets, rainy days and trials in my life, but, hey, that's the human condition, isn't it? I know that if I can change myself and the people around me, then I am doing my part to make the world a better place. I am optimistic, confident, financially solvent, and have a great relationship. What happens when I die? I'm not really sure, but I am trusting in something good. If I get discouraged and depressed, I soon pull myself out of it. I am physically fit and like to take care of myself.

10 – I am on a mission to help others. I can honestly say I am the happiest now that I have ever been. I understand something of the world and my place in it, and have travelled extensively. I have balance and an appreciation for others with whom I share this planet. I know I am only on Earth for a short while, so I am going to act and live in a way that reflects credit upon my existence. I know there are bad things happening in the world, but I am determined to keep active in helping others, because, in so doing, I achieve a comforting sense of peace and tranquillity.

It is my opinion that the universe is conspiring to do me good. I believe that this life is but a foretaste of something marvellous to come. I don't fear death. Why should anyone threaten me with heaven? I strive to exercise those virtues that others can look up to. I make mistakes, but constantly learn from them. I know I can never be perfect, but have a sense that I am being honed and refined for something in my future. Earth is the School of Hard Knocks, and experience, which I am amassing, is what you get when you didn't get what you wanted. I know I can never be perfect, but am willing to strive for excellence. I am a work constantly in motion. I have no regrets. I am in the world, but not *of* the world. On this incredible journey called life, I am passing through to some ultimate destination. I cannot wait to get there and experience my destiny.

Which one applies to you?

CHANGING STATES

While we are alive, we experience *states*. These are emotional conditions that determine our mood or outlook on life. The mistake of many is to manipulate their states in an incorrect or temporary fashion to move out of conditions that frustrate and depress them. Coffee, tea, and stimulants such as sugar, drugs and adrenalin highs are all used to achieve *changes in state*. These are never permanent or long-lasting, and the resultant *loss of any state we gain* vexes us. We experience a negative shift in mood, so we seek to regain the high. This is the classic addiction profile.

What everyone ultimately strives for is a *state*. An emotion. Physical possessions are a means of achieving these states. Ask any fifteen-year-old girl in the Western world what, out of all the things on Earth, they would have, and most would say *"Brad Pitt!"* And yet Brad, like all humans, is nothing but several yards of intestines, a squashy brain, lots of gooey red stuff and all the vices common to the human condition. What the girl wants is the *state* she believes she will experience from owning Brad Pitt. The satisfying feeling of jealous girlfriends, a beautiful man and the social status among her peers of being seen with one of the most unavailable but desirable men on the planet.

A seventeen-year-old male would probably want a Ferrari. But notice that a Ferrari is nothing but metal, glass, rubber, smelly oil and a bunch of electrical wiring. This boy wants what he believes the Ferrari will do for him. He is striving for an ultimate *state*.

We are satisfied when we achieve a state that brings us balance and equilibrium. Think of the days when the sun is shining and all's well with the world. All religions, including humanism, seek to equip us with the tools for achieving this balanced state, in which we are, to coin the cliché, 'at one with the world'. All belief systems, to be successful, must offer answers to the four most fundamental questions of the human condition:

- ➢ Who am I?
- ➢ How did I get here?
- ➢ What am I supposed to do here?
- ➢ Where am I going when this life is over?

Leading motivational trainer and businessman Brian Tracy believes: *"To be truly happy, you need a clear sense of direction. You need a commitment to something bigger and more important than yourself. You need to feel that your life stands for something, that you are somehow making a valuable contribution to your world."*[604]

Much misery comes from not possessing any sort of answers to the above. Unhappiness is not being able to accept or forgive ourselves for who we are or what we have done or become. And yet, world-renowned behavioural expert Anthony Robbins triumphantly declares: *"Your past does not equal your future!"*

---

[604] Tracy, Brian, *Maximum Achievement*, Simon & Schuster, New York: 1993, p.29

Just because we were broke yesterday, does not mean the future holds the same. Just because we had cancer, depression, schizophrenia or heart disease last week, does not mean we have to suffer these things in our future. Robbins and Tracy declare our future moveable; that life is uniquely an experience during which we must learn to become masters of our own destiny. The fact is, no-one can do it for us. The purpose of life is to survive, grow and learn. To do this, we must take control over our decision-making processes and destiny. We must take action. This takes a quality known as *personal initiative.*

There are several ways to force a change of state without resorting to chemicals and food. The first is to alter your body language. Those who are depressed have body language which suits depression. If you are depressed, practise straightening your body and pacing around the room with a sense of purpose. Fix yourself in the mirror with an irresistible and handsome smile. If you change your body language, your state will invariably move in the same direction.

Changing your attitude, or angle of attack, is the second method. This is altering your mental body language and has the same effect as the first point above. Removing negative stimuli from your life, such as newspapers, gloomy friends and other baleful influences, will cause a state change all on its own.

GOAL-SETTING AND THE 'WELCOME STATE'
Goals are destinations on a road-map. They can be very modest or epoch-shaping. The correct goals benefit not only yourself but others. Negative people develop goals that will enslave others, enrich themselves and grant the ability to control and manipulate their environment. Thus they achieve a *state*. Hitler ate two boxes of chocolates and invaded Russia the following morning. At the time, Russia was nothing but pot-holed roads, lean dogs, unfortunate-looking automobiles and angry Bolsheviks. Did Hitler really want Russia and the world for their own sakes, or was Hitler not striving for the ultimate, EMOTIONAL *state*?

Setting goals and achieving them brings self-worth, confidence and *the welcome state*. The welcome state is one in which the person sees no threat to their survival currently on the radar screens. They experience peace because they know that taking their own action has a long history of achieving survival and stability. Therefore they feel 'in control' and masters of their own destiny.

SURVIVAL – THE MOST DOMINANT HUMAN DYNAMIC

Your organism is constantly striving to survive, both physically and mentally. Threats to the organism's survival will trigger a survival state, which will be experienced with all the concomitant, UNCOMFORTABLE emotions of frustration, anger, unhappiness, or, in the case of a physical threat, pain and somatic symptoms. *The purpose of this survival state is to goad you, using its uncomfortable emotions or physical pain, into taking action to resolve the threat*. Notice that when you begin to take action to resolve the threat, those uncomfortable emotions diminish. You gain a sense of purpose and direction.

There is nothing wrong with experiencing negative emotions, if we understand that these are designed to spur us into *taking action*. Frustration at being perpetually short of money is designed to goad us into designing a vehicle which will propel us out of hardship, which is a threat to our survival. Taking no action to resolve the survival threat, as a result of experiencing these negative emotions or pain, guarantees the continuing survival threat to the organism and its likely extinction. Simply changing our state with stimulants, tranquillisers, food or drink will not remove the original threat our brain has detected.

TAKING ACTION

Consider that if we are experiencing physical or emotional pain, our brain has perceived that there is a survival threat and is warning us of it. Our brain or body wants us to take action. To do this, we must

> ➢ Identify the nature of the survival threat
> ➢ Identify the course of action which will guarantee the removal of the survival threat
> ➢ Take this action CONSISTENTLY.

The purpose of this book, and others I have written, indeed the goal of my organisation, is to provide information that can help us

> ➢ Identify the nature of the survival threat
> ➢ Identify the course of action which will guarantee the removal of the survival threat
> ➢ Take this action CONSISTENTLY.

The implementation of the remedy is something the individual must carry out. *No-one can do this for us*. Many organisations around the world, which deal with behavioural issues, are devoted to educating others on how to take action consistently. All successful and happy people know how to carry out the three tasks above, each time they receive a survival threat. The best business training courses in the world always teach the primary value of *taking action*.

EXERCISE – THE PHYSICAL
Taking action physically is also important. The science of Natural Hygiene promotes exercise to get oxygen into the system to encourage a dynamic circulation, elimination and mobility for your marvellous human machine. Quite simply, if you are doing good for your body, you will feel so darned fine, you will quit your job and begin promoting the Natural Hygiene lifestyle full-time like the dedicated nutritional evangelical you have become, for the rest of your extended happy days.

I love exercise, having lived in California for a number of years. But before you can come to terms with the need for it (exercise, not California), you have to see, like swimming, how far you will sink without regular movement. I am hardly a zealot with exercise, as many are, but I do my part and have developed a discipline over the years that has served me well, and I have been disease-free for the last seventeen years, not only as a result of exercise, but also thanks to the various factors covered in this book.

I have to say though, the one thing that impressed me most about Californians who lived healthy outdoor lives down in those beach communities like Malibu, Santa Monica, Playa del Rey and Redondo Beach, was that they actually enjoyed themselves, looked great and were living life to the full. Months later, I too was part of that euphoria that is healthy Southern California.

I was amazed when, as a pale Englander, I had first arrived in Los Angeles to see tanned and fit octogenarian men sailing by on roller-blades and vital, pretty ladies in their seventies playing volleyball on the sandy beaches before picking up their bikes and cycling along the famous bike-path to one of the great restaurants along Santa Monica Bay for a scrumptious chow-down, consisting of - you guessed it - platefuls of high-water-content, unrefined plant dietary. Certainly the many folks I spoke to were motivated, fit... *and happy!*

WORKING THE BODY
Exercising is something we all must do, because living things DO move, and the more they move, the more alive they feel. Look at a Jack

Russell puppy. It's bouncing off the walls with excitement and couldn't get into more drawers and mischief if you paid it (and no, it doesn't have ADHD). Inactivity is a relatively recent phenomenon with humans, ever since the abandonment of the horse and the advent of mass transport earlier in the 1900's. Many facets affecting health, like high meat and dairy consumption, drug abuse, environmental contamination and polluted food, water and air, are also quite new to us, and so are the health tragedies we are suffering as a result. It often helps to put these things in perspective. We haven't always done many of the things we do or don't do today. And with health and sickness, we are very much reaping the results of our activity or inactivity. Obesity is at an all-time high, as we examined earlier. Our convenience society, coupled with our new chemical junk diets and personal toxin fripperies, is, as they say where I'm from, doing us in. And exercise has all but gone out the window. Unhealthy people are *unhappy* people.

CONSISTENCY! CONSISTENCY! CONSISTENCY!

The key with exercise is don't overdo it, just work the muscles progressively and get cycling to raise a light sheen for a hour or so, and genteelly glow if you are a female. If you are a man, go ahead and sweat and stink all you want. Sweating's good, because the body is eliminating from the lymph massage with the exercise you are giving it. Do not use antiperspirants EVER AGAIN, as the aluminium and other compounds block up your lymph nodes, giving rise to major problems down the road when internal toxins can be driven back into the body, denied any means of escape and damage the lymph and breast. Remember, the idea is to get everything moving both inside and outside the body.

An ideal starting exercise regimen for 16- to 85-year-old kids is laid out below. Ensure no more than one minute's rest between the sets of any particular exercise, in order to prevent the body cooling down and to maintain the muscle stress. It is a good idea to work with the trainers available in the gyms to maximise the benefit of correct and safe techniques in exercising. But once you've got the techniques down, *"The sky's the limit, baby!"* as Ted Turner would undoubtedly say:

THE WEIGHT/CYCLING REGIMEN

15 minutes warming up with light cycling or rowing.
Barbell squats (3 sets x 15 repetitions (reps))
Bench press (3 sets x 15 reps)
Lat pull-downs (3 sets x 15 reps)
Seated rowing (3 sets x 15 reps)

Sit-ups (2 sets until muscle failure)
30 minutes light cycling to finish off, raising the sweat, sheen or glow.

NOTES:

**Before embarking on an exercise regimen of
any sort, it is advisable to consult your
health practitioner, especially if you suffer
from a serious illness.**

➤ Those over 65 should exercise, OF COURSE, but the gym you join will advise on how to ease into the regimen with the minimum of difficulty. Use gym instructors to design a custom program for you, if you do not know how to do this.

➤ Ensure that the weight used is enough to get your muscles failing at around the 15th repetition. The weight will then need to be increased to fail you at the 15th rep as you gain strength during the program.

➤ Exhale as you load the muscles with weight (the positive), inhale as you release the weight (the negative).

➤ The burn you feel in muscle exercise is the result of oxygen metabolism and is known as lactic acid. A few deep inhalations and the burn soon passes.

➤ On your days without weights, do some light cycling for 45 minutes in the gym. I always read while I am doing this, to make the time even more productive and take my mind off what I am doing. Walking doesn't get the heart rate up enough, although walking is great exercise over the long-haul. The idea is to raise the heart rate on a consistent basis to about 75% of your maximum during aerobic exercise. Heart monitors are often provided by the gym for such monitoring.

Do the weight exercises as early in the day as your schedule allows, three times a week, such as Mondays, Wednesdays and Fridays. The intermittent days, Tuesdays, Thursdays and Sundays, should be set aside for muscle recovery. So the week will typically look as follows:

MONDAY – WEIGHT/CYCLING REGIMEN
TUESDAY – 45 MINS CYCLING OR LAP SWIMMING
WEDNESDAY – WEIGHT/CYCLING REGIMEN
THURSDAY – 45 MINS CYCLING OR LAP SWIMMING
FRIDAY – WEIGHT/CYCLING REGIMEN
SATURDAY – 45 MINS CYCLING OR LAP SWIMMING
SUNDAY – A NICE WALK! BUT OTHERWISE OFF

Seems like a lot? Probably by today's standards. Yet a few hundred years ago, your ancestors cheerfully did comparably active workouts as part of their daily chores and thought nothing of it. How soft and lazy we have become.

Do the above regimen for four weeks during the Natural Hygiene program. After four weeks, expand the workout under advice from your qualified gym instructor to train specific muscle groups, if this is your wish. If you continue with these core exercises however, you will see great results. "Consistency! Consistency! Consistency!" over the next few months will reap enormous benefits in both physical and mental well-being.

Ladies: Do not fear 'becoming muscular'. You have 1/100th the adrogen hormone of males and you would quite literally have to take anabolic steroids to get bulky. By exercising properly and naturally, you will tone your muscles, burn excess fat and your body will approach its lean body-weight.

SUNLIGHT

And isn't it strange how we have all been taught to fear the sun? Most already know about the scare concerning the planet's supposed ozone (O_3) depletion. Tales abound about holes above the North and South Poles two and a half times the size of Europe. Chlorofluorocarbons (CFCs) released through industrial activity supposedly rise into the atmosphere and are broken down into chlorine particles by the ultraviolet energy of the sun. These radical chlorines, we are told, in turn destroy ozone molecules at the rate of 1 Cl to 100,000 O_3. A thin layer of ozone in the stratosphere is responsible for shielding the earth from the sun's damaging radiation spectrum emissions. The shield is apparently now 5% depleted. Scientists estimate that at 17% depletion, we may as well forget about putting away for that pension. Did you know the US government actually spent $19 million of taxpayers' money to find out whether the belching and farting of cattle damaged the ozone layer?

Let's now learn a few things about ozone. O_3 is a poisonous gas that is a product of the chemical reaction of the sun's light meeting the earth's atmosphere. Ozone does indeed act as a barrier in the upper atmosphere filtering out the sun's radiation and thus behaves as a shield, protecting us. The thing is, very little ozone is produced at the earth's poles simply due to the fact that the sun's light does not play on these regions directly but strikes at an angle without producing O_3. Which means, there have always been ozone holes at the poles and in surrounding areas.

There is no *global* ozone catastrophe. Indeed the facts such as they are indicate that man's ozonic depredations are extremely minor when compared with the damage caused by volcanoes and their aerosols. One eruption, such as Mount St Helen's, will do more to damage the ozone layer than 10,000 years of spraying stink pretty under our arms.

It is true that areas in proximity to the poles are not adequately protected by ozone for the foregoing reasons of sunlight-angle and so produce problems for humans and animals, if they are not adequately nourished and protected. In the extreme south of Chile, ranch cattle developing conjunctivitis to an abnormal degree have been reported staggering into one another. In southern Argentina, farm labourers become severely burned after spending just 20 minutes in the sun. Skin cancer in humans in the danger zones blanketing the poles and adjacent areas is also a recognised serious issue, and seems to be on the rise, but only because of the encroaching metabolic deficiencies in the humans concerned. Simply put, too much of anything is going to do you harm. Too much water and you'll drown. Is that a good reason for giving up water?

In recent years, when the ozone layer was measured across the planet (not just at the poles), it was found to be thicker than the first time we examined it! The pillorying of R-12 air-conditioning refrigerant as being the chemical responsible for destroying the earth's protective shield is as pathetic as the idea that the propellants (CFCs) released through spraying deodorant under our arms indirectly cause cancer to schoolchildren in Tierra del Fuego. For starters, R-12 is heavier than air and sinks. Secondly, not even normal convection currents would carry R-12 into the atmosphere to sufficient heights and in adequate volume to do any damage. It would take a sustained and prolific misuse of R-12 for at least 100 years to make any measurable impact on the ozone layer and this simply has not happened.

The result of outlawing R-12 and replacing it with an environmentally friendly alternative in car air-conditioning systems has effectively caused an overall increase in the price of automobiles. This in turn has led to increases in all society's related sector costs as a result. No doubt some enterprising economist in government got a big bonus for dreaming up that one. Not bad for a tax for which no one can be blamed. Was this the same guy or girl who dreamt up the lottery (tax on greed)?

393

So have some sun. It's good for you, and great for your mental conditioning. You get Vitamin D by the bucket-load, and your intestines are lined with Vitamin D receptors, which means that calcium absorption can increase up to 20 times if these receptors are full.[605] Skin cancer will only be a concern if you a) abuse the sun over a protracted period of time while having... b) inadequate nutrition and no Vitamin B17 in your diet[606] (factors which have made skin cancer appear to be on the increase over the past few decades); or c) use sunscreens with known carcinogens in them which will permeate the skin into the bloodstream and accumulate to damage the body, creating healing trophoblastic reactions which then do not terminate (cancer).

Do not burn yourself, but tan gently over a period of time. If you are fair-skinned, you must of course take a lot less sun than darker-skinned types. We looked at the need for the human body to have sunlight earlier when we learned that we have three glands behind the eyes – the hypothalamus, the pineal and the pituitary glands. Sunlight is absolutely required to stimulate these into releasing their hormone payloads for the benefit of our regular health. Many societies spend all day in the sun and do not have the chemical toxic loads we have in the industrial world and so do not suffer from the cancer scourge that is currently afflicting us. Anyone who tells you the sun is harmful in reasonable amounts is a menace.

---

[605] Barefoot Robert, *The Calcium Factor*, op. cit.

[606] Day, Phillip, *Cancer: Why We're Still Dying to Know the Truth*, Credence Publications, 2001; Ransom, Steven, *Great News on Cancer in the 21st Century*, Credence Publications, 2002

The *Food For Thought* Dietary Regimen

- ➤ Eat properly constituted, organic, whole, living food, a high percentage raw. Excellent recipes are provided in our companion guide, *Food For Thought*.
- ➤ The ideal balance is: 80% alkali/20% acidic ash foods. Most diets today comprise 90% acid/10% alkali!
- ➤ Ensure meat components are not more than 10% of the total diet. Fish, deep and cold caught, is good, excepting those below.
- ➤ Avoid the foods below.
- ➤ Hydrate the body (4 pints of clean, fresh water a day).
- ➤ Detoxify (eat fruit before noon on an empty stomach). A full account of what to do can be found in *Health Wars*.
- ➤ Reduce meat and dairy intake (eliminate if sick).
- ➤ The basic supplement program (see 'A Guide to Nutritional Supplements').
- ➤ Exercise (to get everything moving!).
- ➤ Rest.
- ➤ Reduce environmental toxicity (dangerous jobs using dangerous chemicals, radiation, etc.).
- ➤ Use safe personal care products.
- ➤ Use safe household products.

FOODS TO AVOID

- ➤ Pork products (bacon, sausage, hot-dogs, luncheon meat, ham, etc.) These are high in nitrites and are known homotoxins which can cause high blood urea and dikitopiprazines, which cause brain tumours and leukaemia.[607]
- ➤ Scavenger meats (inc. ALL shellfish and other carrion-eaters – see Leviticus 11 in the Bible). Carrion-eaters, pork and shellfish in particular, concentrate toxins of other animals in their tissues, which we then consume to our detriment. The same goes for the elimination organs of commercially raised animals, such as liver and kidney, which can be high in drug and pesticide residues.
- ➤ Aspartame/saccharin, artificial sweeteners. These are known mental impairment problems and cancer risks.

---

[7] Day, Phillip, *Food for Thought*, Credence Publications, 2nd Ed., 2002; "Adverse influence of pork consumption on human health", *Biologic Therapy*, Vol. 1, No. 2, 1983

- ➤ Refined sugar/flour/rice. Restricted amounts of wholegrain bread are OK. Use only wholegrain rice. No sugars should be consumed other than those contained naturally in whole foods.
- ➤ Hydrogenated & partially hydrogenated fats (margarine).
- ➤ Junk (processed) food, including fizzy sodas and other soft drinks containing sugar, artificial sweeteners or phosphoric acid, which are drunk out of aluminium cans.
- ➤ Fat-free foods. Fat is essential! See 'A Guide to Nutritional Supplements'.
- ➤ Olestra, canola, soy, etc. Avoid fake or synthetic fats. Soy, in its unfermented state (meat and milk substitute products), disrupts the hormone (endocrine) system, blocks the absorption of calcium and magnesium, and acts like estrogen in the body. Small usage of unfermented soy and fermented soy products (soy sauce and miso) are OK.
- ➤ Polluted water (chlorinated or fluoridated – see *Health Wars* section, entitled 'Water Under the Bridge').
- ➤ The abuse of caffeine products.
- ➤ The abuse of alcohol products.
- ➤ Excess salt. It's better to spice food with ground kelp to maintain a healthy iodine intake!

THE FOUR PILLARS OF MENTAL HEALTH
- ➤ Eliminating allergies
- ➤ Maintaining blood sugar balance
- ➤ Avoiding toxins and pollution
- ➤ Ingesting optimum nutrition

For a full analysis of 'food as it should be', see *Food For Thought*, the food recipe companion to *The Mind Game* (see 'Other Books by Credence').

A Guide to Nutritional Supplements

The following section, compiled by Credence researchers and other contributors, outlines nutritional components that have been studied and used for specific purposes in relation to conditions covered in this book. The purpose of this section is to inform and not to recommend any particular course of action or product. Health advice from a qualified health practitioner trained in nutrition is always advised. Please note that Credence has no commercial affiliations with companies discussed in this section.

SMART NUTRIENTS AND BRAIN FOOD

The human brain is responsible for man's superior mental power. It is the command centre for intellect, memory, awareness, motor control, and sensory perception - the internal regulator of all body processes. The brain's mental energies diminish as chronological age advances. The impact of aging, poor circulation, nutrient-depleted food, polluted air and water, toxic chemicals, and lifestyle stressors can severely impair your body's ability to supply nourishment to the brain. Increase blood flow is very important to the very narrow blood vessels throughout the body increasing the supply of oxygen to vessels that may receive very little oxygen due to their constricting size. The muscles and nerve cells of the brain are composed of phosphatidylserine and phosphatidylcholine. The following ingredients, both of ancient and recent discovery, are known to help enhance circulation and mental/physical energy.

DMAE (dimethylaminoethanol): DMAE is the precursor for choline, which in turn can cross the blood-brain barrier to manufacture the memory neurotransmitter molecule acetylcholine. DMAE has been shown to improve cognitive abilities when taken in doses ranging from 100–300mg. In a 1996 study in Germany, those patients taking the placebo showed no change in their EEG brain patterns, while those on DMAE demonstrated improvements in their brainwave patterns in those parts of the brain which play an important role in memory, attention and flexibility of thinking.[608]

DMAE supports the health of the brain's nerve fibres. Also known as centrophenoxine, it has been shown to decrease lipofuscin in the

---

[608] Dimpfel et al., "Source density analysis of functional topographical EEG: monitoring of cognitive drug action", *European Journal of Medical Research*, Vol.1, No.6 (19th March 1996): pp.283-290

brain. With age, the number of lipofuscin-containing neurons in the cortex increases. An increase in lipofuscin results in a concomitant decrease in spontaneous neuronal action potentials and age-related neuropathies. Centrophenoxine is an anti-lipofuscin compound that prevents this age-related increase in lipofuscin. Centrophenoxine also increases acetylcholinesterase activity in the hippocampus thus reversing the age-related decline of the cholinergic system and possibly mediating its effects on cognitive and neuronal synaptic function.

DMAE, marketed as the drug Deaner or Deanol, was shown by Dr Bernard Rimland at the Autism Research Institute in San Diego to be almost twice as effective in treating children with ADD/ADHD than Ritalin, without the side-effects.[609]

5-HTP: 5-HTP (5-hydroxytryptophan) aids in maintaining healthy serotonin levels in the brain to combat feelings of depression, frequent headaches, and muscle aches and pain. 5-hydroxytryptophan is a compound native to the body and use to synthesise serotonin. Decreased levels of serotonin have been associated with depression, frequent headaches, and muscle aches and pain. Supplementation with 5-HTP has the potential to alleviate many of these ailments.

Ginkgo biloba extract: Contains the flavonone glycosides quercetin and kaempferol. It improves blood flow, especially in the microvasculature in the body. In the brain, this improves memory and capacity for learning.[610]

Bacopa monniera extract: Bacopin, the active chemical constituent found in the herb Bacopa monniera, is an excellent antioxidant that helps support mental function and memory. Bacopa monniera extract is used to improve mental performance, memory, and learning. It is useful when stress and nervous exhaustion are decreasing mental function. It acts as an adaptogenic, a tonic for the nervous system, a circulatory stimulant, and a cerebral stimulant. It is also used to promote longevity, and for nervous deficit due to injury and stroke. Other traditional uses include epilepsy, insanity, nervous breakdown and exhaustion.

---

[609] Holford, Patrick & Hyla Cass, *Natural Highs*, Piatkus Books, 2001, p.139
[610] Blumentahl, et al, Complete German Commission Monographs, *Therapeutic Guide to Herbal Medicine*, op. cit.

Phosphatidylserine (PS): Phosphatidylserine contains the amino acid serine and is one of the brain's phospholipids. It plays a vital role in brain nerve cell membrane functions. Phosphatidylserine makes up approximately 105 of the total phospholipids in nerve cell membranes. Phosphatidylserine helps activate and regulate membrane proteins and play major roles in nerve cell functions, such as the generation, storage, transmission and reception of nerve impulses. As we age, our cellular membranes begin to change, and become stiffer. Proper functioning of the nerve cell membrane requires that it be more fluid, which phosphatidylserine accomplishes. It also acts as a glutamate blocker, thereby preventing excitotoxic damage to the cell. Those having hypoglycaemia or a strong family history of one of the neurodegenerative diseases should avoid excitotoxins in their food and probably should take these supplements at an early age, beginning in their twenties or thirties. Phosphatidylserine boosts the brain's energy supply, thereby protecting vulnerable brain cells from injury.[611]

When Dr Thomas Crook, from the Memory Assessment Clinic in Bethesda, Maryland, gave 149 people with age-associated memory impairment a daily dose of 300mg of PS or a placebo, those only taking PS experienced a vast improvement after 12 weeks in their ability to match names to faces – a recognised measure of memory and mental function.[612]

Centella asiatica extract: Centella asiatica, the ancient Ayurvedic herb commonly called gotu kola, maintains healthy blood flow, helps to balance the nervous system, and encourages proper brain function and enhanced mental capacity. It also contains compounds knows as asiaticosides. Asiaticosides are converted to Asiatic acid in vivo and have been research thoroughly for their ability to elevate antioxidant levels in the blood and decrease the time necessary for wound-healing. The increase in antioxidant levels could be beneficial to those suffering from

---

[611] Crook, T, et al, "Effects of phosphatidylserine in age-associated memory impairment", *Neurol.*, (1991), 41:664-649; Cenacchi, B, et al, "Cognitive decline in the elderly: A double-blind, placebo-controlled multicenter study on efficacy of phosphataidylserine administration", *Aging Clin. Exp. Res.*, (1993), 5:123-133; Engle, R, et al, "Double-blind, cross-over study of phosphatidylserine vs. placebo in subjects with early cognitive deterioration of the Alzheimer type", *Eur. Neurophycolpharmacol.*, (1992), 2:149-155; Kidd, P M, "A review of nutrients and botanicals in the integrative management of cognitive dysfunction." *Altern. Med. Rev.* June, 1999, 4:144-61

[612] Crook, T, et al., "Effects of PS in age-associated memory impairment", *Neurology*, Vol.41, No.5, (1991), pp.644-9

cerebral insufficiency. Centella asiatica, a source of vitamins A, B, E, and K, and magnesium, is used to support the improvement of memory, and enhance the body's fight against insomnia, fever, headache and inflammatory skin problems. It also promotes bloodflow by strengthening the veins and capillaries.[613] In India, the herb is used to assist against skin disease, syphilis, rheumatism, in the treatment of leprosy, for mental illness, epilepsy, hysteria, and for dehydration. In Southeast Asia, the herb supports prompt bladder activity, physical and mental exhaustion, diarrhoea, eye disease, inflammations, asthma, and high blood pressure. Additional effects of Centella asiatica (gotu kola) include psychotropic and pharmacological effects. In forced swimming behavioural tests, an extract of Centella asiatica caused a significant reduction in the duration of the immobilisation phase. These tests show the sedative and antidepressive effects of Centella asiatica.

Pregnenalone: Pregnenalone, a steroid naturally produced in the body, supports the brain's natural capacity for recalling facts and events. Pregnenalone is synthesised in the body from cholesterol. The brain has the capacity to use cholesterol to make pregnenalone and other steroids. Pregnenalone can be metabolised into progesterone or can be converted into DHEA. DHEA in turn can be converted into androgens, estrogens and other steroids (as many as 150 different steroid hormones). Pregnenalone also improves visual perception - colours are brighter. Shapes and forms are more noticeable increasing one's awareness of the environment. In addition, pregnenalone is a potent anti-depressant and can affect memory capabilities. Pregnenalone can accumulate in the body, especially the brain and nervous system, so effects may take time to manifest.

Phosphatidylcholine: Phosphatidylcholine contains phosphory-lated choline and is one of the brain's phospholipids. It plays a vital role in brain nerve cell membrane functions. Phosphatidylcholine makes up approximately 50% of the total phospholipids in nerve cell membranes. The cell membrane acts as a master switch controlling entry of nutrients, exit of waste products, movements of charged ions through the membrane, membrane shape changes, and cell-to-cell communications. The membrane-based ion pumps, transport molecules, enzymes, and receptors that manage these master-switch activities are the membrane proteins. These membrane protein concentrations and positioning are effected by the phospholipid composition and structure.

---

[613] Kidd, P M, ibid.

Phosphatidylcholine can come from the diet as phosphatidylcholine or choline. In addition, it can be synthesised in the body using free choline. Good dietary sources (in decreasing order of concentration) of phosphatidylcholine and choline are eggs, beef steak, cauliflower, butter, oranges, apples, whole-wheat bread, and lettuce. Dietary phosphatidylcholine is cleaved by the pancreatic enzyme phospholipase B that leads to small amounts of choline entering the blood system. Phosphatidylcholine is synthesized in the body through two different pathways, the CDO-choline pathway and the PE methylation pathway. In the latter pathway, phosphatidylethanolamine is converted to phosphatidylcholine, freeing ethanolamine and consuming choline.

Phosphatidylethanolamine: One of the brain's phospholipids. It plays a vital role in brain nerve cell membrane functions. Phosphatidylethanolamine makes up approximately 25% of the total phospholipids in nerve cell membranes. Phosphatidylethanolamine is present in foods at approximately equal concentrations as phosphatidylcholine. Phosphatidylethanolamine can be converted to phosphatidylcholine in the liver, generating most ethanolamine in the body. Phosphatidylethanolamine can also be synthesized from free ethanolamine and diacylglycerol by the CDP-ethanolamine pathway. Smaller quantities of phosphatidylethanolamine can be reversibly converted to phosphatidylserine upon demand. Additionally, phosphatidylethanolamine can be converted from phosphatidylserine catalysed by a Vitamin B6-requiring enzyme.

Vinpocetine: Vinpocetine, the active compound in the herb periwinkle, helps the body maintain healthy circulation to the brain in support cerebral capacity. Found in the lesser periwinkle *Vinca minor*, vinpocetine has been shown to be an excellent vasodilator and cerebral metabolic enhancer. It improves glucose transport (uptake and release) through the blood-brain barrier throughout the brain, providing increased nutrients for cellular respiration. Vinpocetine is also a phosphodiesterase-1-inhibitor that in turn suppresses the production of TNF-alpha (responsible for inflammatory cytokines in the nervous system).

Researchers at the University of Surrey in the UK gave 203 people with memory problems either vinpocetine or a placebo. Those taking vinpocetine demonstrated a significant improvement in cognitive performance. Russian research has also shown that vinpocetine is potentially helpful for those with epilepsy.[614]

Phosphatidylinositol: Phosphatidylinositol contains the sugar inositol and is one of the brain's phospholipids. It plays a vital role in brain nerve cell membrane functions. Phosphatidylinositol makes up approximately 5% of the total phospholipids in nerve cell membranes. Phosphatidylinositol plays a vital role in the transmission of some hormonal signals. Phosphatidylinositol is the major source of inositol-1,4,5-triphosphate (IP3). IP3 is a modified sugar that has proven to be a versatile molecule participating in signalling events within many types of body cells (e.g., calcium signalling). Phosphatidylinositol is necessary to convert arachidonic acid to prostaglandins and thromboxanes.

NADH: NADH (niacinamide adenine dinucleotide) enhances proper neurotransmitter function - the electrochemical transmission of nerve impulses between the brain and body. Niacinamide adenine dinucleotide is required by the brain to synthesize various neurotransmitters. With age, the level of NADH diminishes resulting in a subsequent decrease in energy production and neurotransmitter levels. This in turn alters brain chemistry and can affect mental function. Theoretically, supplementation with NADH should improve one's mental capacities.

Huperzine: Also known as Huperzine A, is a purified alkaloid isolated from the Chinese club moss *huperzia serrata*. It inhibits the breakdown of the neurotransmitter acetylcholine. Acetylcholine is rapidly broken down in the brains of Alzheimer's patients and age-related memory disorders causing dementia. A shortage of acetylcholine appears to contribute to memory loss and other cognitive defects. Huperzine disrupts the enzyme acetylcholinesterase that breaks down acetylcholine. Current research is ongoing to use Huperzine to protect the brain against damage from strokes, epilepsy and chemical weapons. Studies conducted in China on Huperzine A have indicated its efficacy as an acetylcholinesterase inhibitor. Because cholinergic neurons are responsible for memory, theoretically an acetylcholinesterase inhibitor could improve memory.[615]

---

[614] Hindmarch, I, et al, "Efficacy and tolerance of vinpocetine in ambulant patients suffering from mild to moderate organic psychosyndromes", *Int'l. Clin. Psych.*, Vol.6 No.1 (1991): pp.31-43

[615] Xu, S, et al, "Efficacy of Tablet Huperzine-A on Memory, Cognition, and Behaviour in Alzheimer's Disease", *Acta Pharmacologica Sinica*, (1995), 16:391-395

INGENIOUS (Neways International)

Enhanced brain nutritional support complex. The specially selected ingredients for Ingenious are well known in ancient Chinese, Ayurvedic, and Western medicine for helping provide nutritional support to the brain's system to enhance circulation and revitalize mental energy. Ingenious is effective in supporting the body's natural processes, improving brain function and increasing cerebral and peripheral blood flow, circulation and oxygenation to the brain.

Ingredients: Vitamin B5 (calcium pantothenate), DMAE, 5-HTP, Ginkgo biloba extract, Bacopa monniera extract, Phosphatidylserine, Centella asiatica extract, Pregnenalone, Phosphatidylcholine, Phosphatidylethanolamine, Vinpocetine, Phosphatidylinositol, NADH, Huperzine.

ESSENTIAL FATS (inc. Vitamin F)
EFA Recovery Plus &
Omega-3 EPA (Neways International)

EFA Recovery Plus is a daily essential fatty acid mix that contains omega-3 and omega-6 fatty acids. It was designed to help balance one's diet with a 40/30/30 caloric ratio of the three macronutrient sources, carbohydrate, protein and fat, for optimal health and better performance. EFA refers to the 'essential fatty acids' required in our diet, because these fatty acids cannot be synthesised by our body. 'Recovery' refers to EFA's role in restoring and maintaining general health as well as biochemical recovery following physical exercise and work.

The two major energy sources for the production of ATP energy during exercise are carbohydrates in the form of muscle glycogen and fats in the form of fatty acids. Fat is the most misunderstood of the three macronutrient sources. The association between a high-fat diet and serious health problems is widely advertised. This is the reason for today's trend to buy 'fat-free' food products. However, it is important to know that dietary fat consists of three basic types of fatty acids: (1) saturated, (2) monounsaturated, (3) polyunsaturated.

Saturated fat, 'bad fat', found in most animal fat, margarine, shortening, etc. can raise blood cholesterol levels. Partially hydrogenated oils contain trans-fatty acids that are also classified as 'bad fats'. Unsaturated fat, 'good fats', are composed of cis-fatty acids typically found in vegetable oils, cold-water fatty fish (e.g., salmon, herring, etc.), avocado, nuts and some beans. These foods are known for their ability to reduce blood cholesterol levels.[616]

It is just as important to regulate the kinds of fat we ingest as the amount of fat itself. Unsaturated fats play a beneficial role in our body. Fats are the most concentrated source of energy in the diet. Many sources of fat provide important nutrients, carry fat-soluble vitamins, A, D, E, and K through the bloodstream, maintain healthy skin, and are crucial for foetal brain development. The typical Western diet does not include a sufficient amount of EFAs, especially those referred to as omega-3 fatty acids. EFA Recovery Plus is a combination of the natural sources of all cis-fatty acids as: alpha-lipoic acid, linoleic acid (omega-6), EPA (omega-3) and DHA (omega-3). These fatty acids are essential. Essential fatty acids are involved in a variety of biochemical processes. EFAs are vital in the role of energy production for muscle cells during exercise and assisting in muscle relaxation.[617]

In addition, EFAs affect the control of blood coagulation.[618] They also affect the release of CCK, a hormone that signals the brain that you're full and to stop eating.[619] EFAs are involved in maintaining conduction velocities for sensory and motor nerves.[620] EFAs are also present in cell membranes and support suppleness of skin[621] and help to lower high blood pressure.[622]

[616] Siguel, E, "A new relationship between total-high density lipoprotein cholesterol and polyunsaturated fatty acids", *Lipids*, 1996 Mar;31 Suppl:S51-6

[617] Barbiroli, B, Medori R, Tritschler H J, Klopstock T, Seibel P, Reichmann H, Iotti S, Lodi R & P Zaniol, "Lipoic (thioctic) acid increases brain energy availability and skeletal muscle performance as shown by in vivo 31P-MRS in a patient with mitochondrial cytopathy", *J. Neurol.* 1995 Jul;242(7):472-7

[618] Andriamampandry, M, Freund, M, Wiesel, M L, Rhinn, S, Ravanat, C, Cazenave J P, Leray, C, Gochet, C, "Diets enriched in (n-3) fatty acids affect rat coagulation factors dependent on vitamin K", *C. R. Acad. Sci. III* 1998 May;321(5):415-21

[619] Matzinger, D, Degen, L, Drewe, J, Meuli, J, Duebendorfer, R, Ruckstuhl, N, D'Amato, M, Rovati, L, Beglinger, C, "The role of long chain fatty acids in regulating food intake and cholecystokinin release in humans", *Gut* 2000 May;46(5):689-94

[620] Julup, O, Mutamba, A, "Comparison of short-term effects of insulin and essential fatty acids on the slowed nerve conduction of streptozoticin diabetes in rats", *J. Neurol. Sci.* 1991 Nov;106(1):56-9

[621] Horrobin, D F, "Essential fatty acid metabolism and its modification in atopic eczema", *Am. J. Clin. Nutr.* 2000 Jan;71(1 Suppl):367S-72S

[622] Lee, R M, "Fish oil, essential fatty acids, and hypertension", *Can. J. Physiol. Pharmacol.* 1994 Aug;72(8):945-53

Alpha-lipoic acid is a sulfur-containing essential fatty acid. Alpha-lipoic acid is directly involved in the availability of brain and skeletal energy during exercise.[623] Alpha-lipoic acid has been used in Europe to help the body control diabetic effects.[624]

Alpha-linolenic acid is an omega-3, polyunsaturated, cis-fatty acid found in flax seed oil. Alpha-linolenic acid is converted to EPA and DHA.

Linoleic acid is an omega-6, polyunsaturated, cis-fatty acid found in safflower oil. Linoleic acid in incorporated in phospholipids – phospholipids are key components of healthy cell membranes.[625] Linoleic acid is converted to special prostaglandins[626] – prostaglandins control blood-clotting.

Omega 3 Fats

Food processing has wrought havoc on daily intakes of Omega 3 fats. It is estimated that the population today may be consuming around one sixth of the Omega 3s that our ancestors ingested back in 1850, due mainly to today's food choices and processing.[627] Omega 3 fats are more susceptible to corruption during the cooking process. EPA and DHA are omega-3 polyunsaturated fatty acids – the 'good fats'. Eicosapentaenoic acid (EPA) and docosahexaenoic acid (DHA) are in high concentrations in cold-water fish (e.g. salmon, tuna, mackerel and herring). EPA is used to support against high cholesterol and to form membranes surrounding cells.[628] EPA is required for the production of prostaglandins, which

---

[623] Barbiroli, B, Medori, R, Tritschler, H J, Klopstock, T, Seibel, P, Reichmann, H, Iotti, S, Lodi, R, Zaniol, P, "Lipoic (thioctic) acid increases brain energy availability and skeletal muscle performance as shown by in vivo 31P-MRS in a patient with mitochondrial cytopathy", *J. Neurol.* 1995 Jul;242(7):472-7

[624] Ziegler, D, Reljanovic, M, Mehnert, H, Gries, F A, "Alpha-lipoic acid in the treatment of diabetic polyneuropathy in Germany: current evidence from clinical trails", *Exp. Clin. Endrocrinol. Diabetes* 1999;107(7):421-30

[625] Raederstorff, D, Moser, U, "Influence of an increased intake of linoleic acid on the incorporation of dietary (n-3) fatty acids in phospholipids and on prostanoid synthesis in rat tissues", *Biochim. Biophys. Acta* 1992 Dec 2;1165(2):194-200

[626] Mentz, P, Hoffmann, P, Lenken, V, Forster, W, "Influence of prostaglandins, prostaglandin-precursors and of a linoleic acid rich and free diet on the cardiac effects of isoprenaline and vasodilators", *Acta. Biol. Med. Ger.* 1978;37(5-6)801-5

[627] Ibid.

[628] Mizota, M, Katsuki, Y, Mizuguchi, K, Endo, S, Miyata, H, Kojima, M, Kanehiro, H, Okada, M, Takase, A, Ishiguro, J, et al., "Pharmacological studies of eicosapentaenoic acid ethylester (EPA-E) on high cholesterol diet-fed rabbits", *Nippon Yakurigaku Zasshi* 1988 Apr;91(4):255-66

control blood clotting and other arterial functions.[629] DHA is a component of human brain tissue[630] and the retinal tissue.[631] DHA serves in the transmission of nerve impulses in the nervous system.

Omega 3 Deficiency Symptoms: Dry skin, lack of co-ordination or impaired vision, inflammatory health problems, memory or learning ability impaired, tingling in the arms or legs, hard to lose weight, high blood pressure or triglycerides, prone to infections.

Omega 6 Fats

Gamma-linolenic acid (GLA) is an omega-6 polyunsaturated cis-fatty acid found in evening primrose oil that helps to increase circulation. Research has shown that it aids in the reduction of platelet aggravation, lowers cholesterol and may reduce the risk of cardiovascular disease.[632] Evening primrose oil added to the diet of alcoholics undergoing withdrawal dramatically reduces symptoms and, in the long-term, improves memory.[633] This feature prompted researchers to see whether the oil would improve the memory of Alzheimer's patients. During a controlled trial, significant improvements were seen.[634] Other sources of Omega 6 fats are the seeds of hemp, pumpkin, sunflower, safflower, sesame, corn, walnut and wheatgerm oil. Omega 6 fats must have adequate levels of zinc, magnesium, B6 and biotin accompanying them to drive the enzyme that makes the conversion to GLA.[635]

Omega 6 Deficiency Symptoms: High blood pressure, eczema or dry skin, PMS or breast pain, dry eyes, blood sugar imbalance or diabetes,

---

[629] Bell, J G, Tocher, D R, MacDonald, F M, Sargent, J R, "Diets rich in eicosapentaenoic acid and gamma-linolenic acid affect phospholipid fatty acid composition and production of prostaglandins E1, E2 and E3 in turbot (Scophythalmus maximus), a species deficient in delta 5 fatty acid desaturase", *Prostaglandins Leukot Essent. Fatty Acids* 1995 Oct;53(4):279-86

[630] Ward, G R, Huang, Y S, Xing, H C, Bobik, E, Wauben, I, Auestad, N, Montalto, M, Wainwright, P E, "Effects of gamma-linolenic acid and docosahexaenoic acid in formulae on brain fatty acid composition in artificially reared rats", *Lipids* 1999 Oct;34(10):1057-63

[631] Neuringer, M, "Infant vision and retinal function in studies of dietary long-chain polyunsaturated fatty acids; methods, results, and implications", *Am. J. Clin. Nutr.* 2000 Jan;71(1Suppl):256S-67S

[632] Scheer, James F, "Evening primrose oil – It's essential", *Better Nutrition*, 1998 Jun;60(6)60-64

[633] Pfeiffer, Carl & Patrick Holford, op. cit. p.31

[634] Ibid.

[635] Ibid.

chronic fatigue, multiple sclerosis, alcoholism, depression and mood swings, excessive thirst.

Prostaglandins

Essential fats are, as their name suggests, essential for creating prostaglandins. These are extremely active, hormone-like substances which variously keep blood thin, relax blood vessels, thereby assisting in lowering blood pressure, boost immunity, assist in maintaining the water balance in the body, decrease inflammation, and assist the operation of insulin for correct blood sugar balance.[636] Prostaglandins (series 1 & 3) themselves cannot be supplemented, due to their short-lived and volatile nature. However, an adequate intake of essential fats will equip the body with the raw materials it needs to create them. These two supplements from Neways assist in doing just that. The intake ratio between Omegas 6 and 3 should ideally be around 2:1.

EFA Recovery Plus ingredients: Alpha-lipoic acid, Linoleic acid, Alpha-linolenic acid, Gamma-linolenic acid, Eicosapentaenoic acid (EPA), Docosahexaenoic acid (DHA).

Omega 3 EPA ingredients: Eicosapentaenoic acid (EPA), Docosahexaenoic (DHA), Vitamin E, natural D-alpha tocopherol.

VITAMIN F: The polyunsaturated fatty acids (PUFA's) have been described as 'Vitamin F', a classification that once again hit rough waters with the medical establishment. Saturated fats have no hydrogen atoms missing in their carbon chains, whereas PUFA's may have two, three, four, or more double-bond linkages in the carbon chain with four, six, eight, or more hydrogen atoms missing. PUFA's are long-chain and extra-long-chain fatty acids which naturally occur in nature and are used by the body to prevent hardening of the arteries, normalise blood pressure, enhance glandular activity and assist in physical growth early in life. Despite the American Medical Association loudly denouncing the moniker 'Vitamin F' as quackery, PUFA's have rightly gained prominence in recent years as essential, life-sustaining nutrients. And what are essential, life-sustaining nutrients if not a vitamin?

VITAMIN C (ascorbic acid/ascorbate)

Dr Linus Pauling, often known as the 'Father of Vitamin C' and twice awarded the Nobel Prize, declared that large intakes of up to 10g of the vitamin each day aids anti-cancer activity within the body and also assists

---

[636] Pfeiffer, Carl & Patrick Holford, op. cit. p.29

in repairing damaged arteries and removing arterial plaque (atherosclerosis) for heart disease sufferers. Pauling was largely derided for making these declarations (yet he lived to be 94!), but today, large doses of Vitamin C are used by many practitioners for cancer patients in nutritional therapy, who believe Pauling was right and that the popular nutrient is indispensable to the body in its fight to regain health from cancer.

Vitamin C has been shown to reduce the symptoms of schizophrenia, including hallucinations, hearing voices and dementia. [637] Several studies have suggested that Vitamin C may reduce levels of the pollutant and memory-impairment metal lead in the blood. Epidemiological studies have shown that people with elevated blood serum levels of Vitamin C had lower levels of blood toxicity. An examination of the data from the Third National Health and Nutrition Examination Survey, enrolling 4,213 youths aged 6 to 16 years and 15,365 adults 17 years and older from 1988 to 1994, found a correlation between low serum ascorbic acid levels and elevated blood lead levels. The authors conclude that high ascorbic acid intake may reduce blood lead levels.[638]

An analysis of the Normative Aging Study, which enrolled 747 men aged 49 to 93 years from 1991 to 1995, found that lower dietary intake of Vitamin C may increase lead levels in the blood.[639] A study of 349 African American women enrolled in the project Nutrition, Other Factors, and the Outcome of Pregnancy found that vitamin-mineral supplementation resulted in increased serum levels of ascorbic acid and decreased serum levels of lead. The authors concluded that maternal use of a vitamin supplement with ascorbic acid and Vitamin E might offer protection from lead contamination of the foetus during pregnancy.[640]

Because smoking lowers levels of ascorbic acid in the body, researchers theorised that Vitamin C supplementation may affect blood lead levels in smokers. A clinical study was performed on 75 adult men 20

[637] Milner, G, "Ascorbic acid in chronic psychiatric patients – a controlled trial", *Brit. J. Psychiatr.*, 109, 294-299, 1963

[638] Simon J A, Hudes E S, "Relationship of Ascorbic Acid to Blood Lead Levels." *Journal of the American Medical Association*, 1999;281:2289-2293.

[639] Cheng Y, Willett W C, Schwartz J, Sparrow D, Weiss S, Hu H, "Relation of nutrition to bone lead and blood lead levels in middle-aged to elderly men. The Normative Aging Study." *Am. J. Epidemiol.* 1998 Jun 15;147(12):1162-1174.

[640] West W L, Knight E M, Edwards C H, et al., "Maternal low level lead and pregnancy outcomes." *J. Nutr.* 1994 Jun;124(6 Suppl):981S-986S.

to 30 years of age who smoked at least one pack of cigarettes per day, but had no clinical signs of ascorbic acid deficiency or lead toxicity. Subjects were randomly assigned to daily supplementation with placebo, 200 mg of ascorbic acid, or 1,000 mg of ascorbic acid. After one week of supplementation, there was an 81% decrease in blood-lead levels in the group taking 1,000 mg of ascorbic acid daily.[641]

Dosage recommended by Linus Pauling for prevention is between 600mg and 3g a day – or up to 10g/day for those who have been diagnosed with cancer.[642] High levels of Vitamin C can cause diarrhoea and may be contra-indicated with certain chemotherapy treatments. Vitamin C is especially useful when combined in moderate amounts with Calcium d-glucarate, as formulated in the Neways product D-Toxarate (see D-Toxarate in this section).

VITAMIN P (bioflavonoids): the other part of the Vitamin C 'complex'. Dr Albert Szent-Gyorgi, 1937 Nobel Laureate for his isolation of Vitamin C, later found other factors intrinsic to the action of C. Originally believed to be a single nutrient, Vitamin C became the subject of further testing by Szent-Gyorgi, who fought long and hard to have the co-factor (bio)flavonoids included in the C complex. Coining the new bioflavonoids 'Vitamin P', Szent-Gyorgi argued that they were essential for proper functioning of the human organism, derived from plant pigments known as the flavonols and flavones. Bioflavonoids are widely accepted today for their health benefits and are available in hydroxylated and methoxylated forms. They are derived from the pith of fruits (mostly citrus). The term 'Vitamin P', on the other hand, has been less well received by the medical czars.

THE B-COMPLEX
B, B, B1, B2, B3, B5, B6, B8, B9, B12, B15, B17
One of the most important groups of nutrients for mental health is the B-group. A dip in the intakes of any member of the group will cause problems, and fast. Together however, working in synergy with a sensible, varied diet, the great effects of the 'B's can be startling. B vitamins are water-soluble and rapidly pass out of the body, so a regular intake of a good B-complex is essential. We have variously looked at the B-Vits in my

---

[641] Dawson E B, Evans D R, Harris W A, Teter M C & W J McGanity, "The effect of ascorbic acid supplementation on the blood lead levels of smokers." *J. Am. Coll. Nutr.* 1999 Apr;18(2):166-170.
[642] Use Vitamin C powder, rather than the tablets, which contain binders and fillers.

other books as we've made our way through the nutrition maze, so let's sum up.

Vitamin B (choline) is the base ingredient of lecithin. Choline helps in the formation of the 'memory' neurotransmitter molecule, acetylcholine, and has been used to great effect in treating Alzheimer's. It is often used medically in the form phosphatidylcholine (see section entitled 'Phosphatidylcholine').

Vitamin B (inositol) is another B nutrient used to treat mental illness. Bi-polar mental disorders, characterised by interchangeable periods of depression and euphoria, have responded well to high doses of the nutrient. Inositol is mentioned repeatedly in the scientific literature in connection with treating panic attacks and anxieties.[643]

Vitamin B (PABA), also known as paraaminobenzoic acid, is a component of B9 (folic acid) and acts as a co-enzyme in the body. PABA assists other B vitamins in making red blood cells, metabolising proteins, and helping with skin disorders. Nasty red bumps caused by the sun respond well to PABA applied externally or 400mg internally. Many skin lotions have PABA to help prevent wrinkling of the skin and greying of the hair. A facial mask comprised equal parts of PABA, aloe vera and honey left on the face while sleeping will tighten loose skin and help some wrinkles to vanish. The face mask is removed the following morning with cotton balls saturated in rubbing alcohol followed by warm water. Not for nothing is this nutrient referred to as the 'Cosmetic B'![644]

Vitamin B1 (thiamine) deficiency leads to beriberi. The nutritional pioneer Dr W Henry Sebrell attributed his razor-sharp memory to a daily supplementation of 150mg of B1 for almost 29 years! Sebrells explains that thiamine is often severely lacking in up to 50% of psychiatric patients. Thiamine binds to lead molecules, thereby assisting in excreting the heavy metal from the body. Sebrell estimated that a daily intake of 100mg of B1 would afford protection against lead poisoning.[645]

Vitamin B2 (riboflavin) appears under the microscope as a yellow, crystalline substance. This vitamin assists in body growth, repair and cell

---

[643] Heinerman, John, *Encyclopaedia of Nature's Vitamins and Minerals*, Prentice Hall, 1998, p.15
[644] Ibid, p.18
[645] Ibid.

respiration. It's excellent too in maintaining the health of the nervous system, the assimilation of iron and, along with Vitamin A, for great vision. Those suffering from chronic fatigue, oily skin and intestinal gas may test positive for low levels of this nutrient and iron.

Vitamin B3 (niacin) deficiency causes depression and psychosis. Subjects of various ages taking 141mg of niacin a day demonstrated a measurable improvement in memory of 10-40% in all age groups.[646] Its RDA is only 18mg in the UK, and yet studies, as we have seen, demonstrate that mega-doses can prove extremely beneficial to 'schizophrenics'. This nutrient is also sometimes prescribed with great effect for rheumatoid arthritis in doses between 150-300mg to improve joint function and mood. May cause skin flushing. B3 can be purchased bound with inositol, which prevents flushing. Regular use of B3 will cause flushing to cease. B3 is also reported in the scientific literature to be useful in treating and preventing certain forms of cancer.[647]

Vitamin B5 (pantothenic acid), as it is also known, has been hypothesised to increase cholinergic activity in the body, specifically the central nervous system. This increase in cholinergic activity could result in increased memory, learning, and cognitive abilities. B5 (pantothenate) is another potent memory enhancer, assisting in the creation of the essential memory neurotransmitter, acetylcholine. Supplementing 250-500mg of B5 along with choline may improve memory.

Vitamin B6 (pyridoxine) is essential for making neurotransmitters. It converts amino acids into serotonin, a deficiency of which brings on irritability, violence, poor memory and a dive in overall cognitive and social performance. Folic acid deficiency encourages anxiety and depression. One study showed that about a fifth of depressed people are deficient in pyridoxine.[648] Supplementation is ideally between 30-100mg a day or more for normal dream recall (B6 can be toxic at high doses. Do not exceed 8000-1,000mg).

---

[646] Loriaux, S, et al., "The effects of niacin and xanthinol nicotinate on human memory in different categories of age – a double-blind study", *Psychopharmacology*, 87, 390-395, 1985; also Heinerman, John, op. cit. p.28

[647] Heinerman, John, op. cit. p.29

[648] Stewart, J W, et al., "Low B6 levels in depressed patients", *Biological Psychiatry*, Vol.141 (1982): pp.271-2

Vitamin B8 (biotin) is known as the energy and beauty nutrient and assists our cells' mitochondria in producing the energy molecule adenosine-triphosphate (ATP). Biotin is used in the transformation of consumed carbohydrates, fats and proteins into energy, which is then stored in the liver and muscle tissue in the form of glycogen. Glycogen, when needed, is released from these stores and readily converted into glucose, which the body then chemically 'burns' as a fuel to produce physical energy. Biotin is very much an enzyme helper and catalyses many enzymatic reactions in the body.

Vitamin B9 (folic acid) was discovered almost simultaneously with B12 and indeed works in conjunction with this essential nutrient. Folic acid is well known in helping to avoid birth defects, such as spina bifida and neural tube defects. Folic acid, like B12, is essential for oxygen delivery to the brain. A deficiency in either causes anaemia. Ideal supplementation for folic acid is around 400mcg daily.

Vitamin B12 (cyanocobalamin) has been shown to improve the rate at which rats learn. Lack of B12 leads to anaemia, confusion and poor memory.[649] Several of these nutrients can be raised to larger doses as part of a program to eradicate chronic shortages, as we have seen, with spectacular results. B12 supplementation is between 10-100mcg a day. Some people have poor absorption of B12 and can benefit from amounts up to 1,000mcg a day.

Vitamin B15 (pangamic acid) is another controversial nutrient, traditionally pilloried by the establishment. B15 has been described as 'instant oxygen', and has been used by Russian athletes for years to gain a competitive edge. Almost all research into this nutrient has come from Russia and has been viewed with outright scepticism by the American medical establishment. Pangamic acid has been variously described as the *"hottest substance to hit the ergogenic scene in recent memory,"* and was apparently capable of delivering *"flashy brilliance"* to orgasms and mopping up free radicals *"like mad"*. It is used in certain clinics today as part of the nutritional support for cancer patients. Some mainstream nutritional references still carry information about pangamic acid; others mention it, but disassociate themselves from its B-vitamin status.

---

[649] Pearson, D & S Shaw, *Life Extension: A Practical, Scientific Approach*, Warner Books, 1982

Vitamin B17 (Laetrile, laetrile and amygdalin) is often referred to as the anti-cancer vitamin. Like B15, this nutrient has been clouded with controversy and been the subject of repeated attacks by the medical establishment. Nevertheless, unlike B15, there is an impressive track record of success with B17, which is contained in the seeds of the common fruits, excluding citrus, and a wide variety of grasses, legumes, pulses, vetches and vegetables. I deal with the subject of Vitamin B17 in some detail in my books *Health Wars, Cancer: Why We're Still Dying to Know the Truth,* and *B17 Metabolic Therapy: A Technical Manual.* B17 is renowned for its analgesic qualities and its ability selectively to target and kill cancer cells, while nourishing non-cancerous tissue. Broken down in the body, one of its by-products, sodium thiocyanate, reacts with the liver precursor, hydroxycobalamin, to form the other vitamin with a cyanide radical, Vitamin B12. (see section entitled 'Apricot Kernels')

FULL-SPECTRUM MINERAL NUTRITION
Maximol (Neways International)
The huge rise in incidences of cancer and other degenerative diseases are primarily due to the depleted vitamin/mineral content in today's Western diet coupled with environmental/chemical toxin factors. The key nutritional ingredients invariably missing for cancer are B17, Vitamin C, zinc and the trace mineral selenium. A recent US study showed an overall drop of 50% in cancer deaths and a fall of 37% in new cancer cases, especially lung, bowel and prostate – among 1,300 volunteers taking general supplements for four years. [650]

Mineral supplementation is most effective in the ionised 'liquid suspension' form, assisted by fulvic acid, where an unusually high percentage of assimilation by the body can be expected. Our bodies use minerals as raw material. These cannot be manufactured by the body, and so have to be present in the food and liquids we ingest. Sadly, as mentioned, our food chain is severely depleted of minerals, resulting in over 150 nutritional deficiency diseases that are now striking our societies with increasing intensity.

To combat this very real threat, mineral and vitamin supplementation, far from being a quaint health fad, <u>is essential for everyone</u> and can literally make the difference between life or death, especially for those with cancer. To combat this threat, Neways has formulated Maximol Solutions, probably the world's most complete liquid nutritional

---

[650] *Daily Mail,* 28th July 1999, p. 31

supplement, which contains 67 essential and trace minerals, 17 essential vitamins, 21 amino acids, three enzymes, and lactobacillus acidophilus.[651] To provide greater absorption of all these ingredients, Maximol contains nature's natural chelator, used by plants and animals for the absorption of minerals and nutrients - organic fulvic acid. It is known that fulvic acid aids in the transport and assimilation of minerals and nutrients into living cells. This may in part be due to its low molecular weight, its electrical potential, and its bio-transporting ability. Fulvic acid aids in the selective trading or supply of minerals and other nutrient stacks inside the cell. Fulvic acid is effective at neutralising a wide range of toxic material - from heavy metals and radioactive waste to petrochemicals.

Before minerals can be utilised, they must first be converted from their particular colloidal state to a micro-colloidal state. Thus, for greater bio-availability, Neways has formulated Maximol Solutions as an organic fulvic acid complexed micro-colloidal solution. In this form, Maximol provides higher percentages of easily assimilated minerals than non-ionised, colloidal mineral supplements, whose particles are often too large for easy absorption.

ANTIOXIDANTS
Revenol (Neways International)
Scientists tell us that vitamins A, C, and E, as well as beta-carotene and other antioxidant bioflavonoids, are vitally important to good health. But there are antioxidant formulae around now that have many more times the power of Vitamin C and Vitamin E. The Neways product Revenol contains antioxidants that are broad-spectrum. Revenol contains antioxidants from maritime pine bark and grape seed pycnogenols extracts - up to 95% in concentration and bioavailability. Revenol also contains curcuminoids, nature's most powerful and aggressive antioxidant, which is around 150 times more powerful than Vitamin E, about 60 times more powerful than Vitamin C, and about 3 times more powerful than antioxidants from maritime pine bark and grape seed pycnogenols extract in neutralising harmful oxidation elements in our bodies. [652]

Revenol also contains ginkgo biloba for the brain and circulatory system; alpha and beta carotene to increase potency; esterfied Vitamin C -

---

[651] Contents may vary by country.
[652] Majeed, Muhammed, et al, *Curcuminoids – Antioxidant Phytonutrients*, Nutriscience Publishers, 121 Ethel Road West, Unit 6, Piscataway, NJ 08854 USA

a bonded form of Vitamin C that increases its power and residual retention in the body (up to 3 days); natural Vitamin E for greater absorption and effectiveness. Micro-spheres are also included which bond to the intestinal wall, allowing up to 400% more of the ingredients to be digested and absorbed.

Each tablet of Revenol supplies over 60 milligrams of curcuminoids and maritime pine bark and grape seed extract. An independent study on antioxidants has been conducted by Russian biochemists. As they announce their findings to the World Health Organization, Revenol is expected to be listed as the world's No. 1 effective antioxidant.

Cascading Revenol (Neways International)

Neways has also released an exciting, further version of Revenol, named Cascading Revenol. Current theory suggests that oxidation elements, or free radicals as they are sometimes known, are unstable molecules hungry to scavenge additional electrons, thereby damaging healthy cells. These factors are especially dangerous for cancer sufferers. Antioxidants such as Vitamin C can help prevent the damage caused by free radicals by completing their compounds, thus rendering them inert. The problem is, after having entered the body, most antioxidant molecular structures will grab one free radical and then change into an inert state, ceasing to be of further radical-scavenging value. The additional problem is that even when an antioxidant neutralises a free radical, the process creates an off-shoot free radical that is slightly different and less potent in variety, which in turn creates another, and so on. Typical antioxidants have a linear application and thus show no ability to address this free radical cascading effect.

However Cascading Revenol's formulation has been designed to regenerate these scavenging molecules so that they can neutralise multiple free radicals. So, instead of only one free radical being destroyed per antioxidant molecule, each molecule is able to change structure and repeat the process again and again. Thus the value of each individual antioxidant molecule increases exponentially. Cascading Revenol's unique action is devastating to the free radical onslaught that damages cancer sufferers and in my opinion is an essential component in any nutritional support program.

IMMUNE BOOSTING
Hawaiian Noni Juice (Neways International)
The fruit juice of *morinda citrifolia* contains a polysaccharide-rich substance with marked anti-tumour activity, according to recent studies into the famous fruit.[653] This research, performed at the University of Hawaii, has resulted in exciting new and scientifically reputable evidence for the potential benefits of Noni fruit juice in the treatment of cancer. Neways Authentic Hawaiian Noni features all the health-enhancing benefits of the noni plant as well as raspberry and blueberry extracts – both powerful antioxidants.

DETOXIFICATION
Cleansing Tea (Neways International)
Colon cleansing, while not a pleasant topic to address, is a subject that cannot be overlooked in the quest for extended youth, weight loss, and total health. Mucoid plaque and impacted toxic metabolites can be removed with a modified diet as well as with certain purgative agents that can assist in restoring the colon and intestines to full function. It is essential to allow the body to clean itself of detritus that has collected in the digestive system over the years, hampering the body's ability to absorb the nutrients it craves through the intestinal lining. Cleansing Tea, with its formulation of special herbs, is great at getting it all moving again, and is an ideal adjunct to any program of wellness.

D-Toxarate (Neways International)
As we have already learned, every day we are exposed to harmful substances in our environment. The air we breathe, the food we eat, and even objects we touch are contaminated by substances that threaten our health in many ways we are only just beginning to understand. D-Toxarate is formulated with two important ingredients to help many of these substances pass through the body without harmful effects. Calcium d-glucarate, the first ingredient, can help eliminate some agents that potentially harm our cells. The second ingredient is ascorbic acid, or Vitamin C, an antioxidant with the interesting property we examined earlier- it reduces blood-lead levels.

---

[653] Hirazumi, A & Eiichi Furusawa, "An Immunomodulatory Polysaccharide-Rich Substance from the Fruit Juice of *Morinda citrifolia* (Noni) with Antitumour Activity", Dept of Pharmacology, John A Burns School of Medicine, Hawaii, HI 96822 USA

VitaCell - Resveratrol, Maitake, Lycopene combination (Neways International)

The human body is a miraculous system of organs, with several different mechanisms for removing harmful substances from the body, repairing damaged cells or accidental mutations, replacing older cells with new cells, and removing ill or dead cells from the body. Three novel substances have recently gained attention in the scientific community for their potential anti-cancer activity: resveratrol, maitake mushroom, and lycopene. Together, these products act as antioxidants, detoxify through the enzymatic pathway, protect hormone receptors, encourage cells to go through natural differentiation and apoptosis processes, and support the immune system's efforts to police the entire system.

CALCIUM, MAGNESIUM BALANCE
Osteo Solutions (Neways International)

This calcium, magnesium and Vitamin D supplement is one of my favourites, and is ideal for those seeking to bolster levels of these particular minerals and vitamins in the body for supreme health. Calcium and magnesium are essential to combat irritability, lack of sleep, hyperactivity and that famous 21st century 'wound up' feeling. An ideal sleeping aid is 600mg of calcium to 400mg of magnesium.

Next to zinc, magnesium is probably the second most deficient mineral in Western populations. Deficiency symptoms include muscle twitches, cramps, tremors or spasms, high blood pressure, irregular heartbeat, constipation and fits and convulsions. An ideal intake is around 500mg a day. Food sources include dark, leafy-green vegetables, nuts and seeds.

Calcium, as we discuss in detail in *Health* Wars, is a vital precursor to so many chemical reactions that affect both the physical and mental workings of the body, including bone structure and the all-important acid/alkali balance. Calcium should be present abundantly in our diets along with *reasonable* sunlight for optimum effects. Calcium and magnesium are ideally supplemented together, as they work superbly in synergy with Vitamins C and D.

ZINC – BACK TO BASICS

Perhaps the most commonly deficient mineral, zinc is critical for mental health. Most British folk don't even get 50% of the RDA, which is 15mg, meaning of course that they are prone to zinc deficiency problems, including schizophrenia, violence, depression, anxiety, anorexia, delinquency, hyperactivity and autism.

As we have seen, there are times when zinc is required in greater amounts by the body. Stress, infections, colds, PMS, using the contraceptive pill, frequent alcohol consumption and blood sugar problems all present problems to the body which result in an increased demand for zinc.

MANAGANESE – THE MENTAL MINERAL
A deficiency of manganese also creates problems that can present themselves as mental disorders. Manganese chloride was an early, successful treatment for 'schizophrenia'. Carl Pfeiffer discovered that almost all mental patients will benefit from extra intakes of zinc and manganese. He found that high levels of copper and iron may displace manganese and over-stimulate the brain to produce many psychotic states. Since manganese is found in foods common to a natural diet, our junk food society today is extremely manganese deficient, with all the attendant problems. Manganese is also poorly absorbed and easily excreted from the body. Manganese supplements usually contain between 5-25mg of the mineral.

Epilepsy is also linked to manganese deficiency, although the mechanisms are not completely understood. Epileptics have been shown to have lower levels of manganese than other people. Epileptics and those suffering from tardive diskinesia may benefit from manganese supplementation.

APRICOT SEEDS/KERNELS
Apricot kernels are an inexpensive, rich and natural source of Vitamin B17, the anti-cancer vitamin. They also deliver the vitamins, minerals and enzymes not found in the pharmaceutical derivative of B17.

> ➢ 7g of seeds per day for life are recommended by Dr Krebs as a nutritional supplement for those exercising cancer prevention, commencing with low intakes. Intake should be distributed throughout the day.
> ➢ Up to 28g of seeds per day are recommended by Dr Krebs as nutritional support for clinical cancer sufferers, commencing with low intakes, working into the higher levels over a period of time. Intake can be scaled according to body-weight (i.e. with children and animals).

In a minority of cases, cancer sufferers may experience nausea when taking seeds. In this event, clinics recommend that dosage is reduced and then gradually increased as tolerance is gained. Kernels should not be consumed if liver function is damaged or impaired. Not all apricot seeds are effective. They must have the characteristic bitter taste indicating that the active B17 ingredient is present. Not to be swallowed whole. May be pulped, grated or crushed.

Please note: Some cancer sufferers believe that apricot kernels alone are all that is required to fight cancer. Consultation with a qualified health practitioner familiar with Metabolic Therapy is advised for further information. Apricot kernels are usually part of the nutritional support for those exercising cancer prevention *for life* as well as cancer patients undergoing Phase 1 or Phase 2 Metabolic Therapy.

THE BASIC NUTRITIONAL SUPPLEMENT PROGRAM

Remember that the body likes to take nutrients in collectively. Nutrition works best when the various components are allowed to work synergistically. Thus, a basic, but comprehensive supplement program, carried out *consistently* over a period of time, can have very beneficial results.

For the past 17 years, I have been disease-free and have not had a day off work (haven't got the time☺). I put this down to avoiding the minefields, boosting nutrients in the body, staying hydrated and getting exercise and rest. The regimen below can hardly be described as a 'basic' supplement program, in view of the complexities of the amazing nutrients involved, but here it is anyway!

- **Maximol**
- **A B-complex supplement**
- **Vitamin E (600IU a day)**
- **Zinc (25mg, am and pm)**
- **Revenol**
- **Osteo Solutions**
- **Essential fatty acids**
- **Ingenious**
- **Apricot kernels**
- **Vitamin C (1-3 g a day) inc. bioflavonoids**

This program MUST be taken in conjunction with the *Food For Thought* dietary regimen and adequate hydration. It is not a substitute for a good diet!

AN ADVANCED SUPPLEMENT PROGRAM
Can contain any of the above components, plus other items discussed in this guide. Please see a health practitioner who is qualified to diagnose and recommend a comprehensive nutritional program.

And Finally....

Another stunning journey we have taken together.... Phew! But a journey of truth nonetheless. Contained in these pages is the greatest news for those who have been imprisoned by despair, pain and mental anguish. In a sense, we must compel ourselves to return full circle to 'people helping people', instead of cynically committing our friends and loved ones to many often uncaring and brutal institutions.

ORTHOMOLECULAR PSYCHIATRY

There is no question, as we mentioned from the start, that there are wonderful men and women working within psychiatry and psychology, who entered their respective fields to make a difference in the lives of those who needed help. And so, we come to the nub of it. What will these people do now, with all this amazing information at their fingertips? The new science of 'orthomolecular psychiatry', in my view, is the way forward. This is the science of treating mental illness, for want of a better term, with the correct ('ortho') molecules – in other words, examining the patient medically first in order to establish the existence of physical ailments to which the subject may be reacting, and then bringing the full arsenal of nutritional, allergy and toxicological medicine to bear.

Naturally, there is a tremendous amount each of us can do ourselves to ensure that we and our families steer clear of the minefields of food allergies, toxins, malnutrition and blood sugar problems. Changing our lifestyles and diets for the better can only have a tremendous effect on our health. Only a fool would argue otherwise.

THE CAMPAIGN FOR TRUTH IN MEDICINE

I would like to invite you to join me now in helping to catapult this message far and wide across the world. If you have not already done so, I invite you to join the Campaign for Truth in Medicine for free, and enter the ranks of thousands of others who think the same way you do (see CTM section at the end of this book). Public pressure – united and determined – has always won the day, and will always in the future, in spite of any opposition from vested interests and corrupt public servants. The truth will out, and things are indeed beginning to change. View *The Mind Game* as a strong light that needs to be aimed into the dark places. For, as the old Scottish proverb declares, *"It is better to light one wee candle, than to curse the darkness."*

Contacts! Contacts! Contacts!

If you wish to purchase more copies of this book or find out where you may obtain any of Credence's other book and tape products, please use the contact details below. Credence has local sales offices in a number of countries. Please see our website at www.credence.org for further details on how to contact them:

> UK Orders: (01622) 832386
> UK Fax: (01622) 833314
> www.credence.org
> e-mail: sales@credence.org

HEALTH REVIEW MAGAZINE

What other book entitles you to a free magazine subscription and regular e-mail updates completely free? If you have not received these and have purchased this book, contact us on the above numbers.

ECLUB BULLETINS

Twice each month, the Campaign for Truth in Medicine sends out the EClub Internet bulletin to thousands of subscribers worldwide. This highly informative e-mail newsletter is available FREE to customers who have purchased this book or who have requested EClub. This online bulletin contains the latest news and research on cancer, heart disease, mental health and other vital health topics. DO NOT BE WITHOUT THIS GREAT RESOURCE! If you wish to subscribe, log on to the Campaign site at www.campaignfortruth.com and click the 'Join CTM' tab to complete your free application.

Credence Publications
PO Box 3
TONBRIDGE
Kent TN12 9ZY
England
infopack@credence.org

Other Book Titles by Credence

**Scared Sick of Cancer? Don't Be.
Get the Facts... and then get
on with your life !**

CANCER: WHY WE'RE STILL DYING TO KNOW THE TRUTH

by Phillip Day

For more information on the truth behind cancer and Metabolic Therapy, our world-famous book, *Cancer: Why We're Still Dying to Know the Truth* is the excellent starting point. This overview title exposes the ongoing establishment cover-up over the failure of traditional cancer treatments and explains Metabolic Therapy (Vitamins B17/A&E/enzymes), the controversial treatment for cancer and its prevention. This book further details the amazing track record of nutrition and its role within the simple, combined protocol of Metabolic Therapy. Whether you have cancer, or are exercising prevention for you and your family, PLEASE get educated on this vital issue today.

Title: *Cancer: Why We're Still Dying to Know the Truth*
by Phillip Day
First published in April 1999 by Credence Publications
Available at www.credence.org

B17 METABOLIC THERAPY IN THE PREVENTION AND CONTROL OF CANCER
- a technical manual -
compiled by Phillip Day

From the desks of some of the world's leading cancer scientists comes the empirical proof of Vitamin B17 and its co-factors in the treatment and prevention of cancer. These explosive findings have been the cause of the real cancer war, where vested interests have moved to vilify and denigrate nutrition in order to protect their highly lucrative cancer incomes.

B17 METABOLIC THERAPY

in the prevention and control of CANCER

a technical manual

compiled by
PHILLIP DAY

- Find out why 18 'primitive' cultures do not get cancer in their isolated state.
- What three nutritional components have been found vital in the prevention and the treatment of cancer?
- What can you do to change your diet in ways which will give you maximum protection from cancer and other associated ailments?
- Why do animals not get cancer in the wild, yet succumb to it when 'domesticated' by humans?
- Discover the amazing research of Professor John Beard of Edinburgh University and American Biochemist Ernst T Krebs Jr which shows what cancer actually is. Remove your fear of this disease forever.
- Why are huge budgets continually spent on 'fighting the war against cancer' when this information has been in the public domain for 50 years?
- Examine the actual technical theses and trials carried out by doctors and scientists that validate this amazingly simple protocol.
- Find out what you can do today to join the global movement to eradicate cancer from the 21st century!

Phillip Day: *"Now comes the empirical information for doctors, scientists and laymen alike, which can be used at a local, state or global level to eradicate cancer and its heartache from the human race forever. Each of us has a chance today to be great – to remove far from us the greed, entrenched error and ignorance that has allowed cancer to flourish like an evil bloom in our midst. In a sense, cancer will remain around only as long as it takes humankind to achieve that rare level of maturity, when he will treasure his own well-being and that of his friends and loved ones above the tempting lure of wealth, prestige and renown."*

Title: *B17 Metabolic Therapy – A Technical Manual*
by Phillip Day
First published in 2002 by Credence Publications
Available at www.credence.org

GREAT NEWS ON CANCER IN THE 21ST CENTURY
by Steven Ransom

THERE IS TIME!
A cancer diagnosis calls for decisions – decisions that because of circumstances, are so often made in haste. *Great News on Cancer in the 21st Century* is the first book that tells us there is time to consider the options! Within these pages is everything you need to know about taking the next step.

Did you know for instance that vested interests in the cancer industry will be having a direct impact on the advice you are receiving from your doctor? Why aren't we being told about the validated, non-conventional treatments that are saving and enhancing lives daily? Instead, we are offered profitable chemotherapy and radiation treatments that damage the immune system – sometimes irreparably. Get informed on the dangers associated with these treatments – including the

426

facts and figures they don't tell you! Learn how to interpret the misleading information for yourself.

Cancer mis-diagnosis is on the increase. Are you making life-changing decisions without a second opinion? Breast cancer screening/ mammography, for example. How dangerous is it? Find out about the simple breast self-examination procedures that are just as effective and pose no danger to women's health, and discover the great news that will lift the current fear associated with breast cancer. Read the powerful testimonies of people who are being helped tremendously with various non-conventional treatments - stories of doctors unable to believe the disappearance of supposedly incurable cancers! This summary represents just a fraction of the wealth of information you will uncover in *Great News on Cancer in the 21st Century*.

"Excellent and well researched. Congratulations! I will certainly be directing all my cancer patients to your book." **Dr Bill Reeder**

"Informative and empowering. This book should be required reading for anyone who values his or her health." **John J Moelaert** - author of ***The Cancer Conspiracy***

"Dear Steve, thank God you wrote this book! Thank you, thank you, thank you!" **Edie Matthews**

"Dear Steve, I must blame you for a sleepless night. Just brilliant! I have been immersing myself in all of this information for a while now, but never have I found it written so well!" **Ledonna James**

HEALTH WARS
by Phillip Day

PRESS RELEASE: Western healthcare is now the third leading cause of death in Britain, according to a UK health research organisation. England-based Credence Research, citing statistics which demonstrate that drug-dominated medicine is now the third leading killer in most industrial nations, warns that the true death toll may be far higher than even its reported figures.

Credence Chief Executive Phillip Day states: *"225,000 Americans are killed every year by Western healthcare, according to the American Medical Association. In Britain, the official figure of 40,000 is in reality far higher, if you examine the proper markers. 1 in 5 Australians will be killed every year by their doctors, through incorrect drug-prescribing, botched medical procedures, infections in hospitals and, the main killer, <u>correct</u> drug prescribing. This worldwide allopathic catastrophe is well known to the authorities who, in reality, are unable to do much about it within the current healthcare system, for the reasons we report."*

Credence, whose recently released publication, *Health Wars*, deals with this unsettling phenomenon, states: *"90-95% of the diseases currently killing populations, at least in the industrial nations, are nutritional deficiency and/or toxin related conditions, such as heart disease, cancer, diabetes and stroke. To understand completely why medicine continues to fail with these problems, and worse, be guilty of its own unique slaughter of the citizenry, one need look no further than the fact that doctors receive almost no formal training in nutrition. Thus, doctors are not trained to understand the underlying metabolic problems of at least 90% of diseases, which can be treated effectively, even in their late stages, or completely prevented, using simple, and unfortunately un-patentable nutrition."*

On the toxin disease front, the medical establishment is equally dismissive and trivialises the real chemical and environmental causes, according to Credence. To illustrate why this happens, Day points out that the very industry responsible for producing and selling chemicals, which routinely kill and maim the public, also manufactures the public's medicines. *"Don't expect the chemical industry to gain a morality on this issue overnight. It is hamstrung by stark conflicts of interest. The urgent call for reform needed to prevent further tragedy on the scale we face must come from the public itself."*

On Credence's recently released book, Day declares: *"The purpose of 'Health Wars' is to highlight these problems and to urge citizens to pressure their governments for immediate reform. Compounding its failures, British healthcare has ironically been brought to its knees by the crippling costs of the very drugs and treatments, which have been, and continue to be, the main instigators of these frightening death statistics. Credence has been looking at mortality. But how many citizens out there have been crippled or maimed by healthcare practices, such as vaccinations, errant drug prescribing and unnecessary surgeries? Recent reports show that the NHS must budget every year for at least £2.8 billion in compensation claims alone. That's enough to build and fully staff 28 new hospitals <u>every twelve months</u>."*

Credence states that medical science has known for years that the answers to heart disease, cancer, stroke and other illnesses lie completely in nutrition and lifestyle changes, not radical surgeries, toxic drugs or radiation. To prove this point, the company cites at least 18 cultures alive today who do not apparently suffer from these health problems. *"Interestingly,"* Day elaborates, *"we tend to call these peoples 'primitive' and 'less developed'. But they know enough about nutrition to ensure that they survive in sterling health, in many cases to over 100 years of age. The authorities know this too, and do nothing. Why? Because Western healthcare today is a multi-trillion-dollar industry worldwide, and you cannot pay CEO salaries and shareholder dividends using apples, oranges and chemical-free, organic vegetation."*

Day believes that health reform is inevitable, and that the public can do much to precipitate the process by getting educated and politically active: *"A proper healthcare industry must have nutritional education at its heart,"* he states. *"This is the most basic body science. We are what we eat. But the people will have to fight a war with their industrial and political peers first, in order to secure the return of their unalienable right to drink fresh, uncontaminated water, to eat fresh, uncontaminated food and to breathe fresh, uncontaminated air."*

Title: *Health Wars*
by Phillip Day
First edition published June 2001 by Credence Publications
Available at www.credence.org

TOXIC BITE
by Bill Kellner-Read

Toxic Bite
an investigation into truth decay

Bill Kellner-Read

Most people go to the dentist at some point in their lives, and many go regularly. But who really questions what happens when we are in the dentist's chair? Can we be sure that we are receiving the best, long-term treatment for such an important and necessary part of our body?

Finally there's a new book that demystifies dentistry and lets you take control of your own dental health. *Toxic Bite*, by British dentist Bill Kellner-Read, gets to the bottom of some startling questions:

➢ Could your gum disease be responsible for heart disease or stroke?
➢ What products are we using every day that contribute to wider toxic illnesses?
➢ And what about those extractions? Do we really need that tooth pulled?
➢ Should we really be extracting children's teeth for orthodontic correction?
➢ What are the longer-term consequences of having less teeth in our mouth?
➢ What about the other correctional work being carried out today?
➢ Is there a link between nutrition and gum disease?

You might not have toothache. But what about back-ache, neck-ache, jaw-ache, migraine or those constant blinding headaches? It may well be an underlying dental problem that is contributing to wider systemic disease, chronic pain and discomfort in your body.

For the best in toxin-free tooth, mouth and body care, read *Toxic Bite* - the latest addition to the Credence roster of top-selling healthcare titles.

Title: *Toxic Bite*
by Bill Kellner-Read
First published in 2002 by Credence Publications
Available at www.credence.org

FOOD FOR THOUGHT
compiled by Phillip Day

Need a guide on where to go with your food? What better way to embrace the dietary concepts laid down in *The Mind Game, Cancer: Why We're Still Dying to Know the Truth* and *Health Wars* than to obtain a copy of our official recipe book.

This delightful guide takes you through the main concepts of acid/alkali, Vitamin B17 dishes, the proper combining of foods, the problems with meat and dairy in excessive amounts, fruit consumption techniques, smart foods, a host of detox menus, 5-10% meat and dairy recipes, snacks, pro-active sickness dieting, children's dishes and proper supplementation. Whether you are suffering or just want to make a change for your extended future, sensible nutrition comes to life in *Food For Thought*, bringing you the most delicious foods that WON'T KILL YOU!

Title: *Food for Thought*
Compiled by Phillip Day
First published in August 2001 by Credence Publications
Available at www.credence.org

PLAGUE, PESTILENCE AND THE PURSUIT OF POWER

by Steven Ransom

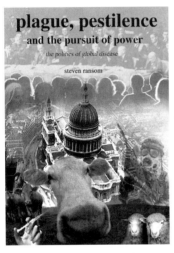

plague, pestilence
and the pursuit of power
the politics of global disease
steven ransom

Almost every day, it seems, we are hearing reports of some 'highly infectious' disease breaking out somewhere across the world - the recent flu pandemics, AIDS decimating Africa, tuberculosis on the rise again, measles, and meningitis on the increase. And in the animal kingdom, we've seen Bovine Spongiform Encephalopathy (BSE), poultry flu, swine fever, more BSE and now foot and mouth, wreaking havoc across our countryside. One could be forgiven for thinking that we are quite literally surrounded by virulent illness. But not everything is as it seems – not by a long way.

In this book, we discover that these so-called 'epidemics' are NOT the deadly illnesses we have been led to believe by our respective governments, national papers and news programs. With all the above-mentioned illnesses, the facts being disseminated have been grossly misleading, accompanied, in many instances, by a deliberate intent to scare and deceive. Welcome to the shocking world of the politically manufactured epidemic - the 'psycho-plague'.

The formula is quite simple. Using the mainstream media as their chosen vehicle for change, powerful vested interests are deliberately instigating national and international fearsome headlines. Through these channels, the problem – the epidemic – the psycho-plague, is manufactured. A crisis has now been firmly embedded into the mind of the populace. **"We must have a solution!"** we cry. Lo and behold, a governmental/corporate solution is speedily proffered.

In reality, the epidemic needing 'swift state intervention' has been nothing more than a Trojan Horse either for creating immense profit for various pharmaceutical industries or, as we shall discover, for ushering in

432

unsavoury, global super-state ideology. Throughout this whole process, we are being taught what to think about health and disease, but not how.

In examining the facts laid out before us, we soon realise that our battle is not so much against pathological disease, as against corrupt and self-serving desires, birthed in the minds of man. This book contains the supporting evidence to make this case. You are invited to consider the evidence for yourself.

But this book also maps out a positive way forward. For, in discovering the true nature and causes of these 'epidemics', a longer lasting remedy can now be planned for the future.

Plague, Pestilence and the Pursuit of Power is dedicated to those who want to find out what really goes on behind the closed doors of Big Business and Big Government and to those who wish to see truth reign in conventional science and medicine.

Title: *Plague, Pestilence and the Pursuit of Power*
by Steven Ransom
First published in June 2001 by Credence Publications
Available at www.credence.org

WORLD WITHOUT AIDS

by Steven Ransom & Phillip Day

World Without AIDS dismantles one of the world's greatest fears and lays bare the deceit, fraudulent science and needless fearmongering that lie at the heart of this supposed global epidemic. Over ten years in the making, this impeccably researched book gives an eye-opening account of what vested interests can get away with, given a trusting public, an almost limitless supply of money and scant scruples. It also explains the non-existence of HIV, the bankruptcy of the HIV test, the real causes of immune suppression, the AIDS-devastating-Africa myth and the appalling dangers of the establishment-approved medications prescribed to those who have been written off as 'HIV positive'.

Title: *World Without AIDS*
by Steven Ransom and Phillip Day
First published in June 2000 by Credence Publications
Available through credence.org

All titles can also be obtained from the distributor whose details are in the *Contacts!* section of this book.

The Campaign for Truth in Medicine
"a force for change"

WHAT IS CTM?

Campaign for Truth in Medicine is a worldwide organisation dedicated to pressing for change in areas of science and medicine where entrenched scientific error, ignorance or vested interests are costing lives. Its ranks comprise doctors, scientists, researchers, bio-chemists, politicians, industry executives and countless members of the world public, all of whom have made one observation in common. They have recognised that, in certain key areas of global disease, drug treatments and overall healthcare philosophy, the medical, chemical and political establishments are pursuing the wrong course with the maximum of precision, even when their own legitimate and erudite scientific research has illustrated the dangers of pursuing these courses.

CTM BACKS ITS PEOPLE'S CHARTER

CTM's People's Charter catalogues these key problem areas - for example AIDS, cancer, the mental health concerns discussed in this book, heart disease and vaccinations - all where the preponderance of evidence demonstrates severe cause for concern over deadly errors in basic science, resulting in needless loss of life. CTM's charter also highlights industry's every-day use of potentially harmful contaminants and biohazards, such as toothpaste's sodium fluoride, shampoo's sodium lauryl sulphate and cosmetic's propylene glycol, which have long been linked to long-term serious health risks and death. CTM's purpose is to present this damning evidence to its members, to the public at large and to the establishments and individuals involved in these errors, in order to press for immediate change and cessation of their use for the benefit of humanity. The People's Charter is periodically amended to reflect current issues and new areas of concern.

CTM STANDS FOR TRUTH

For decades members of the public and a significant proportion of their medical and scientific professionals have become increasingly angry and frustrated at what they see as establishment indifference and even downright hostility towards much-needed changes in healthcare, especially in areas where the proven solution is substantially less profitable than the current status quo.

PROMOTING THE TRUTH

CTM believes in promoting the truth in these matters, thereby exposing those morally bankrupt and compromised politicians, corporations and individuals responsible. This method of action is viewed as a top priority. CTM is dedicated to pushing for immediate change, in order that immediate relief from many of the diseases and their causes, currently afflicting us, may be implemented, the remedies for which, in certain cases, have been a matter of existing scientific knowledge for decades.

The Journal of the American Medical Association (JAMA) implicitly reports that western healthcare, along with its drugs, treatments and hospitals, is now the third leading cause of death in the United States, next to heart disease and cancer. If we examine this astonishing fact, also highlighted by US consumer advocate Ralph Nader in the early 1990's, we come to realise that the Western healthcare paradigm is adopted by almost all developed nations and many other developing countries around the world. Thus this tragic statistic of iatrogenic death can be fairly considered to be global in application.

This would be serious enough on its own, yet the true extent of this orthodox medical catastrophe is unfortunately far more devastating. Western medical establishments are in possession of key life-saving information that can immediately and drastically reduce current and future global incidences of cancer, heart disease, AIDS and other treatable, non-fatal conditions. But in almost all cases these institutions have chosen neither to adopt these measures, train their healthcare practitioners in these practices, nor publicise the latter to a generally trusting world populace. Thus these government personnel and their associated medical luminaries, who have wilfully kept this life-saving information from their doctors and the public, may justifiably be exposed for becoming the leading cause of death across the planet today.

CTM STANDS FOR DIRECT ACTION

CTM believes that, in certain cases, legitimate direct action is warranted against these institutions and individuals to halt their wilful and harmful actions and hold them to account. In these circumstances, CTM calls upon its membership to organise and act in a unified, lawful and mature fashion to bring these matters to the attention of the mass communications media, government leaders and heads of state through demonstrations and other appropriate action. CTM is dedicated to being part of the people's movement in this regard; a powerful and irresistible force for change, compelling vital reform TODAY for a safer and healthier world for our children and children's children.

CTM IS FREE FROM VESTED INTEREST FUNDING

Through its network of worldwide professional contacts, CTM has constant access to well-researched information on key health issues. CTM brings its members highly readable and jargon-free information, such as that contained in this book.

CTM HAS ALL THE NECESSARY CONTACTS

...at local and central government/corporate level, responsible for particular health legislation and legislative change. Names, addresses, contact details and relevant template letters are supplied with all CTM newsletters.

CTM IS A HEALTH ADVOCACY ORGANISATION

with purpose and direction. It is a conduit through which the individual minority voice can become a powerful and respected, collective majority voice for change.

WHAT YOU CAN DO NOW

CTM invites you to visit its web-site to learn more about how you can join this worldwide movement FOR FREE and receive regular bulletins and further information on these fascinating subjects as they develop. Be part of a different future. One that celebrates life!

**Campaign for Truth in Medicine
PO Box 3
Tonbridge
Kent
TN12 9ZY UK
e-mail: info@campaignfortruth.com
www.campaignfortruth.com**

Index

439

B

443

F

H

I

448

M

N

Q

R

456

W

Acknowledgements

Many thanks to all who contributed in small or large measure to make this book a reality, including all you independents, dug in deep around the globe, who pitched in mightily on this one. Many thanks especially to all at CCHR, including Brian D, without whose help I would still be rifling the trash cans in Beverly Hills. Thank you to Sheryl for the web wonders and technical, Steve R and domestic research for rubbing the sleep from your eyes when you didn't have to. A big hand to Wendy W and her four horses over in the States for their brilliant insights. Tig B, wherever you are at the moment – no, I am not posting your bail... again. Dave and Kay, have you lost my number?

To the cherubs at Credence, including Edward for his anchor, Steve Russ for his captaincy, level head and constance. To Kate and Lucy for keeping things going even as you both expanded. Jenny, just on board - you go, girl! Eddie, take a bow for your invaluable contribution. Sandra, Shirley, Lilibelle, Gwen, Bruce F, Paul and Sue – take a pink sticky elephant and put it on your lapels. Sharlene and Margie and all your soldiers worldwide, here we go again! Thanks for all your teamwork and skills. And to little Ashley for keeping me read on the endless plane trips.

To Credence International and Events Management, who pick up the ball from here, especially those Australian dahlings, Kirstyn, Dora and Marlene (A1, A2 & A3). Heidi in South Africa, Tina in Canada, Carl and Kerry in the States, Ora in Deutschland, and Thiru and Kumar up near the Line of Control (please keep your heads down, fellas).

And to the two most wonderful ladies in my life, the indefatigable Blanche, who has faithfully braved all weathers, and to my eternal Samantha, who endures the long hours and tragi-comedy that is life on the road, without whom... well, just without whom.

And so to bed for all of us. It's been a long day.

Zzzzzz.

461

About The Author

Phillip Day was born in England in 1960. He was educated at the leading British education establishments Selwyn and Charterhouse, and throughout his '20's had a successful entrepreneurial career founding businesses in sales and marketing. With a firm grounding in business and the ways of the media, Phillip's research career began after he became interested in wars going on in the realms of health and politics over issues that were being deliberately withheld or misreported to the public.

His research into AIDS and cancer, as two examples of the medical establishment's entrenched scientific error and brazen profiteering to society's great cost, culminated in two books that have captured the public's imagination around the world: *CANCER: WHY WE'RE STILL DYING TO KNOW THE TRUTH* and *WORLD WITHOUT AIDS*. Phillip's book, *HEALTH WARS*, released in 2001, deals with a whole spectrum of diseases, whose causes and pathological make-up render them simple and relatively straight-forward to combat. This information, deliberately not promoted by the medical establishment, forms the basis of the promotional and educational work in which Phillip's research and investigational units are engaged.

Today Phillip's schedule takes him all over the world, lecturing on the subjects of entrenched scientific error and the little-known groundbreaking research doctors and biochemists have made to break the back of diseases for the benefit of everyone. His goal is to educate the public directly on these issues, a task both the medical establishment and mainstream mass communications media have failed to address to their great shame, due to deep-rooted vested interests and ulterior agendas.

Phillip heads up the publishing and research organisation Credence, which collates the work provided by researchers all over the world. Credence's intention is to work with the establishments and organisations concerned to resolve these life-threatening issues, and to provide the necessary information for citizens to make their own informed choices in these vital matters.

Phillip Day currently lives in Kent, England.